Elementary Statistics

First Edition

Elementary Statistics

A Guide to Data Analysis Using R

FIRST EDITION

Nancy L. Glenn Griesinger
TEXAS SOUTHERN UNIVERSITY

Daniel Vrinceanu
TEXAS SOUTHERN UNIVERSITY

Monica C. Jackson
AMERICAN UNIVERSITY

William C. Howell
AMERICAN UNIVERSITY

LIBRARY OF CONGRESS
SURPLUS
DUPLICATE

SAN DIEGO

Bassim Hamadeh, CEO and Publisher
John Remington, Executive Editor
Carrie Baarns, Manager, Revisions and Author Care
Gem Rabanera, Senior Project Editor
Susana Christie, Senior Developmental Editor
Laureen Gleason, Senior Production Editor
Emely Villavicencio, Senior Graphic Designer
Kylie Bartolome, Licensing Associate
Stephanie Adams, Senior Marketing Program Manager
Natalie Piccotti, Director of Marketing
Kassie Graves, Senior Vice President, Editorial
Jamie Giganti, Director of Academic Publishing

Copyright © 2023 by Cognella, Inc. All rights reserved. No part of this publication may be reprinted, reproduced, transmitted, or utilized in any form or by any electronic, mechanical, or other means, now known or hereafter invented, including photocopying, microfilming, and recording, or in any information retrieval system without the written permission of Cognella, Inc. For inquiries regarding permissions, translations, foreign rights, audio rights, and any other forms of reproduction, please contact the Cognella Licensing Department at rights@cognella.com.

Trademark Notice: Product or corporate names may be trademarks or registered trademarks and are used only for identification and explanation without intent to infringe.

This textbook incorporates the recommendations of the American Statistical Association's most recent *Guidelines for Assessment and Instruction in Statistics Education* (GAISE) *College Report* (GAISE College Report ASA Revision Committee, 2016). Utilizing the GAISE framework, the goals of this textbook are to (1) cultivate students' logical thinking with statistical as well as coding methods applied to real-world problems, group experiments, and research and (2) leverage R's computing techniques to deepen students' understanding of statistics as well as coding.

Reference: GAISE College Report ASA Revision Committee. (2016, July). *Guidelines for Assessment and Instruction in Statistics Education (GAISE) college report 2016.* www.amstat.org/education/guidelines-for-assessment-and-instruction-in-statistics-education-(gaise)-reports

Cover image copyright © 2022 iStockphoto LP/Olga Tsyvinska.

Interior image copyright © 2013 Depositphotos/foxiedelmar.

Printed in the United States of America.

Brief Contents

Detailed Contents

COGNELLA ACTIVE LEARNING

INSTRUCTIONS FOR STUDENTS

This book has interactive activities available to complement your reading.
Your instructor may have customized the selection of activities available for your unique course. Please check with your professor to verify whether your class will access this content through the Cognella Active Learning portal (http://active.cognella.com) or through your institution's learning management system.

It is necessary to enroll in Active Learning to ensure your professor receives your scores on any graded content. If you are enrolled in a course at a higher education institution where your professor has adopted this book, enroll with your cohort of classmates by either (1) redeeming a code at https://store.cognella.com/codes/redeem or (2) finding your institution and course and purchasing access in the Cognella Student Store at store.cognella.com.

INSTRUCTIONS FOR EDUCATORS

If you are an educator, you will need to adopt Active Learning in order for you and your students to gain access. Please contact your Cognella Sales Representative or email adopt@cognella.com if you need to enroll as an instructor in Active Learning.

Please contact adopt@cognella.com with any Active Learning enrollment questions.

WEB-BASED RESOURCES: ACCESSING QR CODES AND LINKS

The author has selected some supporting web-based content for further engagement with the learning material that appears in this text, which can be accessed through QR codes or web links. These codes are intended for use by those who have purchased print copies of the book. You may scan them using a QR code reading app on your cell phone, which will take you to each website. You can also search for the link using a web browser search engine. Readers who have purchased a digital copy of the book can simply click on the hyperlinks beneath each QR code.

Cognella maintains no responsibility for the content nor availability of third-party links. However, Cognella makes every effort to keep its texts current. Broken links may be reported to studentreviews@cognella.com. Please include the book's title, author, and 7-digit SKU reference number (found below the barcode on the back cover of the book) in the body of your message.

Please check with your professor to confirm whether your class will access this content independently or collectively.

PART I

Introductions to Statistics and R

CHAPTER

1

Introduction to Statistics

CHAPTER OUTLINE

1.1 Constructing a Statistics Study Guide

1.2 Relevance of Statistics

1.3 Two Major Branches of Statistics

1.4 Statistical Software Overview

CHAPTER OBJECTIVES

After completing this chapter, you will be able to do the following:

1. Construct a detailed study guideline for earning a good grade in a statistics class.
2. Understand the relevance of the field of statistics.
3. Understand the difference between the two major branches of statistics.
4. Gain a general overview of the different types of statistical software.

The word ***statistics*** is derived from Latin, ***statisticum collegium***, which means council of state. In the 1700s statistics referred to the analysis of demographic and economic information about the state. This definition was broadened in the 1800s to include the collection, summary, and analysis of any type of data. As was the case hundreds of years ago, the field of statistics remains relevant today in areas including all scientific fields, technology, engineering, and business. In this chapter you will learn about the continual relevance of statistics and the necessity of the software R for statistical analysis, computing, and graphics.

FIGURE 1.1 An Early Times Statistics Story

Chapter Vocabulary

- A variable in statistics is a symbol which works as a placeholder for a quantity that may change.
- Data represent information from observations, counts, measurements, and responses.
- A data set is a collection of data.
- A population consists of all items under study. A sample is a subset of a population.
- Descriptive statistics is the branch of statistics that involves the organization, summarization, and display of data.
- Quantitative data are numerical data.
- Qualitative data are categorical in nature.
- Inferential statistics consists of using samples to make generalizations about populations, performing estimations and statistical tests, determining relationships among variables, and making predictions.
- The probability of an event is the chance of an event occurring.

1.1 Constructing a Statistics Study Guide

Students often ask how to study statistics and prepare for statistics examinations. Our answer to this question is based on pedagogical techniques used by Mobile Math, LLC. The following is a statement from Mobile Math's CEO and founder:

> Mobile Math has an almost 100% college graduation rate for students whom we work with on a regular basis. We attribute our success to hard-working students, and to the way in which we teach our students how to study math. This study methodology, called the "Griesinger Study Plan" is named after the Mobile Math CEO and founder, Professor Glenn Griesinger.
>
> Mobile Math accomplishes its high graduation rate by combining Dr. Glenn Griesinger's decades of university-level teaching experience with elements of Polya's Four Basic Principles of Problem Solving: (1) Understand the problem, (2) Devise a plan, (3) Carry out the plan, and (4) Look back. Polya was a noted mathematician well known for his contribution to pedagogy, specifically mathematics education.

1.1.1 Three Steps to Success

The Griesinger Study Plan guides students through what should be done before, during and after each lecture to succeed in a statistics class. Before class, students should start preparing for the upcoming lecture. During class, students should stay focused on what is currently being covered in the lecture. Staying focused involves turning off devices that can be distracting, such as cell phones, before entering the classroom or before logging into an online class. After class, students should review the lecture, work on any assignments, and then study on a regular basis.

FIGURE 1.2 Mobile Math

Mobile Math Website

Check out this website for assistance with study techniques in statistics: https://mobilemathlab.com/

The *Griesinger Study Plan's* three steps to success in a statistics class are:

1. Preview before each class by reading the book, PowerPoint notes, and so on.
2. Come to class on time, ask questions, and take good notes.
3. Review and study on a regular basis.

Previewing is part of good note taking. Students should preview their lesson prior to each lecture, even if the lesson is initially unclear. The course syllabus typically contains a list of topics to be covered during the semester. Previewing helps to identify main ideas and concepts that will most likely be discussed during the lecture. The preview time is also a good time to write questions to discuss later during the lecture.

When students preview the lecture before class, they will most likely be prepared to ask questions about the lesson, which is a part of step two of the Griesinger Study Plan's three steps to success. Taking good class notes is essential to success, and asking questions is a part of good note taking. Coming to class on time is also part of good note taking. Being on time helps students to be mentally prepared for class.

Arriving to class late causes students to miss lesson introductions and other essential information as professors often share important information, reminders of upcoming quizzes, new classroom rules, and due dates at the beginning of the lecture. In online classes, students should log on at least 15 to 30 minutes early just in case of unanticipated computer glitches.

Finally, students should review and study after each lecture. Because the material is cumulative, all questions about a previous lecture should be answered before the following lecture. Homework should be started within 24 hours of receiving the assignment. Reach out to your professor, teacher's assistant (TA), your tutor, or other students in your class to make sure you understand the material. Students should study each lecture as if they are preparing for an upcoming test in the following lecture.

1.1.2 Personalized Study Guide

Specifically, how can a student study on a regular basis? The *Griesinger Study Plan* suggests constructing a personalized study guide. In addition to a class notebook, students should create a personalized study guide that contains the following items:

- Vocabulary
- Directions
- Formulas
- Examples

Students may use any of the following to make study guides: three-ring binder divided into four sections, four legal pads, four notebooks, four sets of index cards, or any combination of the materials. Some students prefer electronic study guides, while most student are manipulative learners in statistics classes. That is, they learn by writing and manipulating objects. In either case, the study guide should contain lots of colors as colors aid in remembering the material. The study guide should be created as the material is being covered in class. Therefore, studying on a regular basis means to study from the personalized study guide on a regular basis.

Vocabulary is important in statistics because students need to understand what the question is asking in order to get it right. Often, everyday words have a different meaning in a mathematical context. Statistics is a branch of mathematics. Understanding vocabulary also allows for meaningful class discussions.

After understanding the definitions, students can begin to follow directions. In other words, first understand the concept, and then learn guidelines for specific problems. For example, there are five specific steps for constructing a frequency distribution from a data set. These directions will be explained in a future chapter.

Even if a professor allows a formula sheet or programmable calculator, these items should not be used as a crutch. It is important for students to know statistical formulas without having to look them up for several reasons. For instance, knowing and understanding a formula gives students a deeper understanding of the concepts the formula portrays. When students know the formula, they are more likely to know when and how to use the formula. When taking a test, knowing formulas saves time from having to look them up. However, they should be double-checked if time allows.

Examples are an essential part of a personalized study guide. Each concept covered during lecture should be illustrated with at least one example. Examples that will be on a test should definitely be included in the personalized study guide. If a student is struggling with a particular concept, related examples should also be included in the personalized study guide.

Keeping up with a personalized study guide prevents students from falling behind in class. They are also extremely beneficial when studying for cumulative exams like midterm and final exams.

1.2 Relevance of Statistics

In 1654, probability theory grew out of a gambler's dispute between two French mathematicians, Blaise Pascal and Pierre de Fermat. Statistics is a branch of mathematics that has roots in probability theory. Statistics is the science of collecting, interpreting, analyzing, and presenting data. Data consist of information such as observations, counts, measurements, or responses. Statistics is the backbone of all of the sciences. It plays a vital role in every field of science. In addition to the sciences, statistics is relevant to sectors such as business, government, education, and health care.

Recent COVID-19 (coronavirus disease) articles from sources such as the World Health Organization are current examples that illustrate the importance of statistics and statistical models. Figure 1.3 was created by the U.S. Centers for Disease Control and Prevention (CDC). It depicts the coronavirus's ultrastructural morphology, which are the cells and biomaterials that are visible through high magnification microscopes. This new virus is a severe acute respiratory syndrome coronavirus (SARS-CoV-2). It was identified as the cause of an outbreak of respiratory illness first detected in Wuhan, China in 2019, which led to a worldwide pandemic in 2020. The illness caused by this virus is called coronavirus disease 2019 (COVID-19).

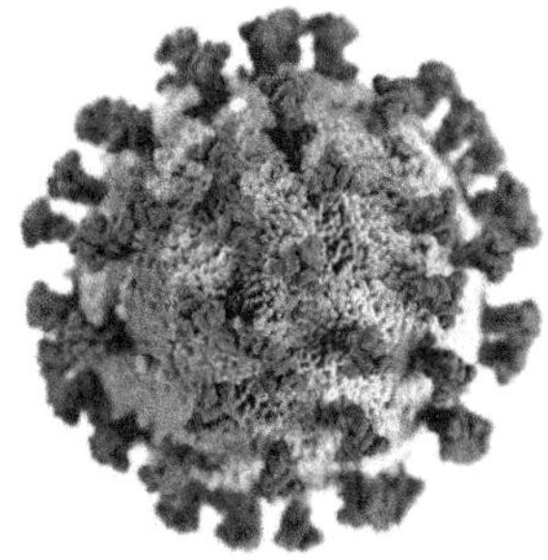

FIGURE 1.3 Coronavirus's Ultrastructural Morphology

1.2.1 Informed Citizen

The field of statistics helps citizens to stay informed about what is happening in the world around them. Knowing how to read, critique, and understand statistics is essential to being an informed citizen. When statistics is used in a misleading fashion, it can trick the casual observer into believing something other than what the data exhibits. Thus, it is important to have a good understanding of statistics because it helps individuals to become more aware of how statistics affects almost every aspect of their life.

For example, citizens are informed about the importance of completing the census. The U.S. Constitution in Article 1, Section 2, mandates a census. As a result, the United States has counted its population every 10 years since 1790. The census still remains relevant today. As with prior U.S. censuses, the 2020 U.S. census data affect the amount of funding a community receives for health care, infrastructure, and education. The census data determine a community's representation in government, which in turn helps communities to plan for the future.

A
COLLECTION
OF THE
YEARLY BILLS
OF
MORTALITY,
From 1657 to 1758 inclufive.
Together with feveral other Bills of an earlier Date.
To which are fubjoined
I. Natural and Political Obfervations on the bills of mortality: by Capt. John Graunt, F. R. S. reprinted from the fixth edition, in 1676.
II. Another effay in political arithmetic, concerning the growth of the city of London; with the meafures, periods, caufes, and confequences thereof. By Sir William Petty, Kt. F. R. S. reprinted from the edition printed at London in 1683.
III. Obfervations on the paft growth and prefent ftate of the city of London; reprinted from the edition printed at London in 1751; with a continuation of the tables to the end of the year 1757. By Corbyn Morris, Efq; F. R. S.
IV. A comparative view of the difeafes and ages, and a table of the probabilities of life, for the laft thirty years. By J. P. Efq; F. R. S.
LONDON:
Printed for A. Millar in the *Strand*.
MDCCLIX.

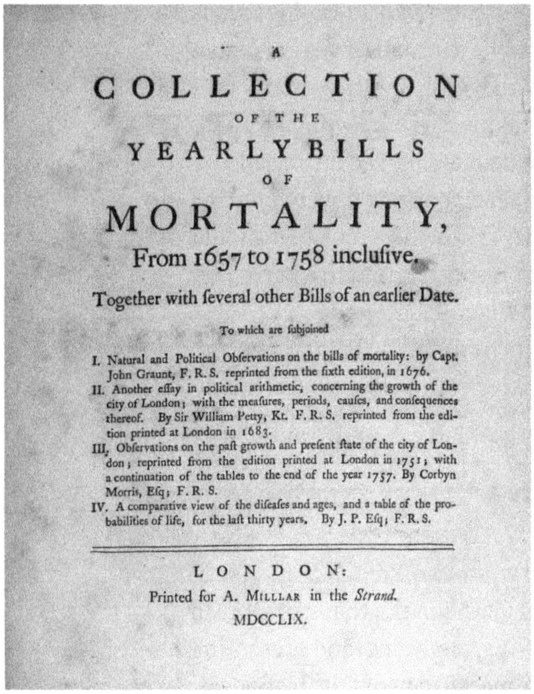

FIGURE 1.4 A Collection of the Yearly *Bills of Mortality*

1.2.2 Effectively Conduct Research

The need to turn large amounts of data into useful information has stimulated both theoretical and practical developments in statistics. Statistical analysis plays an essential role in scientific studies, as it provides evidence that validates results.

Statistics traces its roots back to the mid-17th century London when the commoner John Graunt began reviewing a weekly church publication issued by the local parish clerk that listed the number of births, christenings, and deaths in each parish. Graunt compiled and analyzed the numbers and published them in a book known as the *Bills of Mortality*. Graunt was later elected as a charter member of the Royal Society, the United Kingdom's national academy of sciences. The *Journal of the Royal Statistical Society* was founded in 1887 and remains one of the many highly ranked, relevant statistical journals today (Sutherland, 1963).

1.2.3 Exercises

Understanding Concepts

1. What is the science of collecting, organizing, analyzing, and interpreting data called?

2. Statistics is called the backbone of what? Why is it called that?

3. What is the connection between probability theory and statistics?

4. In 1654, probability theory grew out of what?

5. What can happen to the casual observer when statistics are used in a misleading fashion (i.e., arguing something other than what the data exhibits)?

6. How does statistical analysis play an essential role in scientific studies?

True or false? In Exercises 7–12, determine whether the statement is true or false. If it is false, rewrite it as a true statement.

7. The field of statistics is irrelevant.

8. Statistics is a branch of mathematics.

9. Statistics grew out of probability theory.

10. Probability theory grew out of a gambler's dispute in France.

11. The U.S. Constitution mandates a census.

12. All mathematicians are statisticians.

Skill Building

13. What is your definition of statistics?

14. Give a definition of *data*.

15. One of the most valuable tools for locating available data is the internet. Go to the website https://www.cdc.gov/nchs/nhanes to locate available data sets. Find a data set that you would be interested in studying. Describe the data.

16. What are the variables for your data set described in Exercise 15?

17. What does it mean to be an *informed consumer*?

18. Data can be found from many sources. However, in order to effectively conduct research based on data, you have to be able to trust that the data are real and accurately reflect what is being studied. What are some indications that your data found in Exercise 15 are reliable?

19. Sometimes you cannot find a data set that has the information you want to study. Therefore, you must design a plan to collect the desired data. Think of something that you would like to research. Describe your plan for data acquisition.

20. What are some research questions for your study described in Exercise 19?

Extending Concepts

21. Give an example of a news piece from the last month that uses statistics. Be sure to cite the source and provide the date.

22. Explain why the field of statistics is relevant for the government.

23. Give an example on how the field of statistics is used in business.

24. Why is the field of statistics important in almost *all* branches of sciences?

25. In your own words, explain the importance of statistics in engineering and technology.

1.3 Two Major Branches of Statistics

As seen in Figure 1.5, there are two major branches of statistics, descriptive and inferential. Descriptive statistics involve the organization, summarization, and display of data. Descriptive statistics provide basic information about variables in a data set. As in pure mathematics, a variable in statistics is a symbol which works as a placeholder for a quantity that may change. In Chapter 5 of this textbook, you will learn about random variables, as they are referred to in the field. In statistics, data represent

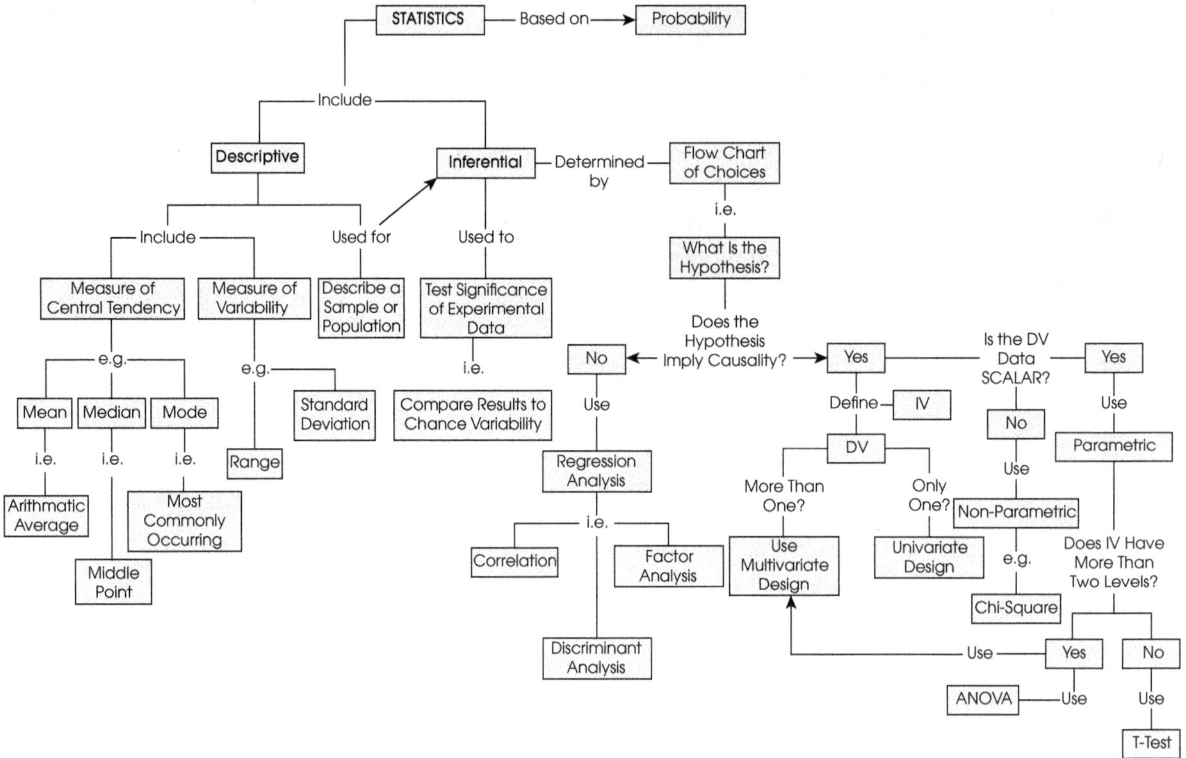

FIGURE 1.5 Branches of Statistics

information from observations, counts, measurements and responses. A data set is a collection of data. Both branches of statistics highlight potential relationships among variables in a data set. Inferential statistics are concerned with making inferences about the population based on conclusions drawn from samples.

Of note, a population is not necessarily a population of people. A fashion designer may conduct a study about the average price of a population of designer handbags. A population consists of all items under study. A sample is a subset of a population. A subset of the fashion designer's population of designer handbags may be handbags made by French designers. When presenting findings from a study such as the French designer handbag study, statisticians typically start with descriptive statistics, then carry out inferential statistics.

1.3.1 Descriptive Statistics

Statisticians use descriptive statistics to describe a situation. Descriptive statistics is the branch of statistics that involves the organization, summarization, and display of data. Descriptive statistics can be displayed graphically or pictorially. In the case of the U. S. Census, once data are collected, the Census Bureau organizes and summarizes the data. The bureau then presents the data in a meaningful form using descriptive statistics such as charts, tables, or graphs.

The type of graph that best represents a data set is determined by the type of data, whether quantitative or qualitative. Quantitative data are numerical data. Qualitative data are categorical in nature. Chapter 3 explores the different types of graphs along with some advantages and disadvantage of each type of graph.

Example:

Studies indicate that living with a spouse is associated with a reduced risk of mortality due to coronary heart disease in middle-aged individuals. However, it remains unclear whether marriage and other living arrangements are important both for the development of heart disease and survival following a heart attack. In a cohabitation study conducted in Finland, living arrangements categorized as married, cohabitating, single and living alone, and living with a nonromantic partner yielded interesting results. The table below presents the number of myocardial infarction fatal and nonfatal events that occurred during the period between the baseline year and the 12-year follow-up. (Kilpi et al., 2015).

Number of Myocardial Infarction (MI) Events

LIVING ARRANGEMENT	MEN	WOMEN	TOTAL
Marital partner	3694	967	4661
Cohabitating	531	130	661
Living with others (nonromantic)	674	214	888
Single and living alone	1017	321	1338
Total	5916	1632	7548

Determine which part of the study represents the descriptive branch of statistics.

Solution:

Descriptive statistics involves statements such as "Men who live with a marital partner have an age-adjusted myocardial infarction rate of 320," and "Women who live with a marital partner have an age-adjusted myocardial infarction rate of 401." Also, the chart represents the descriptive branch of statistics.

1.3.2 Inferential Statistics

The second branch of statistics is inferential statistics. Inferential statistics consists of using samples to make generalizations about populations, performing estimations and statistical tests, determining relationships among variables, and making predictions. A fundamental tool in inferential statistics is probability. The probability of an event is the chance of an event occurring. As described earlier, the theory of probability grew out of gambling. Games of chance such as playing cards, dice, bingo, and lotteries all rely on the laws of probability. Probability also has applications in other areas such as the insurance industry. Probability will be revisited in later chapters.

In addition to probability, inferential statistics involves hypothesis testing. This is a decision-making process for evaluating claims about a population based on information obtained from samples. Hypothesis testing will be discussed in later chapters as well. As with all introductory statistics textbooks, part of this book is devoted to descriptive statistics. However, the majority of this textbook is about inferential statistical methods.

Example:

Refer to the myocardial infarction study from Section 1.3.1. What conclusions might be drawn from the study using inferential statistics?

Solution:

A possible inference drawn for the study is that greater fatality due to myocardial infaection is associated with men who live alone. However, cohabitation is associated with a greater fatality from myocardial infarction in women.

1.3.3 Exercises

Understanding Concepts

1. What are the two major branches of statistics?

2. What is the branch of statistics that involves the organization, summarization, and display of data?

3. What is the branch of statistics that uses samples to generalize information about populations, perform estimations and statistical tests, determine relationships among variables, and make predictions?

4. In statistics, what represents information from observations, counts, measurements, and responses?

5. In statistics, which branch includes charts and graphs?

6. In statistics, which branch includes testing claims about the population based on samples?

True or false? In Exercises 7–12, determine whether the statement is true or false. If it is false, rewrite it as a true statement.

7. Quantitative data are categorical data.

8. Level of pain (1–10) is an example of quantitative data.

9. If the probability of an event is zero, the event will not occur.

10. An inference is an uneducated guess.

11. A sample is a subset of a population.

12. In statistics, a population is not necessarily a population of people.

Skill Building

13. How are descriptive statistics different from inferential statistics?

14. Give an example of a research study that would use descriptive statistics.

15. Describe an example of a research study that would use inferential statistics.

16. David conducts a study to find out the average time U.S. college students spend on social media (e.g. Instagram, Twitter, Facebook, etc.). David surveys 300 students on a local college campus by asking them that exact question. David finds that the average time students spend using social media is approximately 4 hours per week. Is this an example of descriptive statistics or inferential statistics? Why?

17. A college professor is interested in finding out if the students in a basic statistics class would prefer to learn statistics through examples related to politics or public health. The professor surveys all the students, and the results show that 81% of the students prefer public health examples, and 19% prefer examples in politics. Are these statistics examples of descriptive statistics or inferential statistics?

18. On election day, a student asks the first 100 voters if they are pleased with the presidential candidate on the ballot. Of the respondents, 52% say "yes." Is 52% an inferential statistic?

19. A popular late-night snack among college students is pizza. Students conduct surveys to find out the favorite type of crust on their campus: deep dish, thin crust, Neapolitan, or something else. They survey 300 students. Here are the number of people and percent that chose each type of crust:

CRUST TYPE	PERCENT	TOTALS
Thin	46	138
Deep Dish	13	39
Neapolitan	17	51
Other	24	72

The table shows that 46% of the respondents preferred thin crust pizza. Is the 46% a descriptive or inferential statistic?

20. Refer to the table in Exercise 19. The number of students that prefer deep dish crust pizza is 39. Is the number 39 an example of an inferential or descriptive statistic?

Extending Concepts

21. Is the number of dots that can appear of the faces of a die numerical or categorical data?

22. Does it make sense to start an analysis of some data with inferential statistics and follow up with descriptive statistics? Explain your answer.

23. Does "population" in statistics refer to a group of people or animals?

24. A student notices that other students in the statistics class with larger shoe sizes tend to have higher grades. Would the student use descriptive or inferential statistics to test the claim that students with larger shoe sizes have higher grades?

25. Does more data lead to better or worse predictions ?

1.4 Statistical Software Overview

Unless the size of the data set is small, statistical analysis done by hand or by using a calculator becomes really tedious, and the use of a computer becomes necessary. Computer software can help to do statistical analysis in the following areas:

- Organize, archive, assess quality, and carefully curate data sets
- Perform character and string manipulation to organize data in tables and lists
- Perform calculations according to formulas and algorithms established by the best statistical practices and methodologies
- Create informative reports that include various visualizations, plots, and diagrams that can concisely summarize vast amounts of information.

Numerous choices of computer solutions can be employed to execute the four statistical tasks listed above with different levels of facility, quality of results, and operational costs. In general, it can be argued that the more expensive the software, the better and easier to obtain the desired results. However, that may not be always true, or advisable, for the task at hand. Broadly, the software for doing statistics can be either part of a generic scientific computing software system or a specialized package.

Another dimension for consideration is the cost of software. *Open source*, or publicly available software, comes with minimal costs. Open source software benefits from having hundreds of highly qualified contributors and evolves continually over time. However, commercial software emerges from small, but motivated and goal-oriented teams and offers quality guarantees and significant technical support. Cost issues due to intellectual property rights could get in the way of updating and evolving commercial software. In the end, statistical software choices depend on the personal taste, familiarity, and, of course, budget.

1.4.1 Generic Scientific Computing Software

Many generic programming languages and programming environments, not specifically designed for statistics, have been adopted for performing scientific computing for various reasons. A researcher who is well versed in one generic software and who needs to perform occasional statistical analysis usually prefers to work with familiar tools. The advantage of learning any of these tools is that the skill learned by doing statistics with any of these languages will be easily transferable for other computational projects. Skills learned with one software package are usually transferable to other packages.

Here we discuss several scientific computing software options and how they are used for statistical analysis.

Python. Python is a popular scripting language among computer scientists, and it is increasingly popular for doing computational work. Specifically, researchers use the *SciPy* package as it offers a large number of functions for statistical work such as probability distributions and simulations. For numerical vectorization operations, *NumPy* package is an excellent choice. The *Matplotlib* package offers a variety of visualization and plotting functions. *Pandas* package has functions for connecting to various data sources and formats. *Statsmodels* is a Python module that provides classes and functions for the estimation of many different statistical models, as well as for conducting statistical tests, and statistical data exploration. In Python, all packages are free of charge, publicly available, and actively maintained.

MATLAB. MATLAB is a commercial software specializing in numerical linear algebra. A number of add-on packages are available for conducting statistical analysis, with a large number of functions covering many methods and techniques. MATLAB also includes excellent graphics capabilities.

Mathematica. Mathematica is a commercial symbolic algebra package with extensive numerical and graphics capabilities. Built-in functions can be used to do statistical analysis and tests, such as ANOVA. Mathematica adopts a functional language in which objects are represented by functions that can be chain linked to obtain solutions for complex problems. Mathematica also offers access to extensive and comprehensive data sets, and data format import and export.

C++ and Fortran. These are generic programming languages that create executable programs after compilation. Compilers for them are available commercially, but also as open source—the most notable compiler being *gcc*. Some statistical functionality can be found in more general mathematical and computational libraries such as *GSL*, *Boost*, or *Cephes*. Programing statistical analysis with C++ or Fortran requires more effort, but the solutions are expected to be much more efficient than any other approach.

1.4.2 Specialized Software Packages

A large number of software packages and environments are dedicated exclusively for dealing with statistical problems. Most of these solutions are commercial and have been developed for many decades, although many of them are also offered as free editions.

In addition to R, the most popular specialized software packages include the following:

- SPSS (Statistical Package for Social Sciences) is a program maintained by IBM used extensively in social sciences, marketing, surveys, government, and education research. SPSS was developed in 1968. PSPP is a free software alternative to IBM SPSS Statistics, developed in the late 1990s.
- SAS (Statistical Analysis System) is a software suite for data mining and retrieving. SAS is particularly good with large data sets. Its statistical analysis capabilities are especially useful in health services-based research and business analytics.
- STATA (statistics and data) is a general-purpose package created in 1985 and used for research in economics, sociology, political science, and epidemiology.
- Minitab is a package developed in 1972, which automates calculations and creations of graphs and reports allowing the user to focus more on data analysis and interpretation.

Object-Oriented Programming. Some statistical software has the quality of being designed following an object-oriented programming paradigm. The advantage of object orientation is revealed, for example, when performing regression analysis. A traditional statistical package such as SAS and SPSS will dump a mountain of output onto the screen. By contrast, an object-oriented program will return an object that encapsulates the relevant attributes together with methods that manipulate those attributes in various ways. *Polymorphism* refers to a quality of objects that makes a single function able to differentiate by the type of input and to process different objects in different ways. *Inheritance* means that a complicated object can be built from previously defined simpler ones, with no need to replicate code.

Functional Programming. Central to functional programming, also known as procedural programming, is the idea that any aspect to programming can be encapsulated in a function that has some input arguments, activates some side effects, and returns a value. This value can in turn be the argument of another function. A solution of a programming problem is therefore expressed as a chain of nested functions that create a processing pipe for the data from retrieval to reporting. For example, the compound command in R: `nrow(subset(G, z==1))` extracts all records that have the variable *z=1* from the data set G, and reports the number of such rows. The double equal "==" operator compares two values and returns True or False values.

The scripting language R for statistical data manipulation and analysis, which has been adopted for this book, occupies a unique position in the statistical software ecosystem. R is open source and has a very wide base of users and developers. It offers a rich, multipurpose, general programming language with both object-oriented aspects for developers and expert users. R also has a functional interface with thousands of commands. It was inspired by the statistical language S, an allusion to another one-letter language, C. As such, it offers a wealth of methods and interfaces that facilitate statistical computing. It is rich with methods of acquiring and importing data from many sources, and it comes by default with many quality data sources. The scripting language R is able to produce publication-quality graphics and automated reports. The R language is very expressive and free of unnecessary constructs we would need to use when working with a general-purpose language such as Python or C. Thus, R is experiencing a surge in popularity, as one of the preferred tools used by practitioners in modern data science and data analytics.

The purpose of this textbook is twofold. First, it provides a solid foundation in the field of statistics. Second, it offers a solid foundation in statistical computing using R. These foundations rely on a well-constructed personalized statistics study guide. The beginning section of this chapter provides students with step-by-step directions for creating such a study guide.

1.4.3 Exercises

Skill Building

1. What is a key difference between object-oriented programming and functional programming?

2. Define *software package*. Give an example of a popular open-source software package.

Extending Concepts

3. If you were in charge of conducting a statistical analysis of a large data set (e.g., one billion data points), what kind of statistical software would you use: commercial or open source? Explain and argue your choice.

4. Which statistical tasks are handled better by a functional programming style, and which tasks benefit from an object-oriented programming style?

5. Is Mathematica an object-oriented programming language?

6. If a function needs to perform one million calculations of a data set containing one million pieces of data, what programming language would you chose to implement your solution: R or Fortran? Explain your answer.

7. Explain why inheritance is a desired feature in software development.

Summary

Use these questions as a self-assessment checklist for this chapter:

1. How would you define the field of statistics?

2. What are the two major branches of statistics?

3. What are the different types of statistical software?

4. Have you started constructing your statistics study guide as outlined in this chapter?

References

Kilpi, F., Konttinen, H., Silventoinen, K., & Martikainen, P. (2015). Living arrangements as determinants of myocardial infarction incidence and survival: A prospective register study of over 300,000 Finnish men and women. *Social Science & Medicine, 133*, 93–100. https://doi.org/10.1016/j.socscimed.2015.03.054

Sutherland, I. (1963). John Graunt: A tercentenary tribute. *Journal of the Royal Statistical Society: Series A (General), 26*(4), 537–556.

Figure Credits

Fig. 1.1: Source: https://commons.wikimedia.org/wiki/File:Manuscript_Waste_(8680589579).jpg.
Fig. 1.2: Copyright © by Mobile Math, LLC.
Fig. 1.3: Source: https://commons.wikimedia.org/wiki/File:SARS-CoV-2_without_background.png.
Fig. 1.4: Source: https://commons.wikimedia.org/wiki/File:Birch_-_Yearly_bills_of_mortality%2C_1759_-_062.tif.
Fig. 1.5: Source: https://commons.wikimedia.org/wiki/File:Statistics_overview.pdf.

CHAPTER

2

Introduction to R

CHAPTER OUTLINE

2.1 Why R?

2.2 Installing R, RStudio, and Packages

2.3 Getting Started With R and RStudio

2.4 Data

2.5 CRAN (Comprehensive R Archive Network)

2.6 R and RStudio

CHAPTER OBJECTIVES

After completing this chapter, you will have acquired skills to:

1. Install R and RStudio.
2. Understand the basics of R and RStudio.
3. Implement various ways to enter data into R and RStudio.
4. Comprehend how to use CRAN.
5. Apply knowledge about R and RStudio.

R is one of the most widely used languages for statistical computing, analysis, and graphing in fields such as the sciences, finance, banking, health care, e-commerce, and marketing. Major internet-related companies such as Google, LinkedIn, and Facebook all use R for many of their operations. In this chapter you will learn the importance of digital fluency in today's world. You will also learn the fundamentals of statistical computing and graphics with R.

FIGURE 2.1 Digital World

Chapter Vocabulary

- **Big data** refers to the challenge of handling extremely large data sets that keep growing in various fields.
- A **script** is a list of commands that are stored in files and used to reproduce a calculation as if the commands are typed individually from the command line.
- **Identifier** is a name given to entities of a computer language, such as variables, data types, objects, or functions.
- A **factor** in R is a variable that takes a limited number of different values in order to represent a categorical variable. Factors may be displayed as numbers or strings, but conventional operations that make sense for numbers or strings are not defined for factors. A factor functions as a label for a possible value for a categorical variable.
- **Code fragments** are snippets or pieces of code that occur regularly in a program and may be collected for reuse.
- To **chain** a function is to pass an intermediate result onto the next function.
- A **Boolean expression** in programming is an expression that returns a value of true or false.
- In programming, a **type** is a set of possible values for a set of operations.
- **Markup language** instructions are textual descriptions of the style and formatting of documents that need to appear on computer screens or printed on paper. Markup documents are simple text files that are easy to store and transmit between computers. HyperText Markup Language (HTML) is used to encode documents displayed in a web browser. LaTeX is a markup language and document preparation system for high-quality typesetting that is often used for mathematical or scientific publishing.
- **Markdown** is a simplified and reduced markup language.
- **Bitmap graphics** are computer representations of images that use colored pixels in file formats such as joint photographic experts group (JPEG or JPG), graphics interchange format (GIF), and bitmap (BMP).
- **Vector graphics** are computer representations of images that describe them in terms of geometric elements and features without using grids of pixels.

2.1 Why R?

Unlike general purpose programming languages like Fortran, C, or Java, R is not designed by software engineers for software development. The development of the programming language R was started by statisticians as an interactive environment for data analysis and exploration. Because of its easy use with intuitive names and easy syntax, especially when dealing with multidimensional numerical quantities such as vectors and matrices, R gradually has been adopted by other communities of computational scientists as well. The predecessor of R is the S programming language that was created in 1976 and later updated to S-Plus. R was released in 1995 at the University of Auckland in New Zealand. At the time, R mainly was used in academia and in research as a free version of S-Plus.

R has since had a phenomenally successful evolution as a statistical analysis package. R has a vibrant community of users both nationally and internationally. Moreover, it has several advantages over its commercial competitors, which most often have prohibitive costs and are feature-locked. In contrast, extensions to R are constantly being developed and released quickly by its large and supportive community of users through the Comprehensive R Archive Network (CRAN). These extensions can be added to any user's existing version of R to upgrade its capabilities. Because of CRAN and its extensibility, R is always evolving.

QR Code Sidebar 2.1

Comprehensive R Archive Network (CRAN): https://cran.r-project.org

2.1.1 Big Data Applications

Recently, R's popularity has been boosted by its adoption by researchers in data science, machine learning, and artificial intelligence. It is clear that R will continue to develop and grow over the next decades and far beyond. R allows users to do practically any type of statistical analysis or graphic representation. Researchers that use R extend beyond academia to companies such as Google, Facebook, Pfizer, Merck, Shell, the Intercontinental Hotels Group, Bank of America, Sun Trust, and governmental agencies such as the U.S. Food and Drug Administration.

There currently is a big data trend for handling larger data sets in governmental agencies, academia, and corporations and also a movement for merging statistics and data science. Therefore, students enrolled in elementary statistics courses from both scientific and nonscientific disciplines need to be able to use R to download data files, download computer code, and write R programs. This textbook addresses both national and English-speaking international students' needs by guiding them from the very basics of R to its more complex, challenging uses.

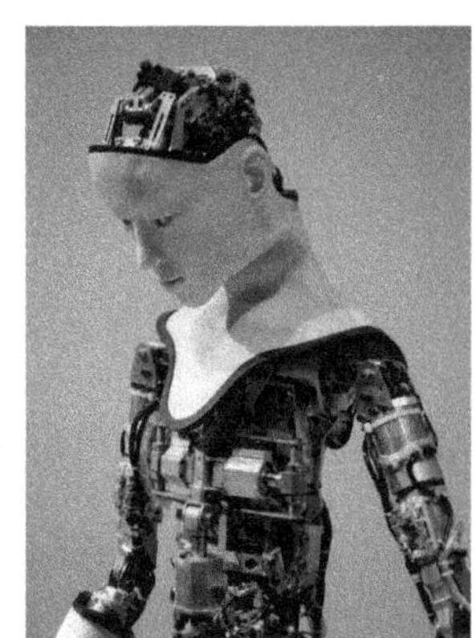

FIGURE 2.2 World of Artificial Intelligence

2.1.2 Main Features of R

Interactivity, a fundamental trait of R, is an indispensable feature in data science because the ability to quickly explore data is a necessity for success in data science. Every R session can be saved as a script, which can be easily executed at any time. These scripts serve as a record of the work performed and of all steps and analyses done, which can then be re-executed on a different data set. An expert programmer with a background in computer science may be surprised that R does not follow many of the programmer's conventions. However, the liberties taken in the design of the R language serve the goal of empowering the practitioner and making it as easy as possible to analyze data quickly, obtain detailed reports, and produce publication-quality data visualization, all in one package.

R has the following features:

- R is free, open source, and widely available for all major operating systems, Windows™, MacOS™, and Unix/Linux™, so that R programs can be shared and executed by anyone.

- R makes it easy to share ideas, techniques, and accomplishments. An increasingly large user base that shares their work through a package repository and forums has been active for the last 20 years.
- R's performance can be improved, and extensions can be built in other programming languages such as C, C++, and Fortran. This makes it easy to port and reuse software that has been polished and already used in different contexts.
- R has extensive capabilities for creating publication-quality graphics and reports, interactive web pages, and so on.
- R can be used as a functional programing language, but at the same time it has object-oriented underlying constructs that could be useful for some projects or programming styles. A number of excellent features such as integrated development environments (IDE) are available.
- R is easy to learn just by reading code. It has an extensive help system, detailed documentation that comes complete with code examples, and vibrant online communities.

2.1.3 Pros and Cons of R

However, like any human artifact, R is not perfect or suitable for every need. It has certain shortcomings, some of which are listed below:

- Most code is written by non-programmers in haste to solve a pressing problem. Hence, they are not always paying attention to software engineering best practices. The code may not be elegant, fast, or easy to understand. Source code control or automated testing is rarely used in conjunction with R programming.
- Some inconsistencies stemming from over 20 years of evolution by a diverse user base are to be expected. The language is littered by many special cases and language quirks.
- Because R was invented in an era when human interaction with computers was limited to text consoles, R may have a steeper learning curve.
- The fact that many operations and results can be expressed in several different ways in R has lowered the adoption barrier by offering the possibility of different programming styles. Unfortunately, this has been a source of confusion and frustration.

Programming in R can be done in many different ways. The simplest way does not require any software installation on a personal computer. Instead, R programming environments are offered by some websites, simply through a browser. An example of such a service is RStudio Cloud. You can discover many such services after a quick search. Facilities for programming in R also come in software packages that need to be installed. For example, the Anaconda programming framework, designed in principal for Python-driven data science, has a full-featured R component. Most practitioners however prefer to install R on their computer right from its creators, following the steps explained in the next section.

2.2 Installing R, RStudio, and Packages

Being open source and free to use, R and all the packages that form the R ecosystem are very straightforward to install on a computer in a variety of ways, including compilation from source code. In this section, you will learn how to download R and RStudio. To get started, first download R.

2.2.1 Installing R

The easiest way to install R is through CRAN as detailed below:

1. Browse to http://www.r-project.org
2. Click the "download R" link under the "Getting Started" heading.
3. Select a CRAN location and click the corresponding link. CRAN is a network of servers around the world that store identical, up-to-date versions of R code, documentation, libraries and packages. You should choose such a site, called a mirror, to be geographically close to you in order to get fast downloading speed and to minimize the network load.
4. Click the "Download R for ..." link at the top of the page. Choose the platform appropriate for your computer, such as Windows, MacOS X, or Linux. Each platform offers essentially the same experience regardless of the operating system.
5. Click on the file containing the latest version of R under "Files," and select the version recommended for your operating system.
6. After downloading R, click to start the installation program. It is safe to choose the default options during the setup. One such option is the location of installation. R can be installed in the default system location, but it will work as well from a folder within the user's home directory. It even works when installed on a flash drive.

2.2.2 Installing RStudio

Because RStudio is an integrated development environment for R that works with the standard version of R available from CRAN, you need to have already installed R version 2.11.1 or higher in order to run RStudio.

1. Browse to http://www.rstudio.com/products/rstudio/download/ and download RStudio Desktop for your system.
2. Follow the installation and setup procedures.

Again, it is safest to choose the default options when in doubt. You are now ready to start your first session in R. The following section demonstrates how to open your first session in R.

2.3 Getting Started With R and RStudio

This section contains some examples of how to use R and RStudio for creating graphical representations of the data as well as methods for computing some basic statistics. It is important to obtain the explanation of outputs from the help menu of R and RStudio for complete understanding.

QR Code Sidebar 2.2

RStudio Cloud: https://rstudio.cloud

QR Code Sidebar 2.3

The R Project for Statistical Computing: http://www.r-project.org

FIGURE 2.3 Keyboard Lights

QR Code Sidebar 2.4

Download the RStudio IDE: http://www.rstudio.com/products/rstudio/download/

Note that the "R and RStudio" sections of this textbook are not designed as manuals for the software. The idea is to introduce some basic procedures so that you can get started with applying the statistics you have learned in each chapter. The goal is also to see some of R's and RStudio's capabilities.

2.3.1 Basics of R

The most basic way of interacting with R during a work session is through the R console, where R gives a response after each line of typed commands. A sequence of commands can be saved in a script file in the R Editor window and then executed at once, with the response for each command echoed on the console as text. A typical interactive console session might look like this:

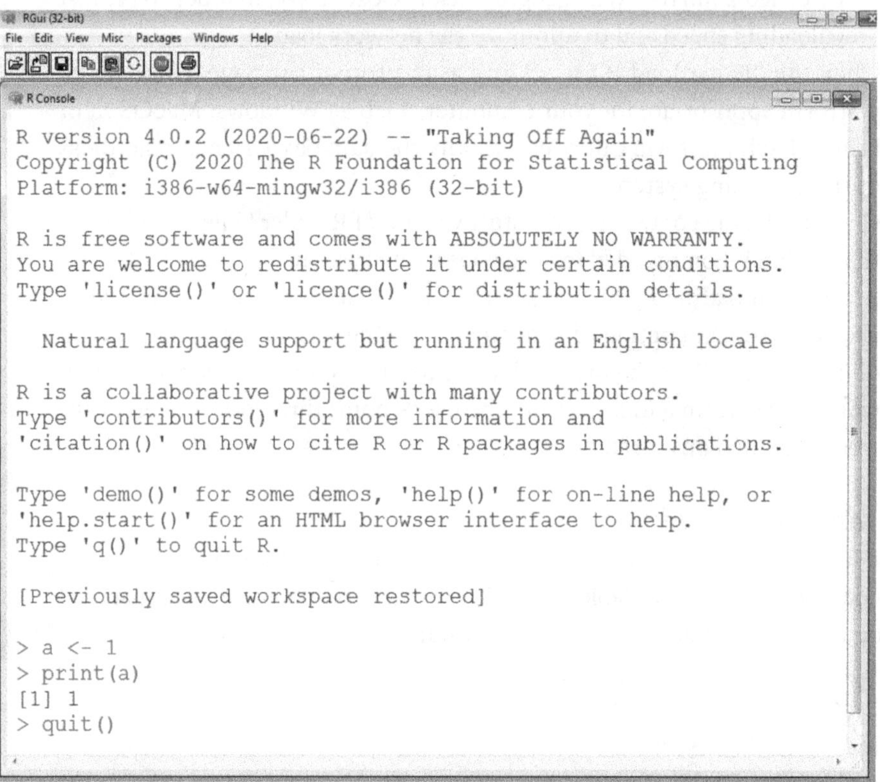

FIGURE 2.4 A Console in Windows

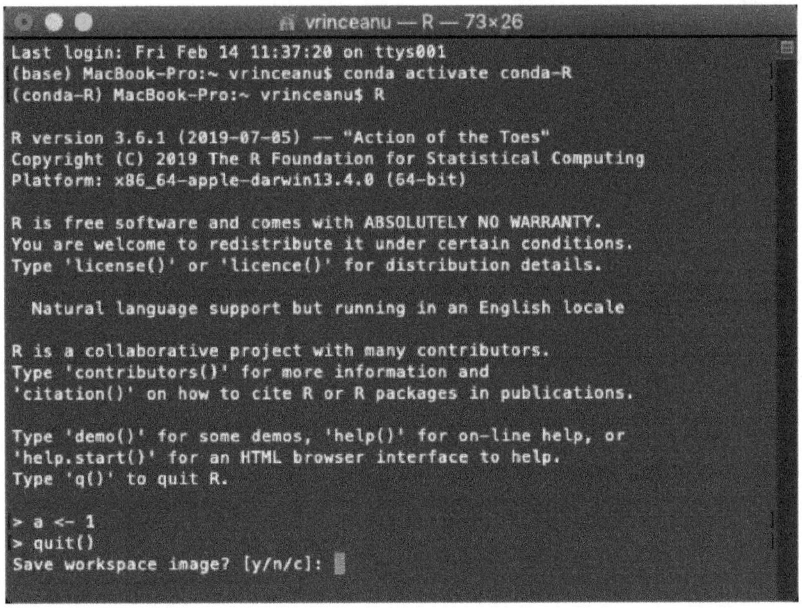

```
vrinceanu — R — 73×26
Last login: Fri Feb 14 11:37:20 on ttys001
(base) MacBook-Pro:~ vrinceanu$ conda activate conda-R
(conda-R) MacBook-Pro:~ vrinceanu$ R

R version 3.6.1 (2019-07-05) -- "Action of the Toes"
Copyright (C) 2019 The R Foundation for Statistical Computing
Platform: x86_64-apple-darwin13.4.0 (64-bit)

R is free software and comes with ABSOLUTELY NO WARRANTY.
You are welcome to redistribute it under certain conditions.
Type 'license()' or 'licence()' for distribution details.

  Natural language support but running in an English locale

R is a collaborative project with many contributors.
Type 'contributors()' for more information and
'citation()' on how to cite R or R packages in publications.

Type 'demo()' for some demos, 'help()' for on-line help, or
'help.start()' for an HTML browser interface to help.
Type 'q()' to quit R.

> a <- 1
> quit()
Save workspace image? [y/n/c]:
```

FIGURE 2.5 Interacting With R From a Terminal Window in MacOS X

Figure 2.5 displays a prompt '>' after a welcome message indicates that the system is ready to receive and process commands that can be typed on the keyboard. After you press *Enter*, the system will start processing, present the result as text in the console, and display the prompt again when ready to receive a new command. This programming interface technique is known as a *read-eval-print loop* (REPL).

As there are many possible commands with a myriad of options and variants, you might feel overwhelmed. However, the command `help(`*topic*`)` will display a detailed multipage explanation about any command, which can be scrolled by pressing *Space*. Pressing *q* will terminate the help command interaction and return the R prompt. The R session itself terminates by executing the command `quit()` or simply `q()`. Please note the set of parentheses `()` after each command. This is because every R command is actually a function, and a function is recognized by an identifier followed by a list of arguments enclosed between parentheses. Even if there were no arguments, parentheses must be present. Otherwise, R will try to get a variable or an object with that name, instead of the function with that name (*quit* in this case).

Conveniently, R can be used as a quick calculator. Try using the console to calculate a 15% tip on a meal that costs $15.50:

```
0.15*15.50
```

```
## [1] 2.325
```

For the rest of this section we will cover the very basics of the R programming, which will allow you to start learning how to use it for statistical analysis in subsequent chapters of this book, when more advanced R commands will be introduced in the context of specific statistical concepts. This section contains the basic building blocks that are required to gain more advanced R skills.

Although it might seem that some of these building blocks might not be immediately obvious, later in this book you will appreciate having mastered these topics. Learning R is cumulative.

Every computer language has variables that can store values. In R, variables have data type and structure, but they do not have to be declared before use. For example, with commands

```
a <- 1
b <- 2.3
a <- "aha"
```

we assign the value 1 to variable a, and b will hold numerical value 2.3, and finally, a will store the character string "aha," so that its old value 1 will no longer be available. Unless there is an error, R will not print anything in response to these commands. However, those objects are now defined and stored in places identified with the names a and b and can be retrieved or used anytime in an expression like this:

```
a
```

```
## [1] "aha"
b
```

```
## [1] 2.3
```

```
print(a)
```

```
## [1] "aha"
```

```
d = sqrt(b^2 - 2*b + pi)
```

as long as the R session is saved before logging out. Note that we omitted the input prompt ">" and indicated the R answer by "##" for clarity.

Objects can be simple numbers or strings or more complicated constructs such as functions and data frames. Note that we used = instead of <- to the same effect of assigning the value of the mathematical expression $\sqrt{b^2 - 2b + \pi}$ to variable d. We did not use a variable *c* in order to avoid confusion with the function *concatenate*, which is one way to form a vector in R. Furthermore, R is case-sensitive. For example, c is not the same as *C*.

There is essentially no difference between the two ways to make assignments, although some people consider that <- is more expressive. Unlike other programming languages, the mathematical constant π is available right away in R as the predefined variable *pi*.

The command ls() lists the collection of all variables created during a session, called the workspace. A specific variable can be removed from the workspace with command rm(). At the end of a session, we have the option of saving the workspace in the R Console window for continuing or documenting the work. However, it is often better for beginners to not save their work in the R Console window when logging out because a built-in R function can accidentally be overwritten. It is instead advised to save all work in the R Editor window. Saving in the R Editor window always needs to occur before compiling and running new or edited code.

```
ls()
```

```
## [1] "a" "b" "c"
```

Functions in R may take zero or more arguments. Some arguments might be optional, thus having a default value defined by the function. For example, the logarithm can be calculated as follows:

```
log(8)
```

```
## [1] 2.079442
```

You can get details about this function by typing the following into the R Console window:

```
help("log")
```

For most functions this also works:

```
?log
```

The help page displays the exact definition of this function, what result to expect when used, and which arguments are expected by the system. For example, the documentation says: "The general form *log(x, base)* computes logarithms with base *base*." Here *log* needs *x* and *base* to run, but this function will work even when only *x* is given. It assumes a natural logarithm by default. The function `args` shows a quick look at arguments of a function, without opening the help system.

```
args(log)
```

```
## function (x, base = exp(1))
## NULL
```

This means that we can use the function like this:

```
# here we calculate the log in base 2 !
log(8, base=2)
```

```
## [1] 3
```

If a line of code starts with the symbol #, then all the text following it will be ignored. This symbol is used to mark comments and reminders intended to be read by humans, not computers.

The most common way of storing data in R is the data frame. Conceptually, the data frame is a list of vectors. If each vector is imagined as a column of elements, the data frame looks like a matrix with rows for each record and columns for each field. In R, a vector is a collection of objects of the same type, while a list is a collection of heterogeneous or different elements. All vectors in a data frame have the same size.

Vectors are the most fundamental data type in R. Even a scalar is represented as a one-component vector. Here is a demonstration of creating a vector:

```
area.codes <- c(713, 281, 382)
area.codes

## [1] 713 281 382
```

Note that the vector's name in this example contains a dot "area.codes." Unlike some other programming languages, R does not apply any special meaning to the dot, which can be used in variable naming.

Vectors have all elements of the same type. They may be logical, integers, numerical, or a string of characters. A factor is a special type of datum useful for storing categorical data and therefore can have a limited set of enumerated values, named *levels*. For example, we build a vector of directions, get its length, and display the set of labels associated with each category (levels):

```
wind <- factor(c("north", "west", "south", "east", "north", "west"))
length(wind)
## [1] 6

levels(wind)

## [1] "east"  "north" "south" "west"
```

Small vectors are easy to create by typing their components inside the concatenate `c()` function, but larger ones are easier to create with special commands like `seq()`, which generates a list of consecutive numbers, or `rep()` which replicates one value across a vector.

In the example below we combine a vector of five consecutive numbers, by using the much simpler operator : instead of `seq()`, with a vector that contains the value 10 repeated 5 times, and then print a slice of the vector by using the colon operator : to generate a range of indices.

```
grades <-c(c(2:6), rep(10,5))
print(grades)          # print the whole vector

##  [1]  2  3  4  5  6 10 10 10 10 10

print(grades[4:8])    # print only elements 4 through 8
## [1]  5  6 10 10 10
```

This code fragment shows some typical R usage. The comment character # is used to make a comment on the same line that has some actionable items. Anything following the comment character is ignored (by R, hopefully not the reader) until the end of the line of code. Functions can be chained because their return becomes arguments for other functions, that in turn return values that can become arguments, and so on. The square brackets `[ ]` and parentheses `( )`

are used in very different ways. The square brackets `[ ]` access the elements of a list or data frame and can be used to both extract and assign values to elements. Parentheses `( )` enclose actual function parameters.

Like Fortran and Mathematica, the first element of a vector is the element with index 1. This is in contrast to other programing language like C and Python in which the index of the first element is 0. The vector called "grades" in the example below can be further modified by updating its first and last element and even by adding an extra element at the end:

```
grades[1] = 0
grades[length(grades)] = 11
grades[length(grades) + 1] = 1
print(grades)
```

```
## [1]  0  3  4  5  6 10 10 10 10 11  1
```

A negative index would select all elements other than the one, or ones, specified. Using a Boolean expression inside the `[ ]` brackets will select only elements for which the expression is true, as Boolean expressions only return `"true"` or `"false"` values. Here we discover and print the number of elements of the vector `"grades"` that are less than 6:

```
print(length(grades[grades < 6]))
```

```
## [1] 5
```

Most vector operations are applied element by element. Like in the example above, there is no need to create a loop to obtain the result. Although old-fashioned loops such as `for()` and `while()` work in R similar to any other computer language, you will discover that they are not always necessary in R because most mathematical operations are vectorized, meaning they are done efficiently at once. Actually, you should be aware that if you decide to use old fashioned loops, your program could become much slower. This code fragment

```
grades**3/sqrt(abs(1 - grades^2))
```

```
##  [1]   0.000000   9.545942  16.524729  25.515518  36.510664 100.503782
##  [7] 100.503782 100.503782 100.503782 121.503121        Inf
```

calculates the expression $x^3/\sqrt{|1-x^2|}$ for each element x in the vector `grades`. Note that here we have expressed the power operation in three different, but equivalent, ways: with `**` operator, with function `sqrt()` representing power 1/2, and with operator `^`. The result for the last element is, of course, ill-defined, but instead of bringing the whole program to a halt, R graciously marks this element with a special non-numerical value `Inf` representing infinity. Other non-numerical values that can be used to represent missing numbers are `NA` (not available), or `NaN` (not a number).

Many interesting functions that operate on vectors may return other types such as variables, expressions, or modules. You have already seen that `length(grades)` returns the size of the vector, which is the number of elements the vector contains. The code fragment below shows how the mean, median, maximum, and minimum of the vector grades is calculated:

```
mean(grades)

## [1] 6.363636

median(grades)

## [1] 6
max(grades)

## [1] 11

min(grades)

## [1] 0
```

Among the many thousands of functions available by default in R, or created by other users, chances are you will find functions that will help you solve most statistical problems. Otherwise you have to invent and create your own new functions. Defining and working with new functions in R is very easy, as demonstrated in the example below:

```
# a new user-defined function to print squares of consecutive
numbers
new.function <- function(a){
  for(k in 1:a){
    b <- k^2
    print(b)
  }
}
new.function(6)

## [1] 1
## [1] 4
## [1] 9
## [1] 16
## [1] 25
## [1] 36
```

An R script is a text file, normally with the extension ".R", that contains a sequence of R commands that are to be executed as if typed from the console. Any simple plain text editor can be used to write scripts. Conveniently, the GUI R console program also has a code editor that can be accessed through the "File" menu, and used to save and edit script files. When saving a file, choose a special folder where you can keep all your work, and name the file in a suggestive way. Avoid using spaces in the script file name. A script file can be executed from a Terminal Window in a Mac or Linux computer by typing the `Rscript` command followed by the name of the script.

Within the GUI R console a script is executed by using the `source("name _ of _ file.R")` function. The argument of this function is the name of your script. R searches for this file in the working directory, which by default is your home directory. To change the working directory use the `setwd()` function, or the menu "Misc". The function `getwd()` prints the current working directory. For example, *setwd("C:/Users/Your_Name/Documents/R-Work")* changes the working directory to the directory where you decided to keep R scripts, and `source("my _ script.R")` runs a script saved in this directory. Alternatively, you can select a group of commands in the editor window, and execute them by pressing Ctrl-Enter, (or Command-Enter on a Mac computer).

You are now programming! The beauty of learning R is that these programming skills are transferable to other object-oriented programs like C++.

2.3.2 RStudio and Reproducible Research

RStudio is an integrated development environment for programming in R, meaning that it is an application that uses a graphical interface, as opposed to the simple console, for facilitating development of R code. Learning RStudio is not required to program in R, but by gathering several resources, it can make R programming a little bit easier for some. However, the menu-driven interface and the three, four, or more window panels that present a wealth of information and options can be intimidating for others. Each window serves as a precise scope into the development process. A typical configuration is shown in the figure with the main window and four quadrants.

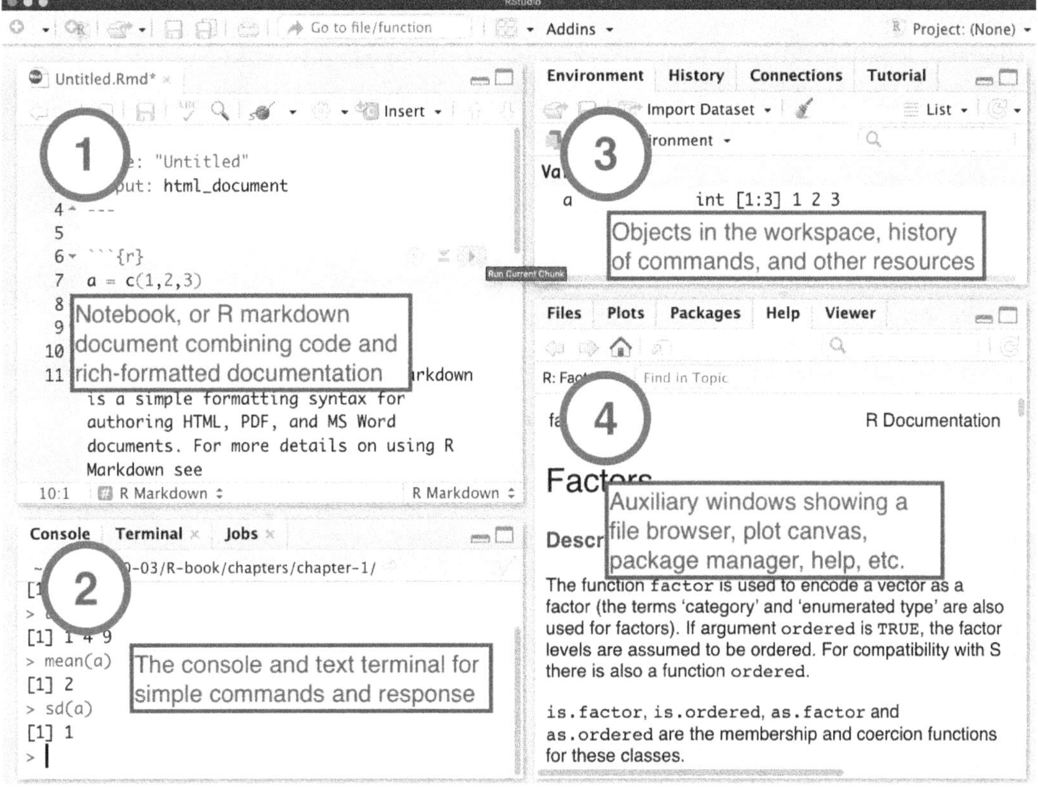

FIGURE 2.6 RStudio Configuration

Some of the panels, as shown in Figure 2.6, are as follows:

1. The source panel is a programming text editor, a notepad where you create R scripts, text files with an ".R" extension. These files should be saved often. R does not actually evaluate the code as you are typing. Evaluating the code is done by sending the code to the R console, then clicking the "Run" button.
2. The console is the central place where code is executed in a session that can be terminated or restarted. You can interact with the console in the regular way by typing commands and receiving the answer. Code can also be passed to it through other mechanisms. Another tab in this panel can open a terminal window with access to a shell environment where you can interact with the operating system.
3. Environment and history panels show the current workspace with variables, data frames, and other runtime introspective information. A history of all commands in the session is also accessible.
4. The files/plots/packages/help panel gives access to a wealth of critical information relating to your R program. The files tab shows the current directory and the files it holds. Plots is a graphical window where the R graphics and other non-text output can be displayed. The packages tab displays a list of packages that are already installed or available for download. Packages that are loaded in the current session are checked, while packages that are installed but not yet loaded are unchecked. The help menu is the place where R documentation can be consulted.

RStudio has the ability to collect not only the executable scripts, but also the output of those commands along with documentation text that can be styled and formatted. Mathematical equations are represented in this format by using LaTeX markup language. The resulting self-contained R Markdown document achieves several important goals:

- The results can be replicated by anyone using only the information in this file and nothing else.
- The methods and procedures used are documented in the same place as the code, so the chances of having the documentation out of sync with the code are much reduced.
- It is robust in the sense that mistakes are easier to spot and correct.
- Reports and nicely formatted documents can be obtained by the click of a button.

2.4 Data

Data are facts or statistics collected together for reference or analysis. Data can be accessed in several ways when using R such as built-in, simulated, and imported. Built-in data sets are typically used for demonstration purposes. Data can be simulated using several R commands. Data can be imported into R from an unformatted text (.txt) file, comma-separated value (.csv) file, Microsoft Excel™ file, and files from other statistical software packages such as IBM SPSS™, or even a resource over the internet.

2.4.1 Ways to Input and Download Data

When working with your own data, the commands `data.entry()`, `edit()`, and other related commands help you enter and manage data. The function `scan()` will simply read numbers you type from the console into a vector until the EOF (end-of-file) signal is received, which can be *Ctrl-D* on a Mac or Linux computer or *Ctrl-Z* on Windows.

The package `datasets` contains a collection of useful, carefully curated data sets. This package is installed by default, and the data frames available are listed with the command

```
data()
```

A specific data frame is selected with the command

```
data(cars)
```

after which the data frame "cars" becomes available for use. For example:

```
summary(cars)
```

```
##      speed           dist       
##  Min.   : 4.0   Min.   :  2.00  
##  1st Qu.:12.0   1st Qu.: 26.00  
##  Median :15.0   Median : 36.00  
##  Mean   :15.4   Mean   : 42.98  
##  3rd Qu.:19.0   3rd Qu.: 56.00  
##  Max.   :25.0   Max.   :120.00
```

To see the first six rows from the table use:

```
head(cars)
```

```
##   speed dist
## 1     4    2
## 2     4   10
## 3     7    4
## 4     7   22
## 5     8   16
## 6     9   10
```

A typical R session starts with data stored in a data frame that can be one of the R default sets or can be obtained by loading a package with the command `library()`.

There are several other ways to obtain data in the form of data frames. Data can be stored in comma-separated values (.csv) text files or in spreadsheet files created by software like Google Sheets™ or Microsoft Excel™. For example, the command

```
dat <- read _ csv(filename)
```

will read the file and create a data frame *dat* with the data from the file.

The package `readxl` has functions for importing Excel spreadsheets into R.

QR Code Sidebar 2.5

https://DataAnalysisUsingR.com/datasets/murders.csv

```
library(readxl)
table <- read _ xlsx(filename)
```

Data in R can also be acquired from databases and by downloading from the internet because the `read _ csv` function can also be used with an URL, not only with local files. For example,

```
dat <- read _ csv("https://DataAnalysisUsingR.com/datasets/
murders.csv")
```

If you need to save a copy of this resource locally then you use the command:

QR Code Sidebar 2.6

https://DataAnalysisUsingR.com/Rcode/tables.R

```
download.file(https://DataAnalysisUsingR.com/datasets/
murders.csv,
 "murders.csv").
```

This command will download and save the data locally to a file. It will erase the content of the file if a file with that name already exists in your file system.

2.4.2 Graphics and Visual Representation of Data

In addition to manipulating vectors of numbers and calculating results, R has a very powerful means of creating and customizing graphical representations of data. R produces publication-quality illustrations and plots for direct and effective communication of complex statistical results and analyses. As a matter of fact, many figures and tables in this book are produced by R scripts that can be obtained online from Cognella Active Learning resources for this textbook.

QR Code Sidebar 2.7

https://DataAnalysisUsingR.com/Rcode/figures.R

With R graphics, first choose the destination medium for all subsequent graphics operations. The metaphor for this is an artist choosing a canvas before starting a painting. By default, the graphics are displayed on the screen using a system-dependent window painting library. Often times, you will want to have graphics saved to a file. There are two major format choices—bitmap and vector graphics.

The family of bitmap graphics formats, such as PNG and JPEG, are customarily used for saving photographs and scanned images in a lossy or lossless way, meaning that values of individual pixels might be averaged and interpolated for the sake of creating smaller-sized files. The limitation in terms of a fixed number of pixels becomes apparent when you try to scale a bitmap graphics to display and "pixelation" of the image occurs. This happens often when the graphics are to be used with different media. For example, it may show fine on a PowerPoint slide on a computer display with a typical density of 72 pixels per inch, but not when printed on a journal page with a laser printer at 600 pixels per inch. Thus, the use of bitmap format should be avoided for publication-quality graphics, unless absolutely necessary.

The vector graphics formats adopt a different strategy for representing graphics in that everything that should appear on the screen or on paper is decomposed into primitive geometrical elements such as lines, squares, circles, glyphs, and so on. The advantage is that it is the responsibility of the end device to create an image that looks as good as possible for the given scale and resolution. The first generation of laser printers used this more economical way of accepting data from computers, instead of arrays of pixels or bitmaps. The computer language used for this is called PostScript, a predecessor of the ubiquitous pdf format. Scientific graphics tend to use this kind of format because it scales easily and looks good even when used with different media.

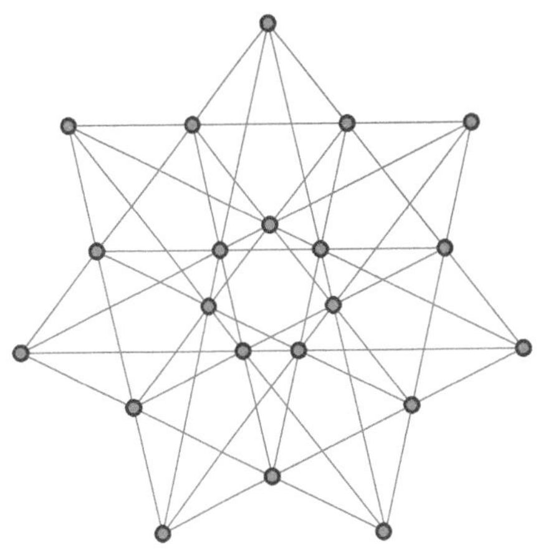

FIGURE 2.7 Grünbaum–Rigby Configuration, Vector Graphics

Once a medium is defined, for example, with a command like `png(file = 'nice_chart.png')` to create a *.png* file with your graphics, R has a large number of functions for drawing on the blank canvas, changing colors, changing line width, and many other graphical features. The R base graphics package provides, by default, simple functions to create many types of graphs. Two alternative graphics packages, *lattice graphs* and *ggplot2,* offer more powerful and advanced functionality but have to be installed and set up separately. They are more complicated to use.

The code fragment below demonstrates a few basic rules for using R's integrated graphics system.

```
x = seq(0, 10, by = 0.1)
y = sin(x)
plot(x, y, "l", xlab = expression(phi), ylab = "sin function")
text(5.0, 0.7, expression(e^{i*pi} + 1 == 0), cex = 1.6)
```

The function `plot()` needs two vectors for the x and y coordinates of the data to be plotted. If only one vector is given, then the x-coordinates will be generated as a default sequence 1, 2, 3, ... The "l" option indicates that the points to be plotted are joined by lines. The labels used along the axes specified by the optional arguments `xlab` and `ylab` can be simple strings of characters or a special function `expression()` that can be used to express Greek letters, superscripts, subscripts, and other mathematical notations that are otherwise difficult to obtain. The function `text()` is used to annotate graphics by placing some text at a given position in the graph's coordinates and magnification expressed by the optional parameter `cex`.

The R graphics system is designed such that simple graphs can be obtained with very few lines of code. At the same time, numerous options and additional functions can be used to customize R graphics with a high degree of precision while creating a large variety of graphs and plots.

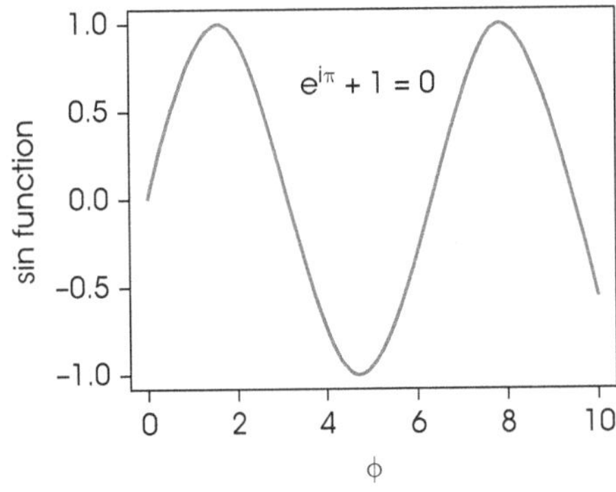

FIGURE 2.8 Sin Function

QR Code Sidebar 2.8

https://DataAnalysisUsingR.com/datasets/first_year_stress.dat

2.4.3 Exercises

Skill Building

1. List the type of data that can be loaded into R or RStudio.

2. What are the main differences between R and RStudio in terms of inputting data?

3. What is a function that is used to manually input data?

4. The data file "first_year_stress.dat" contains data on the perceived stress level of college students during their freshman year on a scale of 1–10 with 10 being high stress level. The data set contains a single column and a snapshot of the first 10 rows is shown below. What is the header for this data file?

STRESS LEVEL
3
8
8
5
4
5
8
6
6
6.5

5. Load the data file that is mentioned in Exercise 4 and assign it a name of `Stress` in R. What command did you use to load the data? How many rows of data are in the data set?

6. The data file in Exercise 4 is missing five rows of data. Those five rows are shown below:

6
7
9
8
8

Add the data in the table above to the `Stress` data frame that you created in R in Exercise 5. Now view the updated data frame to confirm that it is correct. What function did you use? How many records are there now in the combined data set?

7. Export the combined Stress data frame to a .csv file. Which command was used to export the data?

Extending Concepts

8. If `x = c (4, INF, 2, 4, 3, 2, 4, NA)`, what are the levels of `factor(x)`?

9. Write an R command to create a list `z` with two elements that are vectors of length 1 named `x` and `y` with values 1 and 2.

10. Add to the vector in Exercise 9 a third vector of length 1, `w` = 5.

11. Which command will create the string `Hello world` from variables `x = "Hello"` and `y="World"`?

12. Plot in the same graph a blue parabola and an orange exponential function.

2.5 CRAN (Comprehensive R Archive Network)

There are thousands of contributed packages for R. New packages are continuously being written by researchers, professors, and other experts in the field. Most of these contributed packages are available for download from CRAN. Some of the CRAN packages implement specialized statistical methods, while others give access to data or are designed to complement textbooks.

2.5.1 Introduction to CRAN

Almost all aspects of computational science are covered by R's extensions and packages. For example, low-level network connection capabilities and a variety of databases connector are available in R. Coupled with strong numerical algorithms and high quality graphics, the R ecosystem has become the preferred tool for researchers in many fields outside traditional statistics, such as bioinformatics, machine learning, artificial intelligence, and data science. Part of the appeal of R is its very large pool of contributors. Most user-contributed packages are well documented with detailed explanations, case studies, and examples.

Although R is an open-source project supported by a community of developers, some companies strive to provide commercial support and R extensions for their customers.

QR Code Sidebar 2.9

CRAN Task Views

A list of the current packages organized by topics is available at https://cran.r-project.org/web/views/.

2.5.2 Installing R Packages

As of July 2022, there were more than 18,000 packages that vastly extend the default limited capabilities of R. A number of important packages are part of the R standard installation, but many user-created packages implement specialized statistical techniques, graphical devices, import and export capabilities, reporting tools, and data sets. For example, the Bioconductor project provides R packages for analysis of genomic data. The easiest way to install and activate a package is to use the *Packages* tab in the fourth quadrant of the RStudio Desktop environment or to navigate to the "*Tools*" menu and select "*install packages.*" Packages can also be installed from the console. Type *help*("*INSTALL*") or *help*("*install.packages*") for information regarding the process. Browse to https://cran.r-project.org/web/views/ to see a list of packages organized by topic, with a full description of their capabilities.

The functions and variables defined in a package can be used in the programs contained in this textbook after loading the package content with the command `library`. For example, `library(my_package)` will load a package named *my_package*. If you try to load a package and get an error, it probably means that you need to install the package first. Once installed, it remains installed. At this point, it only needs to be loaded with the command `library`. The package remains loaded until you quit the R session.

The command `install.packages('my_package')` will install a package named, for example, *my_package*. This means that the package is downloaded and placed in the correct position in the file system. You can list all installed packages available with function `installed.packages()`.

2.5.3 Exercises

Skill Building

1. CRAN stands for what?

2. What are CRAN packages, and how are they used?

3. Name a CRAN package that is installed in R and RStudio.

4. The definition of the statistical term *mode* is the value that occurs most frequently in a data set. In the data shown below, the sample X has mode 2.

X
1
2
3
2
2
2

Load the CRAN package *DescTools*. Use it to compute the mode of the Stress Level variable from the data set called "first_year_stress.dat" that was used in Exercise 4 of section 2.4.3.

Extending Concepts

5. Search CRAN and find a package that allows you to access and work with international COVID-19 data sets.

6. What is the current number of official packages in CRAN?

7. What is the difference among different mirrors that you are asked to select when using CRAN?

8. How many packages are in your current R installation? Write an R command to print this number by using the command `installed.packages`.

2.6 R and RStudio

2.6.1 Programming Assignments

Exercise 2.1

Two vectors are defined as

```
x = c(1,3,5,7,9)
y = c(2,3,5,7,11,13)
```

Can you guess the results of the following R commands?

```
x + 1
```

```
y*2
```

```
sum(x>5)
```

```
sum(x[x>5])
```

```
sum(y[x>5])
```

```
y[x]
```

```
mean(y[-3])
```

Exercise 2.2
Write an R function that solves a quadratic equation $ax^2 + bx + c = 0$ by taking as input arguments a vector with components a, b, and c and returning a vector with solutions x_1 and x_2.

Exercise 2.3
Explain the difference between a vector and a list in R.

Exercise 2.4
Write a function that shifts a vector to the right one place, for example, to take a vector (3, 5, 7, 2, 1) to produce the shifted vector (1, 3, 5, 7, 2).

Exercise 2.5
Your cell phone bill last year had the following amounts:

```
53 37 44 60 51 57 49 62 55 40 44 63
```

Enter this data into a variable called `bill`. Use the `sum()` command to the find the total amount you spent last year on your cell phone bill. What is the smallest amount spent in a month? Write an R command to show the month you spent the largest amount.

Exercise 2.6
Give an example of two commands in R that provide the same functionality. Give a concrete example that uses the two commands to show that they produce identical results.

Exercise 2.7
Write a program in R that draws a STOP sign, with an octagon filled with red color, and the word STOP written with white letters in the center.

QR Code Sidebar 2.10

https://raw.githubusercontent.com/datasets/gold-prices/master/data/annual.cs

Exercise 2.8
Use the function `read.csv()` to access the URL https://raw.githubusercontent.com/datasets/gold-prices/master/data/annual.cs and create a data frame with historic monthly prices of gold. Name this data frame, for example, `gold`. What is the median price of gold? What was the maximum price of gold, and when?

Exercise 2.9
Write an R program to create a vector that contains 10 random integer values between −50 and +50. Find the average of this vector. Is the average what you expected?

Exercise 2.10
You are keeping a record of your car's odometer each time you fill up the car's gas tank and record the following numbers:

```
45332 45611 46050 46402 46994 47325 47712 48099
```

Enter these numbers in R, and write a program that lists the number of miles between fill-ups. Hint: Investigate and try to use the function `diff()`. Use the function `max()` to find the maximum number of miles between fill-ups, the `mean()` function to find the average number of miles, and the `min()` function to determine the minimum number of miles.

2.6.2 Group Experiments

Cell Phone Bills

Separate into groups that will take a class survey containing one question: "Approximately how much did you spend on your cell phone bill last month? Round your answer to the nearest whole number."

For each group, create a vector in R or RStudio that stores the amount of money each group member spent on their cell phone bill last month.

Question 1:

Use the vectors in R or RStudio to compute the following for the entire class:

1. Average cell phone bill
2. Minimum cell phone bill
3. Maximum cell phone bill
4. Total cell phone bill

FIGURE 2.9 Weight Measurement

2.6.3 Case Scenarios

QR Code Sidebar 2.11

https://DataAnalysisUsingR.com/datasets/freshman_data_phase_one.dat

CASE SCENARIO

Weight Gain

Several studies (e.g., Levitsky et al., 2004) recognize significant weight gain to be a common problem many college students experience during their first year. As a class project, students on a college campus surveyed 95 students to determine if they gained weight during their first semester. The data are in the file "Freshman Data Phase One." The data file is shown below:

STUDENT	WEIGHT GAIN	CURRENT_AGE	FRESHMAN_AGE	EXTRACURRICULAR	GENDER	SMOKER	STUDY	GPA
1	0	21	18	0	1	1	1	3.1
2	0	22	18	1	0	0	0	2
3	7	29	18	1	1	1	1	2.3
4	0	23	19	1	1	1	3	4
5	10	24	18	1	0	1	0	3.2
6	0	21	18	0	0	1	0	3.6
7	5	22	18	0	1	1	2	3.9
8	0	21	19	2	1	1	3	3.3
9	0	21	18	2	1	1	3	3.7
10	0	20	19	1	1	1	3	2.7

The columns represent the following:

Student = Unique identifier for each student in the study

Weight_Gain = The number of pounds gained freshman year

Current_Age = The age of the student at the time of the study

Freshman_Age = The age when the student in entered college

Extracurricular = The number of extracurricular activities the student participated in during college

Gender = 1 means the student identified as a woman; 0 identified as a man

Smoker = 1 means student did not smoke; 0 the student did smoke

Study = The average amount of hours studying per day

GPA = The GPA of the student after their freshman year

1. Does the data file contain column headers? If so, what are they?
2. How are the data values separated?
3. Use R or RStudio to load the data. Call the data frame "fifteen." What is the command line that was used to load the data?
4. Students in this study were also asked "How many times per week do you exercise?" The study's results are shown in the table below:

STUDENT	EXERCISE
1	2
2	1
3	1
4	2
5	1
6	1
7	0
8	2
9	3
10	3

   Use R or RStudio to add this column of data, with the heading "Exercise," to the "fifteen" data frame. One way to do this is `fifteen["exercise"]<-c(2,1,1,2,1,1,0,2,3,3)`. The command `cbind` can be also used here.
5. Export the updated data frame that combines the data from Exercise 4 with the original "fifteen" data frame. What is the command that is used to download the data?
6. R and RStudio have a package that is used to compute descriptive statistics. The package name is *descr.* Install and load the *descr* package. What is the command used to install packages?
7. The package *descr* contains a function called `freq`, which can be used to provide frequencies. A frequency is the number of times that something occurs. One example of a frequency is the number of men and women in the study. Use the command `freq()` to determine these frequencies for the "fifteen" data frame and provide your answer.

Use these questions as a self-assessment checklist for this chapter:

1. Have you installed R or RStudio?
2. Do you know how to get started with R?
3. How many ways can you enter data in R?
4. Have you explored any of the CRAN packages?
5. Have you written any code using R?

Reference

Levitsky, D. A., Garay, J., Nausbaum, M., Neighbors, L., & Dellavalle, D. M. (2006). Monitoring weight daily blocks the freshman weight gain: A model for combating the epidemic of obesity. *International Journal of Obesity (London), 30,* 1003.

Figure Credits

Fig. 2.1: Copyright © Unsplash/Markus Spiske.
Fig. 2.2: Copyright © Unsplash/Franck V.
Fig. 2.3: Copyright © Unsplash/Sam Albury.
Fig. 2.4: Copyright © by The R Foundation.
Fig. 2.5: Copyright © by The R Foundation.
Fig. 2.6: Copyright © by The R Foundation.
Fig. 2.7: Source: https://commons.wikimedia.org/wiki/File:Grünbaum-Rigby_configuration,_vector_graphics.svg.
Fig. 2.9: Copyright © Unsplash/Jennifer Burk.

PART II

Descriptive Statistics and Probability

CHAPTER

3

Descriptive Statistics

CHAPTER OUTLINE

CHAPTER OBJECTIVES

After completing this chapter, you will know how to carry out the following:

1. Design a statistical study.
2. Correctly collect data.
3. Construct statistical graphs.
4. Explain three measures for describing data.
5. Use R and RStudio to simulate data, calculate summary statistics, and construct graphs.

Descriptive statistics give a depiction of data through charts, graphs, and summary statistics. For example, a frequency distribution can provide an overall picture of how water quality varies in a river. Lists of microbiological and inorganic substances are useful for determining the quality of water in places such as the nature trail depicted in Figure 3.1. In this chapter you will learn how to design a statistical study, construct a frequency distribution, and use descriptive statistics to visualize information.

FIGURE 3.1 Statistical Analysis of Water Quality Variables of Rivers

Chapter Vocabulary

- A statistical study is a detailed investigation and analysis of a population, subject, or situation.
- A census consists of data from the entire set of objects that belong to a population.
- The population under study is the set of all outcomes, responses, observations, measurements, or counts of interest.
- A sample is a subset of a population.
- A confounding variable is a variable that may have a hidden effect on an experiment's outcome.
- The placebo effect occurs when a subject reacts favorably to a placebo when the subject has been given a fake treatment instead of an actual treatment in an experiment.
- Blinding is a technique in which the subject does not know whether they are receiving a treatment or a placebo.
- In a double-blind study, neither the subject nor the experimenter knows whether a subject is receiving a treatment or a placebo.
- Randomization is a technique that randomly assigns subjects to different treatment groups.
- In a completely randomized design subjects are assigned to different treatment groups by random selection.
- In a randomized block design, the experimenter divides subjects into blocks and then randomly assigns subjects from each block to treatment groups.
- A block is a group with similar characteristics.
- A matched-pairs design is a specific type of block design in which only two similar subjects are randomly assigned to each block.
- Replication means to repeat an experiment under the same or similar conditions.
- The sample size in an experiment is the number of subjects in the study.
- A convenience sample consists only of members of the population that are easy to obtain.
- In a random sample every member of the population has an equally likely chance of being chosen.
- A simple random sample is a sample in which every possible sample of the same size has the same chance of being selected.
- Strata are subsets that share similar characteristics such as gender, nationality, and marital status.
- In stratified sampling the population is first divided into strata, and elements are then randomly selected from each stratum.
- In cluster sampling, the researcher divides the population into naturally occurring separate groups, then all the members of one or more of these groups (called clusters) are selected. However, not all clusters are selected, as that would be equivalent to selecting the entire population.
- A frequency distribution is a chart, table, or graph that displays the frequency of the various outcomes in a sample.
- The mean of a data set is the arithmetic average.
- The weighted mean is the mean of a data set that has entries of varying weights.

- The median is the middle entry of an ordered data set.
- The mode is the most frequent entry, or entries, in the data set.
- An outlier is a data value that is far removed for other entries in the data set.
- The range is the maximum data entry minus the minimum data entry.
- The coefficient of variation of a data set describes the standard deviation as a percent of the mean.
- Fractiles are values that partition an ordered set into equal parts such that each part contains the same number of values.
- A quartile is a fractile that partitions the data into four equal parts.

3.1 Statistical Studies

A statistical study is a detailed investigation and analysis of a population, subject, or situation. A census consists of data from the entire set of objects that belong to a population. However, it is sometimes too expensive or impossible to study the entire population. The population under study is the set of all outcomes, responses, measurements, or counts of interest. It is typically more feasible to study a sample instead of a population because a sample is a subset of a population. Hence, a statistical study uses a sample to make inferences about the population.

The three major types of statistical studies are observational study, survey, and experiment. In an *observational* study, a researcher observes subjects without manipulating the subjects. A *survey* is a type of observational study in which subjects are asked questions. In an *experiment*, a researcher applies a treatment then observes results. Regardless of the type of statistical study, a correct design is important.

3.1.1 Designing a Statistical Study

Reliable results can be obtained only when a statistical study is designed properly. The first step to designing a statistical study is to identify the variable or variables of interest. Next, identify the population, and clearly state the research question(s). Identifying key variables of interest is important because it provides focus in the study. The next step is to develop a detailed sampling plan. Because the sample will be used to make inferences about the population, the sample needs to be representative of the population.

After devising a detailed data-collection plan, researchers next collect the data. Typically, data are collected and then organized in a spreadsheet. The data are then ready for descriptive statistics techniques, charts, and graphs. The benefit of descriptive statistics techniques is they allow data to be presented in an organized, meaningful way. This aids in interpretation. Conversely, raw data organized in a spreadsheet may be hard to visualize.

Inferential statistics are used to interpret data and make decisions about the population. This step is important because it extends beyond the data that were collected. Inferential statistics allow us to draw conclusions about the population regarding what has occurred, what is currently occurring, or what will occur. Lastly, identify any possible issues in the statistical study. Full disclosure is also important.

Example:

Distinguish between observational study, survey, and experiment:

Cottonii (*Kappaphycus alvarezii*) is a species of sea algae that is one of the most important commercial sources of carrageenans. Carrageenans are used in the food industry worldwide for their gelling and thickening properties (Ateweberhan et al., 2015). In southwest Madagascar, a monitoring program was established to support community-based seaweed farming by providing scientific information on the effects of physicochemical and health factors influencing the growth of cottonii. Six aquaculture site configurations were studied. At each site, a number of growth and health variables were monitored monthly for 14 consecutive months. Determine the type of statistical study that was performed.

Answer:

This was an observational study because researchers observed and measured characteristics of interest such as the effects of physicochemical and health factors influencing the growth of cottonii. However, they did not change existing conditions.

FIGURE 3.2 *Kappaphycus alvarezii*

3.1.2 Experimental Design

Design of Experiments (DOE) is a course that is taught in statistic departments as well as other university departments. DOE details experimentation techniques that are based on statistical principles, which are key to producing unbiased experimental results. Several key elements go into designing an experiment such as identifying possible confounding variables.

A carefully designed experiment starts with being able to control influential variables such as confounding variables. A confounding variable occurs when an experimenter cannot tell the difference between the effect of different factors of the experiment.

Example:

Determine the confounding variable:

The Fortis Healthcare Department of Mental Health and Behavioral Sciences in India conducted a study on patients with mood disorders. One patient was a 32-year-old female, married, and currently pursuing the final year of her doctoral degree. She had been seeking psychiatric treatment for bipolar I disorder for more than a year. She also had a history of five manic episodes prior to her first counseling session.

FIGURE 3.3 Female Sketch

Her therapist utilized a treatment process that was largely based on a traditional cognitive-behavioral model that included a focus on psycho-education, goal setting, cognitive-restructuring interventions, behavioral techniques, and problem-solving strategies. Throughout the patient's treatment, she may have also been gaining insight into her mental state, which could have facilitated therapeutic change. What is the confounding variable (Sondhi et al., 2016)?

Answer:

The confounding variable is patient insight because it may play a significant role not just in determining her willingness towards the therapy but also in contributing to further the patient's therapeutic alliance with the therapist. This in turn could enhance therapeutic outcomes.

The placebo effect is a factor that can affect an experiment. The **placebo effect** occurs with a subject who reacts favorably to a placebo when the subject has been given a sugar pill instead of an actual treatment in an experiment. During an experiment it is advisable to use a technique called blinding to help control the placebo effect. **Blinding** is a technique in which the subject does not know whether they are receiving a treatment or a placebo. In a **double-blind** study, neither the subject nor the experimenter knows whether the subject is receiving a treatment or a placebo.

Another key element of a well-designed experiment is randomization. There are several randomization methods such as simple, block, and stratified. **Randomization** is a technique that randomly assigns subjects to different treatment groups. A simple design is a **completely randomized design** in which subjects are assigned to different treatment groups by random selection. In a **randomized block design**, the experimenter divides subjects into blocks, groups with similar characteristics, and then randomly assigns subjects from each block to treatment groups. A **matched-pairs design** is a specific type of block design in which only two similar subjects are randomly assigned to each block.

Replication and sample size are also key elements of designing an experiment. **Replication** means to repeat an experiment under the same or similar conditions. The **sample size** in an experiment is the number of subjects in the study. The greater the replications and the larger the sample size, the more the experiment's validity improves. Sampling is also a statistics course. Sampling techniques will be discussed in Section 3.2.

3.1.3 Exercises

Understanding Concepts

1. In statistics, what does the acronym "DOE" represent?

2. What is the difference between a population and a sample?

3. Name three randomization methods.

True or false? In Exercises 4–6, determine whether the statement is true or false. It if is false, rewrite it as a true statement.

4. A census is a subset of a sample.

5. The placebo effect cannot affect an experiment.

6. A census consists of a portion of data from the entire set of objects that belong to a population.

Skill Building

7. What are the benefits of doing an experiment instead of an observational study?

8. A medical doctor wants to determine whether a new experimental medication will reduce feelings of anxiety. To investigate this question, the researchers gave this new medication to 60 adult volunteers that were patients of the doctor. Forty-two of these patients claimed that their anxiety symptoms were reduced; therefore, the doctor concludes that the medication was successful. Describe a better experimental design to study this question.

9. Does higher octane in gas make a difference in cars? Different octane levels (e.g., 87 octane and 91 octane) are designed to maximize the car engine's performance. However, the higher the octane level, the more expensive the gasoline. Consider the miles per gallon (mpg) of gas as a measure of a car's performance, with higher mpg being better. Design an experiment to test the claim and determine if the higher octane gasoline is worth it.

FIGURE 3.4 Does Higher Octane in Gas Make a Difference in Cars?

Use the following to answer questions 10–16:

> Many states in the United States have a "hands-free" law when it comes to cell phone usage while operating a car. This means that drivers can use their cellphones only if they can do so without touching them. For example, they can use voice-activated features to make calls and send messages or can talk to people using the speaker

setting on the phone. Some people claim that hands-free driving is just as distracting as using your hands to talk on the cellphone. To test this claim, 100 students were recruited to participate in a study. They were divided into two groups. Group 1 drove an obstacle course while using their hands to talk on a cellphone. Group 2 drove the same obstacle course but were hands-free. The accuracy rating on the obstacle course was measured on a scale of 1–20, with higher scores indicating better driving.

10. Is the research question described above an observational study or an experiment?

11. What are the factors and treatments in the research question?

12. What is the response variable?

13. Is randomization necessary in the research design?

14. Is there a control? If so, what is the control?

15. What are some nuisance or confounding variables in this study?

16. What are the experimental units?

Use the following to answer questions 17–22:

Students who are educated at home are called homeschooled. Do students who are homeschooled perform better academically than students who receive a formal in-school education? To study this research question, the scores (higher scores indicating better performance) of a national academic achievement test were collected and analyzed.

17. What are the factors and treatments in the research question?

18. What is the response variable?

19. Is randomization necessary in the research design?

20. Is there a control? If so, what is the control?

21. What are some nuisance or confounding variables in this study?

22. Is blocking necessary in this experiment?

Use the following to answer questions 23–25:

One popular diet to lose weight is the Keto diet. The Keto diet is one that is low in carbohydrates and high in fat. For example, eggs, cheese, and avocados are foods that are commonly consumed while on a Keto diet, whereas the intake of items

FIGURE 3.5 Keto Diet Meal

such as soda, pastries, and white bread is reduced. It is known that men and women lose weight at a different rate due to more muscle mass typically in a man's body. Researchers compared the weight loss of 60 people, composed of men and women. Thirty were on a Keto diet, and the rest were on a Mediterranean diet (e.g., a diet high in fruits and vegetables). The weight loss after 4 weeks on the diet was compared.

23. Is this an experiment or an observational study?

24. Does this study employ a block design? If so, what is the blocking variable?

25. What are the units/subjects of this sampling design?

Extending Concepts

26. A professor uses a random-number generator to select 25 students from a large class to study how much time students spend doing homework each day. Explain what kind of experimental design is being used.

27. The professor separates the students into groups based on gender before selecting 12 students randomly from each group. Explain what kind of experimental design is being used.

28. Explain why a larger sample size is likely to improve the validity of a statistical study. In a statistical study, validity refers to the extent to which conclusions drawn from the study are accurate and reliable.

29. A researcher divides 100 cancer patients into two groups. One group receives an experimental drug, while the other receives a placebo. After 2 years, the spread of the cancer is measured. Is this study observational or an experiment? Explain why.

30. A researcher collects data about the lung capacity of coal miners compared to the lung capacity of farm workers. The variables are smoking habits and exercise habits. The smoking habits of the two groups are similar, but coal miners tend to exercise less than the farm workers. Which variable is a confounding variable? Explain your answer.

3.2 Sampling

In the field of statistics, samples are selected from the population. That is, a sample is a subset of a population. If a count or measure is of the entire population, then it is called a census. Because it is typically too difficult, too expensive, or impossible to study an entire population, conclusions about a population are determined from samples. This is why samples are extremely important and must be representative of the population from which they were selected.

A sample may be unbiased or biased. Ideal samples are unbiased samples because they produce unbiased statistics. The expected value of an unbiased statistic equals the parameter that the statistic is estimating.

3.2.1 Unbiased Sampling Techniques

There are several ways to obtain unbiased samples. Choose the best sampling method by first stating the research goals. After the goals have been clearly defined, identify sampling techniques that are most likely to achieve these goals, and then test the ability of each method to accomplish the desired goals. Finally select the best sampling technique for achieving the goals. One such sampling technique is a random sample.

In a random sample every element of the population has some probability of being chosen. Sampling may be done with or without replacement. A random sample can be generated using Table D in Appendix A in the back of this textbook. Random samples can also be generated using software such as R. This will be demonstrated in the R section of this chapter. A special case of a random sample is a simple random sample. A simple random sample is a sample in which every possible sample of the same size has an equally likely chance of being chosen from the population.

In stratified sampling, the population is first divided into strata, subsets that share similar characteristics such as gender, nationality, and marital status. Elements are then selected randomly from each stratum. This sampling technique is often used when researchers want to observe existing relationships between subgroups of the population or when they want to highlight a specific subgroup within the population. It is also used when it is important for the sample to contain members from each segment of the population.

A cluster sample is similar to a stratified sample. The difference is that in cluster sampling there are natural groups separating the population such as school districts, zip code, or income level. Another difference is that in cluster sampling the two or more entire clusters are randomly selected. Therefore, in cluster sampling, the researcher divides the population into naturally occurring separate groups, then a simple random sample of clusters is selected from the population.

A systematic sample is a sample in which each member of the population is first assigned a number. The sample elements are then selected in regular intervals from the starting number. The starting number may be chosen from a random number table or by statistical software such as R. Systematic sampling may be used when there is a low risk of data manipulation. However, it should be avoided if there are obvious patterns present in the data. For example, if a researcher is interested in the population that attends a particular restaurant on a given day, they could stand by the door and ask every fifth person to be a part of their survey.

Example:

To address fatality rates due to sepsis in Brazilian intensive care units, researchers conducted a national study. In this study, they first divided the population into geo-economic regions (Machado et al., 2015). They then randomly selected 13% of the intensive care units from each region. Which sampling technique did the researchers use?

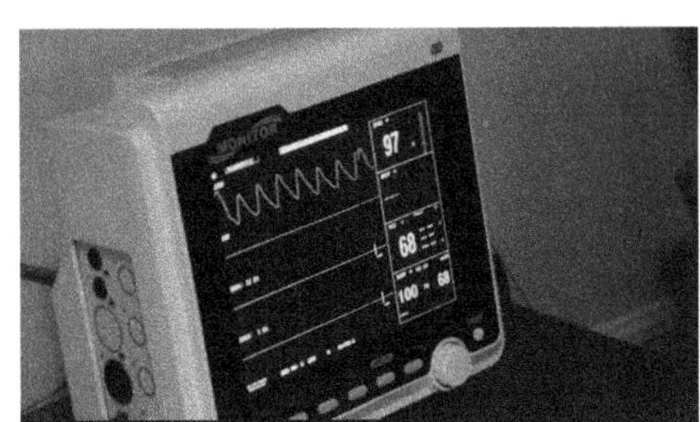

FIGURE 3.6 ECG

Answer:

To ensure that all socioeconomic and geo-economic regions were represented, the researchers used stratified sampling. They first stratified the population, then randomly select 13% of each stratum. This is not cluster sampling because they would have randomly selected two or more entire clusters from the population in cluster sampling.

3.2.2 Biased Sampling

Biased samples result in biased statistics. A biased statistic is not a good estimator of a population parameter because it is either overestimating or underestimating the population parameter.

Example:

Do you recall a U.S. President Alfred M. Landon? During the 1936 U.S. presidential campaign, the *Literary Digest* poll predicted that Landon would receive 57% of the vote to Franklin D. Roosevelt's 43%, making Roosevelt a one-term president (Lohr & Brick, 2017). Actual election results are below.

1936 Election Results

CANDIDATE	PARTY	ELECTORAL VOTES	POPULAR VOTES
Franklin D. Roosevelt	Democratic	523	27,751,597
Alfred M. Landon	Republican	8	16,679,583

They selected 2.4 million names from telephone directories (telephones were a luxury of the wealthy at the time), magazine subscribers, rosters of clubs, and so on. They also had a low response rate, which also contributed to bias. Those who responded were mainly the wealthy.

In 1936 George Gallup conducted an unbiased sample of 50,000 people for the presidential election. Gallup predicted that Roosevelt would win, and he was correct. The Gallup, Inc., is currently an international organization with almost 40 offices worldwide.

Why was the *Literary Digest* poll biased even though the sample size was larger than the Gallup poll?

Answer:

Even though the popular *Literary Digest* conducted one of the largest and most expensive polls of its day, its sampling was biased due to its selection process.

FIGURE 3.7 Opinion Polls

As illustrated, biased sampling is not recommended. A type of sampling that often leads to biased analysis results is convenience sampling. A convenience sample consists only of members of the population that are easy to obtain.

Example:

A researcher would like to determine the median weight of adults in a neighboring county. The researcher stands outside of an all-you-can-eat Chinese buffet in their neighborhood and estimates the weight of every fifth individual who leaves. Is this a biased sample?

Answer:

Even though the researcher employs an unbiased sampling technique, systematic sampling, the sample is a convenience sample because it consists of only members of the population who are easy to contact. That is, the researcher went to a restaurant in the neighborhood. Another factor that may bias the sample is that an all-you-can-eat buffet may be more likely to have overweight clientele as compared to a salad bar, for example.

FIGURE 3.8 All-You-Can-Eat Chinese Buffet

3.2.3 Exercises

Understanding Concepts

1. Why are sampling techniques important?

2. What is a type of sampling that often leads to biased analysis?

3. Are unbiased or biased samples typically preferred?

4. What is the difference between a census and a sample?

5. Which sampling method first divides the population into strata?

True or false? In Exercises 6–10, determine whether the statement is true or false. If it is false, rewrite it as a true statement.

6. A special case of a random sample is a simple random sample.

7. Gender is an example of a stratum.

8. In cluster sampling, the researcher divides the population into naturally occurring separate groups, then elements are selected randomly from each cluster.

9. Both the design of the experiment and data collection technique may cause sampling bias.

10. A biased sample leads to a biased statistic, which is a good estimator of a population parameter.

Skill Building

Use the following to answer questions 11–16:

> To assess the opinions of students about campus food quality at a large university, a reporter for the student newspaper interviews students on the campus.

11. The reporter interviews the first 30 students who walk by and are willing to express their opinions. What type of sampling did the reporter use to collect the data?

12. The reporter randomly selects 30 students from a list of students that have a campus meal plan that allows them to eat regularly on campus. What type of sampling did the reporter use to collect the data?

13. The reporter believes that first-year students who are new to the campus food may respond differently than seniors who have eaten on campus regularly the past 4 years. The reporter is not interested in these differences, only the quality of the food. The

reporter selects 30 first-year students, 30 seniors, 30 sophomores, and 30 juniors to be in the study. Which sampling method will provide the best data to investigate the quality of the food on campus? Why?

14. Which sampling method will provide the least supportive data to investigate the quality of the food on campus? Why?

15. What is the population of interest for this study?

16. Explain the difference between a population and a sample.

17. Researchers are interested in determining the average amount of time that students spend using social media (e.g., Facebook and Instagram). The researchers recruit 250 students to participate in the study. What is the population of interest for this study? What is the sample?

18. Suppose you are interested in studying the impacts of calming music (e.g., nature sounds and Zen music) on reducing math anxiety levels of students taking math exams. You design a study in which 50 students are needed to assess this impact. Describe a sampling design you would use. What type of sampling technique did you choose?

19. An Internet survey on the social media platform Instagram found that 68% of the respondents are not satisfied with the work of the current U.S. president. What sampling technique was used for this Internet survey?

20. The owner of Thompson Consulting, a small consulting firm that specializes in data analysis, surveyed all 20 employees to determine their level of job satisfaction on a scale of 1–10, with 10 being highly satisfied. Do the 20 employees represent the sample or population of interest? Why?

Extending Concepts

21. A computer manufacturer selects three computers at random from each of the six models for testing for defects. What type of sample is this?

22. A school principal chooses three students from each class to find out how many hours they study every day. What kind of study is this?

23. In a large canned-soup factory, a quality control expert randomly selects one of the first 10 cans and every 10th can after that from the batch. What type of sampling is employed?

24. A researcher stops people as they walk by on the street and asks them questions. What type of sampling is this?

25. A researcher measures the fatality rates for COVID-19. Explain why counting the number of deaths only from a population who has been tested for COVID-19 is an example of biased sampling.

3.3 Charts and Graphs

3.3.1 Frequency Distributions

This section focuses on the descriptive branch of statistics, charts, and graphs. A frequency distribution is a chart, table, or graph that displays the frequency of the various outcomes in a sample. Its purpose is to organize and summarize data. They are especially useful when a data set contains a large number of observations. Each table entry contains the frequency of the occurrences of values within a particular group or interval. The several types of frequency distributions include grouped, ungrouped, cumulative, relative, and relative cumulative, which are named according to the way in which the data are organized.

Follow these basic rules when constructing a standard frequency distribution:

Step 1: Determine the number of intervals or classes. This number will be provided in this textbook. However, any number between 5 and 20 typically works. The goal is to choose the number of classes such that the frequency distribution is representative of the data set.

Step 2: Find the class width. The class width is determined by first determining the range of the data set and then dividing this by the number of classes from Step 1. The range is the largest data value minus the smallest data value. If the value for the class width is a decimal, always round up to the next convenient number. For example, round 4.002 up to the number 5.

Step 3: Find all of the lower-class limits. The lower-class limit of the first class is the smallest data value. The lower-class limit of the second class is obtained by adding the class width to the lower class limit of the first class, and so on.

Step 4: Find all upper-class limits. The upper-class limit of the first class is obtained by subtracting one from the lower class limit of the second class, and so on.

Step 5: Determine the frequency of outcomes (how many) for each class. Review the original data set and place a tally mark for each data entry in the row of the appropriate class.

Additional features such as midpoint, relative frequency, and cumulative frequency can be included as well. These features would be incorporated as additional headers in the frequency distribution. The midpoint is determined for each class by adding the two class limits and dividing by two. The relative frequency of a class is the class frequency divided by the sample size. The cumulative frequency of a class is the sum of the frequency of that class plus the frequency of all other previous classes. Of note, the cumulative frequency of the last class is equal to the sample size.

Example:

The ages of all 26 students in an online introductory statistics class are given below. Determine a frequency distribution with the following headings: class, frequency, midpoint, relative frequency, and cumulative frequency. Use five classes:

17, 26, 19, 19, 18, 21, 21, 30, 19, 18, 20, 22, 18, 19, 18, 22, 19, 23, 19, 20, 20, 25, 18, 20, 22, 19.

Answer:

1. The number of intervals was given to be 5.
2. Class width = (30 − 17)/5 = 2.6, round up to 3.
3. Lower class limits: 17, 20, 23, 26, 29
4. Upper class limits: 19, 22, 25, 28, 31

CLASS	FREQUENCY	MIDPOINT	REL. FREQUENCY	CUM. FREQUENCY
17–19	13	18	13/26	13
20–22	9	21	9/26	22
23–25	2	24	2/26	24
26–28	1	27	1/26	25
29–31	1	30	1/26	26

3.3.2 Graphing Data

Graphing aids in the visualization of data. Several types of charts and graphs can be used to visualize the data. Choosing an appropriate graph is the focus of this section.

The first step in choosing a graph is determining whether the data are qualitative or quantitative because there are certain types of graphs for the respective types of data. The table below provides various types of graphs useful for graphing qualitative data. These graphs will be illustrated in the R section of this chapter. To help decide on a particular type of qualitative-data graph, each graph's description along with its advantages and disadvantages are provided.

TYPE OF DATA	TYPE OF GRAPH	DESCRIPTION	ADVANTAGES	DISADVANTAGES
Qualitative	Bar graph	Displays descriptive data in separate columns	• Double bar graph can be used to compare two data sets • Visually strong • Can easily compare two or three data sets	• Graph categories can be reordered to emphasize certain effects • Scaling, labeling, and readability need to be considered when creating a bar graph • Use only with discrete data

(Continued)

TYPE OF DATA	TYPE OF GRAPH	DESCRIPTION	ADVANTAGES	DISADVANTAGES
Qualitative	Pareto chart	Combines a bar graph with a line graph	• Double bar graph can be used to compare two data sets • Visually strong • Can easily compare two or three data sets	• Graph categories can be reordered to emphasize certain effects • Scaling, labeling, and readability need to be considered when creating a bar graph • Use only with discrete data
Qualitative	Pie chart (circle graph)	Displays data as a percentage of the whole; each pie section should have a label and percentage; a total data number should be included; works best for three to seven categories	• Shows percent of total for each category • Visually appealing	• No exact numerical data • Data cannot be reconstructed • Difficult to compare two data sets • An *"Other"* category may be a problem • Total data number is unknown unless specified • Use only with discrete data

The table below provides various types of graphs useful for quantitative data. These graphs will also be illustrated in the R section of this chapter. To help you decide on a particular type of quantitative-data graph, we provide each graph's description along with its advantages and disadvantages.

TYPE OF DATA	TYPE OF GRAPH	DESCRIPTION	ADVANTAGES	DISADVANTAGES
Quantitative	Histogram	Shows discrete or continuous data in a similar way to bar graphs, but without the gap between the columns; usually vertical axis is a frequency count of items falling into each category	• General distribution of the data can be quickly seen • Can compare to normal curve • Visually strong • Easily organizes data sets of all sizes	• Cannot read exact values because data are grouped into categories • Appearance of the distribution of the data can be manipulated depending on numbering scale used • More difficult to compare two data sets than with bar graph

(Continued)

TYPE OF DATA	TYPE OF GRAPH	DESCRIPTION	ADVANTAGES	DISADVANTAGES
Quantitative	Scatterplot	Displays the relationship between two variables or two factors of the experiment; trend line is used to determine positive, negative, or no correlation of data	• Shows a trend in the data relationship • Retains exact data values and sample size • Shows relationship between two different variables	• Hard to visualize results in large data sets • Flat trend line gives inconclusive results
Quantitative	Line graph	Plots continuous data as points, then joins them with a line	• Can compare multiple continuous data sets easily • Interim data can be inferred from the graph line	• Use only with continuous data • Can be misleading due to scale sensitivity • Appropriate only for displaying two variables with one an independent variable being observed exactly once at consistent intervals • Key must be used when graphing multiple data sets together
Quantitative	Frequency polygon	Line graph that emphasizes the continuous change in frequencies	• Can compare multiple continuous data sets easily	• Use only with continuous data • Can be misleading due to scale sensitivity • Appropriate only for displaying two variables with one an independent variable being observed exactly once at consistent intervals • Key must be used when graphing multiple data sets together
Quantitative	Ogive (cumulative frequency graph)	Line graph that displays the cumulative frequency of each class as its upper-class boundary	• Can compare multiple continuous data sets easily	• Use only with continuous data • Can be misleading due to scale sensitivity • Appropriate only for displaying two variables with one an independent variable being observed exactly once at consistent intervals • Key must be used when graphing multiple data sets together

(Continued)

TYPE OF DATA	TYPE OF GRAPH	DESCRIPTION	ADVANTAGES	DISADVANTAGES
Quantitative	Stem-and-leaf plot	Displays each number separated into a stem and a leaf; example of exploratory data analysis (EDA)	• Similar to a histogram, but still contains the original data • Can see how data are distributed • Provides an easy way to sort data • Can be used to easily identify outliers	• Useful only for small data sets from about 15 to 150 data points • More restrictive than histograms because the size of the classes is based on their last digits, which are the leaves
Quantitative	Dot plot	Displays each data entry using a point above a horizontal axis	• Contains the original data • Can see how data are distributed • Provides an easy way to sort data • Can be used to easily identify outliers	• Useful only for small data sets from about 15 to 150 data points
Quantitative	Time-series chart	Displays quantitative entries taken at regular intervals over a period of time	• Can compare multiple continuous data sets easily • Interim data can be inferred from the graph line	• Appropriate only for displaying two variables with the independent variable representing time taken at regular intervals • Key must be used when graphing multiple data sets together
Quantitative	Box plot (box-and-whisker plot)	Graphically represents the 5-number summary (minimum, first quartile, second quartile, third quartile, maximum)	• Easily organizes data sets of all sizes • Displays outliers • Median and interquartile range easily identified • Plots using different sets of data can be easily compared when graphed on the same scale	• Cannot read exact data values except minimum, maximum, and outliers • Data cannot be reconstructed • Mean and mode cannot be determined

3.3.3 Exercises

Understanding Concepts

1. What is the purpose of a frequency distribution?

2. What is the goal in determining the number of classes in a frequency distribution?

3. How is the class width of a frequency distribution chosen?

4. Why is it important to know whether the data are qualitative or quantitative before choosing a graph?

True or false? In Exercises 5–9, determine whether the statement is true or false. If it is false, rewrite it as a true statement.

5. A bar graph is an appropriate graph for qualitative data.

6. A pie chart is also called a circle graph.

7. A histogram is an appropriate graph for qualitative data.

8. The vertical axis in a histogram usually represents the frequency or count of each item falling into each category.

9. A time-series chart is a graph.

Skill Building

Use the following to answer questions 10–14:

> Data are collected from 200 randomly selected faculty members on a college campus to determine their level of satisfaction with their jobs. Some of the survey questions are listed below. Identify each as a quantitative or qualitative variable.

10. How many years have you worked for this university?

11. Rate your level of satisfaction with your job on a scale of 1 to 10.

12. How many miles do you live from campus?

13. Do you share an office?

14. Describe your research area.

Use the following to answer questions 15–19:

> The Survey of Earned Doctorates (SED) is an annual census, conducted since 1957, of all individuals receiving a research doctorate from an accredited U.S. institution in a given academic year. Some of the survey questions are listed below. Identify each as a quantitative or qualitative variable.

15. What is your current job?

16. When you received your doctoral degree, how much money did you owe that is directly related to your undergraduate and graduate education?

17. What is your current annual salary?

18. Do you currently have a job in a field related to your undergraduate degree?

19. What is the geographic location where you work?

20. Malaria is an infectious disease that is one of the leading causes of death worldwide. The journal *Statistica Neerlandica* published a study (this data can be found in the data file "Malaria") that examined the mean number of malaria deaths in 10 West African countries over the 10-year period between 1996 and 2006. Use R or RStudio to make a bar graph of the data.

21. Is it possible to make a pie chart of the malaria data described in Exercise 20? If so, describe how and provide the pie chart. If not, explain why it is not possible to make a pie chart.

22. A popular late-night snack among college students is pizza. Zagat recently researched this question: Is your favorite pizza called deep dish, thin crust, Neapolitan, or something else? The percent of responses for each type of crust is shown in the data file "Pizza Pie." Make a pie chart of the data. What type is the most popular? Would a bar graph be appropriate for these data? Explain why or why not.

23. In a recent survey, 108 students were asked to classify the frequency of their social media use (e.g., Instagram and Facebook) into one of these categories: every day, a few times a week, or once in a while. The data are in the file "Social Media." Make an appropriate graph to display the data. What do the data reveal?

QR Code Sidebar 3.1

https://DataAnalysisUsingR.com/datasets/malaria.dat

QR Code Sidebar 3.2

https://DataAnalysisUsingR.com/datasets/pizza_pie.dat

QR Code Sidebar 3.3

https://DataAnalysisUsingR.com/datasets/social_media.dat

QR Code Sidebar 3.4

https://DataAnalysisUsingR.com/datasets/building.dat

24. College administrators are deciding on whether they should use newly acquired land to build a residence hall, classroom space, or a dining hall. Fifty randomly selected students were asked to provide their opinions during a meeting with the university president. Their responses are in the data file "Building." Make an appropriate graph to display the data. What type of graph was chosen for this data set? Describe the results.

25. How should the bin sizes of a histogram be selected? What do they represent? What type of data is required for a histogram?

26. A coffee shop owner wanted to understand the distribution of the ages of the customers. The owner decided to ask everyone in the coffee shop for their ages. See the responses below:

AGES OF CUSTOMERS AT A LOCAL COFFEE SHOP				
29	67	56	50	19
44	42	24	21	38
13	79	15	50	46
25	20	78	13	31

Create a histogram of the data. What conclusions can be made?

Extending Concepts

27. You want to graph the value of your house over time. Which kind of graph is best to use?

28. A professor collects the grades for a quiz in a spreadsheet. How would the professor create a histogram from this data?

29. Can a professor use a Pareto graph to represent the distribution of grades for a class? Explain why or why not.

30. Explain how an ogive would be used to represent how often students checked social media each day.

31. What would be the best way to graphically study the relationship between the number of siblings and birth order in a sample of students?

3.4 Numerical Data Descriptions

Charts and graphs are used in the descriptive branch of statistics. We begin our discussion of the inferential branch of statistics with numerical data descriptions. Numerical data are those that can be measured. Ways of describing numerical data include central tendency, variation, and position.

3.4.1 Measures of Central Tendency

Just as charts and graphs visually summarize data, measures of central tendency numerically summarize data with a value that is representative of the typical or central entry in a data set. The three measures of central tendency that will be discussed in this section are the mean, median, and mode. We will begin with the mean. The mean is the arithmetic average. The population mean is

$$\mu = \frac{\sum x}{N},$$

where the Greek letter μ (pronounced mu) represents the population mean, the Greek letter sigma Σ indicates a summation of values, and N is the number of elements in the population. The sample mean is

$$\overline{x} = \frac{\sum x}{n},$$

where $\overline{x}$, (pronounced "x-bar") is the sample average, and n is the sample size.

Example:

The ages of all 26 students in an online introductory statistics class are given below. Determine the population mean:

17, 26, 19, 19, 18, 21, 21, 30, 19, 18, 20, 22, 18, 19, 18, 22, 19, 23, 19, 20, 20, 25, 18, 20, 22, 19.

Answer:

$$\mu = \frac{\Sigma x}{N}$$

$$= (17+26+19+19+18+21+21+30+19+18+20+22+18+19+18+22+19+23+19+20+20+25+18+20+22+19) / 26$$

$$\approx 20.4615.$$

The mean can be determined by the R function `mean()`.

In the above example each of the 26 elements in the population has the same weight. However, in some data sets there are entries that have a greater effect on the mean than other values. In this instance, it is more appropriate to determine the weighted mean, which is the mean of a data set whose entries have different weights. A typical example of a weighted mean is a student's course grade. The equation for the weighted mean is

$$\overline{x} = \frac{\sum(xw)}{\sum w},$$

where w is the weight of each element, x.

Another measure of central tendency is the median, the middle entry of an ordered data set. The median is determined by first ordering the data. If there is an odd number of data values, the median is the middle data value in the ordered data set. If there is an even number of data values, the median is technically any real value between the two middle data values. However, most software programs calculate the median as the average of the two middle values in this case. In R, the function `median()` determines the median.

Example:

The ages of all 26 students in an online introductory statistics class are given below. Determine the population median:

17, 26, 19, 19, 18, 21, 21, 30, 19, 18, 20, 22, 18, 19, 18, 22, 19, 23, 19, 20, 20, 25, 18, 20, 22, 19.

Answer:

First, order the data set from the smallest to the largest value:

17, 18, 18, 18, 18, 18, 19, 19, 19, 19, 19, 19, 19, 20, 20, 20, 20, 21, 21, 22, 22, 22, 23, 25, 26, 30.

Notice that since there are 26 entries in the data set, the two middle numbers are the 13th and the 14th entries. The 13th entry is 19 and the 14th entry is 20. Taking the average of the two middle values yield $(19 + 20)/2 = 19.5$. Therefore, the median is 19.5. The notation for the median is typically written as $\tilde{x}$.

The mode is the most frequent entry in the data set. Unlike the mean and median, the mode may be a categorical data value. If the data set is numerical, it is not necessary to order the data, but ordering the data makes it easier to determine the mode. A data set may have more than one mode. If it has two modes, then it is *bimodal*.

Example:

The ages of all 26 students in an online introductory statistics class are given below. Determine the population mode:

17, 26, 19, 19, 18, 21, 21, 30, 19, 18, 20, 22, 18, 19, 18, 22, 19, 23, 19, 20, 20, 25, 18, 20, 22, 19.

Answer:

First, order the data set from the smallest to the largest value:

17, 18, 18, 18, 18, 18, 19, 19, 19, 19, 19, 19, 19, 20, 20, 20, 20, 21, 21, 22, 22, 22, 23, 25, 26, 30.

Because the number 19 occurs the most times, it is the mode of the data set.

In R there is not a built-in function to determine the mode. However, a program can be written in R that will accomplish this. Such a program can use the built-in R function `unique()` to determine the unique values in a data set. Next, use the function `match()` to determine the position of the first occurrence of a value in the data set. Use the function `tabulate()` to count the number of times an integer occurs in a bin. Finally, use the function `which.match()` to determine the position of the element with the maximum value in a vector.

We have presented three ways to represent a typical entry in the same data set—the mean, median, and mode. Each has advantages and disadvantages. The advantage of the mean is that it takes every entry into account. However, it is sensitive to outliers. An outlier is a data value that is far removed for other entries in the data set. The median also takes every entry into account, but it is not affected by outliers. The mode is not affected by outliers either. However, the mode may not exist. That is, there may not be a most frequent data value.

The shape of a frequency distribution indicates the relationship between the three measures of central tendency mentioned. A symmetric frequency distribution has two halves that are mirror images of each other. In a symmetric distribution, the mean, median, and mode are approximately equal. When a distribution is skewed left or negatively skewed, the mean is less than the median and mode. When a distribution is skewed right or positively skewed, the mean is greater than the median or mode.

3.4.2 Measures of Variation

Measures of variation numerically summarize the data with a value that is representative of how spread out values are in the data set. Four measures of variation that will be discussed in this section are range, standard deviation, variance, and coefficient of variation. They are also called measures of dispersion.

The range of a data set is simply the difference between the largest and smallest data value.

Example:

The ages of all 26 students in an online introductory statistics class are given below. Determine the range:

17, 26, 19, 19, 18, 21, 21, 30, 19, 18, 20, 22, 18, 19, 18, 22, 19, 23, 19, 20, 20, 25, 18, 20, 22, 19.

Answer:

Range = maximum data entry – minimum data entry
= 30 – 17
= 13

Another measure of variation is the standard deviation. The standard deviation is a measure of the "average" deviation a data entry is from the mean. The standard deviation is the square of the variance. The population variance is

$$\sigma^2 = \frac{\sum (x - \mu)^2}{N},$$

where the Greek letter σ "sigma" represents the population standard deviation. The sample variance is $s^2 = \frac{\sum (x - \overline{x})^2}{n - 1}$. Instead of computing by hand, we suggest using the R function `sd()` to determine the standard deviation.

When working with two or more data sets, it is sometimes helpful to compare the variation of all the data sets. This can be accomplished with the standard deviation if the units of measure are the same. However, if the units of measure are different, then use the coefficient of variation (CV). The coefficient of variation of a data set describes the standard deviation as a percent of the mean. The only differences between the population and sample coefficient of variation are that the population parameters are replaced with sample statistics.

$$CV_p = \frac{\sigma}{\mu} 100\ \% \text{ and } CV_s = \frac{s}{\overline{x}}\ 100\%$$

Two applications of the standard deviation are based on the empirical rule and Chebyshev's theorem. The empirical rule is also known as the 68-95-99.7 Rule. It goes as follows:

Empirical Rule:
If a distribution is bell-shaped or approximately bell-shaped, then

- Approximately 68% of the data falls within one standard deviation of the mean.

- Approximately 95% of the data falls within two standard deviations of the mean.
- Approximately 99.7% of the data falls within three standard deviations of the mean.

Example:

Given a data set comprised of 2,771 measurements that is bell-shaped with a mean of 493 and a standard deviation of 75, what percentage of the data should lie between 268 and 493?

Answer:

The lower bound (LB) of the interval of values is 268. Therefore,

$$\overline{x} - ks = LB,$$

where $\overline{x}$ is the sample average, k is the number of standard deviations a value is away from the mean, and s is the sample standard deviation. Next, determine k. The formula

$$493 - k(75) = 268$$

implies that $k = 3$. Therefore, the lower bound is $k = 3$ standard deviations below the mean, and the upper bound is $k = 3$ standard deviations above the mean. Because approximately 99.7% of the data falls within three standard deviations of the mean and a bell-shaped distribution is symmetrical, 99.7/2 = 49.85% of the data should lie between 268 and 493.

When you have a bell-shaped distribution and you know the mean and the standard deviation, you can also determine the number of standard deviations a value x is from the mean by computing the standard score, or z-score. To find the z-score use the formula:

$$z = \frac{x - \mu}{\sigma}.$$

We will revisit standard scores when discussing the standard normal distribution.

Chebyshev's theorem is more general that the empirical rule because the number of standard deviations for the empirical rule is limited to 1, 2, or 3. In Chebyshev's theorem the number of standard deviations is any integer greater than 1.

Chebyshev's Theorem:

The portion of any data set lying within k ($k > 1$) standard deviations of the mean is at least $1 - \frac{1}{k^2}$.

Example:

If a group of data has a mean of –73 and a standard deviation of 67.5, what is the interval that should contain at least 93.8% of the data?

Answer:

$1-\frac{1}{k^2}=.938$ implies $k \approx 4$. Both the lower bound (LB) and upper bound (UB) of the intervals are 4 standard deviations away from the mean.

$$\begin{aligned} LB &= \overline{x} - ks \\ &= -73 - (4)(67.5) \\ &= -343 \end{aligned}$$

$$\begin{aligned} UB &= \overline{x} + ks \\ &= -73 + (4)(67.5) \\ &= 197 \end{aligned}$$

Therefore, the interval that contains at least 93.8% of the data is (–343,197).

3.4.3 Measures of Position

A measure of position in a data set describes the location of values in relation to other values in the data set. One such measure is a fractile. Fractiles are values that partition an ordered set into equal parts such that each part contains the same number of values. A quartile is a fractile that positions the data into four equal parts. There are three quartiles, Q_1, Q_2, and Q_3. The first quartile Q_1 is a value that is greater than or equal to 25% of the values in a data set. The second quartile is a value that is greater than or equal to 50% of the data set. The second quartile is also called the median of a data set. The third quartile is a value that is greater than or equal to 75% of the data.

Example:

The ages of all 26 students in an online introductory statistics class are given below. Determine the quartiles:

17, 26, 19, 19, 18, 21, 21, 30, 19, 18, 20, 22, 18, 19, 18, 22, 19, 23, 19, 20, 20, 25, 18, 20, 22, 19.

Answer:

First, put the data in order from the smallest to the largest value:

17, 18, 18, 18, 18, 18, 19, 19, 19, 19, 19, 19, 19, 20, 20, 20, 20, 21, 21, 22, 22, 22, 23, 25, 26, 30.

It is typically easier to start with computing Q_2 because the second quartile divides the data set into two equal subsets—one subset is below the median, and the other is above the median. From previous computations, the median is $Q_2 = 19.5$. The first quartile Q_1 is the median of the subset located below $Q_2 = 19.5$. Because this subset contains 13 values, the middle data value is in the seventh position, $Q_1 = 19$. Likewise, the third quartile Q_3 is the median of the subset located above $Q_2 = 19.5$. Because this subset contains 13 values, the middle data value is in the 20th position in the ordered data set, $Q_3 = 22$.

The quartiles can be used to determine another measure of dispersion, the interquartile range (IQR).

$$IQR = Q_3 - Q_1$$

Example:

The ages of all 26 students in an online introductory statistics class are given below. Determine the IQR:

17, 26, 19, 19, 18, 21, 21, 30, 19, 18, 20, 22, 18, 19, 18, 22, 19, 23, 19, 20, 20, 25, 18, 20, 22, 19.

Answer:

Use the formula

$$\begin{aligned} IQR &= Q_3 - Q_1 \\ &= 22 - 19 \\ &= 3. \end{aligned}$$

The interpretation is that the spread of the ages of students in the middle half of the data of the online introductory statistics class is 3 years.

The IQR can be used to help identify outliers. A general rule of thumb is illustrated in the following example. Because some values are on the border of being outliers, the following example comes with caveats.

Example:

The ages of all 26 students in an online introductory statistics class are given below. Use the IQR to determine outlier identifiers:

17, 26, 19, 19, 18, 21, 21, 30, 19, 18, 20, 22, 18, 19, 18, 22, 19, 23, 19, 20, 20, 25, 18, 20, 22, 19.

Answer:

1. Order the data set:

17, 18, 18, 18, 18, 18, 19, 19, 19, 19, 19, 19, 19, 20, 20, 20, 20, 21, 21, 22, 22, 22, 23, 25, 26, 30.

2. Find the first and third quartiles:

$$Q_1 = 19, Q_3 = 22.$$

3. Find the IQR:

$$\begin{aligned} IQR &= Q_3 - Q_1 \\ &= 3. \end{aligned}$$

4. Multiply the IQR by 1.5:

$$\begin{aligned} 1.5(IQR) &= 1.5(3) \\ &= 4.5. \end{aligned}$$

5. Determine the cut-off value for lower outliers:

$$\begin{aligned} Q1 - 1.5(IQR) &= 19 - 1.5(3) \\ &= 14.5. \end{aligned}$$

6. Determine the cut-off value for upper outliers:

$$\begin{aligned} Q1 + 1.5(IQR) &= 19 + 1.5(3) \\ &= 23.5. \end{aligned}$$

Therefore, values less than 14.5 or greater than 23.5 may be considered outliers. The ages 25, 26, and 30 fit this category. However, because they are not extreme outliers, some experts may not consider them to fall in the outlier category.

Another application of quartiles is a graph called a box plot or box-and-whisker plot. The box plot was invented by John Tukey, the great-grandfather of the first author of this textbook. That is in dissertation terms! That is, the dissertation advisor is the "father" of the graduate student. The advisor of the student's advisor is the "grandfather" of the graduate student, and so on.

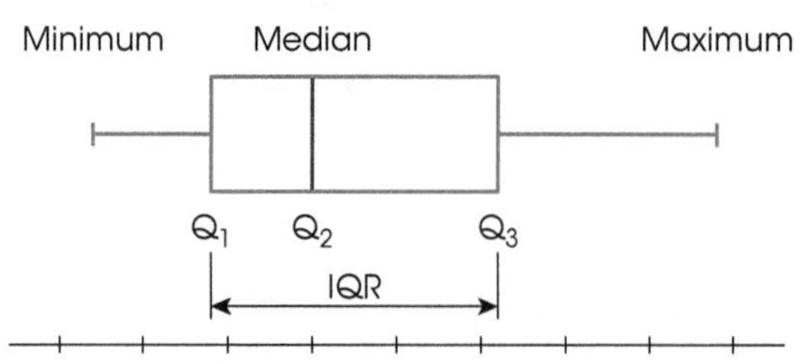

FIGURE 3.9 Box Plot or Box-and-Whisker Plot

The box plot is a graphical representation of the five-number summary, which is the minimum data value, Q_1, Q_2, Q_3, and the maximum data value.

3.4.4 Exercises

Understanding Concepts

1. Name and describe the three main measures of central tendency.
2. Explain why one measure of central tendency would be used over another.
3. Do outliers affect any of the measures of central tendency? If so, how?
4. Which measures of central tendency can be used to describe qualitative data?
5. Which measures of central tendency can be used to describe quantitative data?
6. Explain in your own words what variance is.
7. Why is the standard deviation often preferred over the variance?
8. What is a good measure to use to describe the spread of data using quartiles?
9. What does IQR stand for, and how can it be used to identify outliers?
10. Are the minimum and maximum values in data sets always outliers? Why or why not?

Skill Building

11. Which values does the five-number summary include? Why are these values useful for data analysis?
12. What is a graphical representation for the five-number summary?

Use the following to answer questions 13–20:

> When do students typically arrive for class? This research question was explored using students in an introduction to statistics class. The arrival times of the 20 students in the class were recorded. The class start time was 9:15 a.m. The teaching assistant recorded how many minutes before

QR Code Sidebar 3.5

https://DataAnalysisUsingR.com/datasets/arrival_time.dat

and after the aforementioned start time the students arrived to class. The data are in the file "Arrival Time" and shown in the table below:

WHEN DID STUDENTS ARRIVE FOR CLASS (IN MINUTES)?				
11	-13	-12	21	-14
13	-15	7	-2	89
-130	11	6	28	12
26	0	-2	20	-7

13. Load the Arrival Time data file into R or RStudio. Find the mean and median of the data set.

14. Are there any outliers in the Arrival Time data file? How was this determined?

15. Remove the outliers, and recompute the mean and medians. Did it make a noticeable difference in either?

16. Find the variance and standard deviation. (Be sure to provide the units of measurement.)

17. What are the minimum and maximum values?

18. What is the mode? For this, you can use the function "Mode" from package *DescrTools*.

19. Provide the five-number summary.

20. Make a box plot of the data. Are any outliers displayed in the box plot? If so, how are they displayed? Which quartiles are displayed on the box plot?

Extending Concepts

21. Is the average of a sample greater or smaller than its median?

22. Is the mean more affected by extreme values than the median?

23. What is the name of the most frequently occurring value in a sample?

24. Is the median always a value from the sample?

25. The velocity of cars traveling down a road can be positive or negative depending on which direction they travel. Is the coefficient of variation a good measure for variability of car velocities measured during a week?

3.5 R and RStudio

3.5.1 Programming Assignments

Exercise 3.1

The build-in data frame `mtcars` has data extracted from a 1974 *Motor Trend* magazine. The data frame comprises fuel consumption and 10 aspects of automobile design and performance for 32 car models.

Random Sampling. If we want to sample from the `mtcars` data set randomly, we can use the following code:

```
mtcars[sample(1:nrow(mtcars), 5),]
```

```
##                 mpg cyl  disp  hp drat    wt  qsec vs am gear carb
## Toyota Corolla 33.9   4  71.1  65 4.22 1.835 19.90  1  1    4    1
## Camaro Z28     13.3   8 350.0 245 3.73 3.840 15.41  0  0    3    4
## Mazda RX4 Wag  21.0   6 160.0 110 3.90 2.875 17.02  0  1    4    4
## Toyota Corona  21.5   4 120.1  97 3.70 2.465 20.01  1  0    3    1
## Maserati Bora  15.0   8 301.0 335 3.54 3.570 14.60  0  1    5    8
```

Here we generated five random samples in the range from 1 up to the number of rows in the data set given by `nrows(mtcars)` with the function `sample()`. All columns for the corresponding rows are then displayed.

Stratified Sampling. If we want to be sure that we sample a certain category, we need to sample from the required subsets. Here, for example, we want to be sure to have two random samples from cars with four, six, and eight cylinders, respectively:

```
c4 = subset(mtcars, cyl==4)
c6 = subset(mtcars, cyl==6)
c8 = subset(mtcars, cyl==8)
rbind(c4[sample(1:nrow(c4), 2),],
      c6[sample(1:nrow(c6),2),],
      c8[sample(1:nrow(c8),2),])
```

```
##              mpg cyl  disp  hp drat    wt  qsec vs am gear carb
## Datsun 710  22.8   4 108.0  93 3.85 2.320 18.61  1  1    4    1
## Honda Civic 30.4   4  75.7  52 4.93 1.615 18.52  1  1    4    2
## Mazda RX4   21.0   6 160.0 110 3.90 2.620 16.46  0  1    4    4
## Merc 280    19.2   6 167.6 123 3.92 3.440 18.30  1  0    4    4
## AMC Javelin 15.2   8 304.0 150 3.15 3.435 17.30  0  0    3    2
## Camaro Z28  13.3   8 350.0 245 3.73 3.840 15.41  0  0    3    4
```

We used the function `subset()` to extract records with a given characteristic and function `rbind()` to join together data sets that have similar structure of fields.

Systematic Sample. One way to obtain this sample is to start from a random record and select every other fifth down the list. If we arrive at end of the list, we should continue from the top:

```
seed = sample(1:nrow(mtcars), 1)
mtcars[(seed + 5*(1:4)) %% nrow(mtcars),]
```

```
##                mpg cyl  disp  hp drat    wt  qsec vs am gear carb
## Merc 450SL    17.3   8 275.8 180 3.07 3.730 17.60  0  0    3    3
## Fiat 128      32.4   4  78.7  66 4.08 2.200 19.47  1  1    4    1
## AMC Javelin   15.2   8 304.0 150 3.15 3.435 17.30  0  0    3    2
## Lotus Europa  30.4   4  95.1 113 3.77 1.513 16.90  1  1    5    2
```

Here, starting from a random position `seed`, we go four steps with a stride of 5 because `5*(1:4)` is the same with `c(5, 10, 15, 20)`, and then use the *modulo* operator `%%` to make sure that we do not go outside the bounds of the data set.

Exercise 3.2

Let us explore the categorical variable *gear* from the `mtcars` data set. What are the possible values of *gear*? How many cars are there for each number of forward gears? Use the function `factor()` and the function `table()` to obtain the frequency distribution for this variable:

```
table(mtcars$gear)
##
##  3  4  5
## 15 12  5
```

Obtain the frequency distribution for the `cyl` variable.

```
factor(mtcars$cyl)
```

```
##  [1] 6 6 4 6 8 6 8 4 4 6 6 8 8 8 8 8 8 4 4 4 4 8 8 8 8 4 4 4 8 6 8 4
## Levels: 4 6 8
```

Exercise 3.3

Bar plots and pie charts are very simple and direct ways to represent categorical data. In the example below, the function `par()` is used to set certain parameters for R graphics. Here we want a combined graph with one row and two columns. Reduce the size of the text for the main titles to 0.7 of the default size, which avoids overlap of the two graphs' titles.

```
par(mfrow=c(1,2))
par(cex.main = 0.7)
barplot(table(mtcars$vs, mtcars$gear),
        main="Car Distribution by Gears and VS",
        xlab="Number of Gears", col=c("darkblue","red"),
        beside=TRUE)
```

```
pie(table(mtcars$cyl),
    main="Pie Chart of cars by the number of cylinders",
    xlab="Number of cylinders")
```

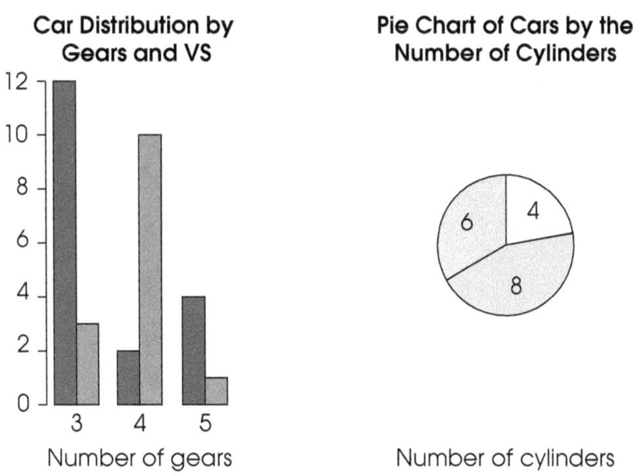

FIGURE 3.10 Example of Bar Plot and Pie Chart

Exercise 3.4

A histogram does two things. First, it collects numerical data into bins to fit a partition of the data's range. The precise way of partitioning the range can be specified in code or calculated algorithmically by default. Second, the frequency of the count in each bin is represented as a bar plot. The example below shows the histogram for the power of engines of cars in `mtcars` data set:

```
hist(mtcars$hp,
     col = "gray",
     main = "Distribution of engine power in the mtcars set",
     xlab = "Power(hp)")
```

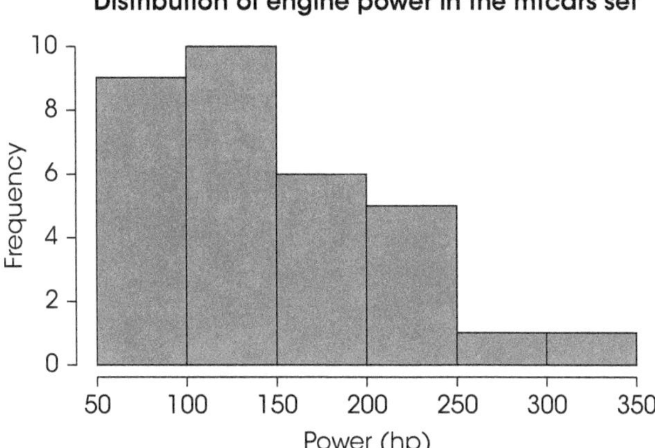

FIGURE 3.11 Example of Histogram

By following this example, build a histogram for the weight of cars in the data set, with a predefined set of breakpoints, by setting the `breaks` parameter, for example, with `breaks = 6`.

Exercise 3.5

A scatterplot is used to represent relations between two numerical variables. The example below demonstrates the dependence of the mileage on the engine power for cars in the *mtcars* data set:

```
plot(mtcars$hp, mtcars$mpg,
     main="Mileage vs. Power for cars in mtcars data set",
     xlab="power(hp)", ylab = "miles per gallon", pch = 10)
```

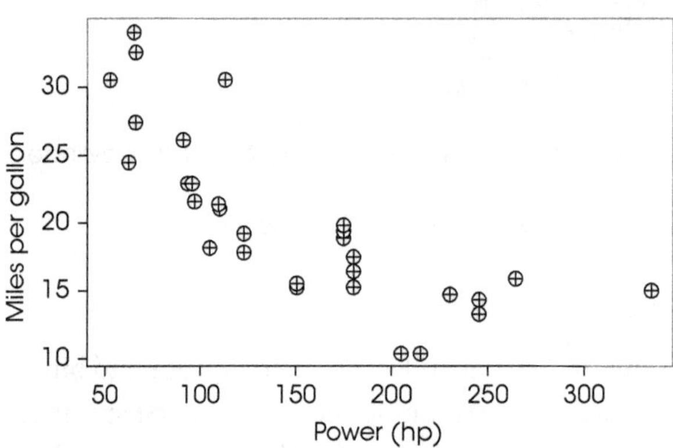

FIGURE 3.12 Example of Scatterplot

Write R code to show a graph for the relationship between mileage and weight of cars.

Exercise 3.6

Use the `mean()` and `median()` functions to find the mean and the median weight of the cars listed in *mtcars* data set.

Exercise 3.7

A function that obtains the mode for a vector uses the `unique()` function to remove duplicates from a vector and `match()` to find the position in the vector of unique elements for each element in the original vector. The function `tabulate()` gets the tally of repeated elements in the vector. Finally, we return the mode, which is a unique member that has the maximum number of occurrences in the list:

```
getmode <- function(v) {
   uniqv <- unique(v)
   uniqv[which.max(tabulate(match(v, uniqv)))]
}
```

Use the function above to determine the mode (the greatest number of cars) for the cylinder variable in the `mtcars` data set by using this function. For example, if `x<-c(2,4,4,1)`, then `getmode(x)` should return 4.

Exercise 3.8

Study the variation in the quarter-mile time variable `qsec` of the cars in the `mtcars` data set by using functions `range()` and `sd()` for range and standard deviation, respectively. Write a function that calculates and reports the coefficient of variation and the *z*-score for an arbitrary numeric vector.

Compare and contrast these measures of variation for the `mtcars$qsec` variable.

Exercise 3.9

There are several ways to investigate the quartile and percentile values for an observation variable in R. The simplest one is function `summary()`. The function `quantile()` calculates the values that cut off the first 25%, 50%, and 100% of the data when it is sorted in ascending order. This function can be customized to find cut values for arbitrary partitions of data.

The function `IQR()` calculates the difference between the upper and lower quartiles. 75% of data is smaller than the *upper quartile*, while 25% of the data is smaller than the *lower quartile*.

Use functions `quantile()` and `IQR()` to analyze the quartiles for the `mtcars$mpg` variable.

Exercise 3.10

The box plot of an observation variable is a graphical representation based on quartiles, as well as its smallest and largest values. It provides a rough visual shape of the data distribution.

In R, it is very easy to obtain a box plot:

```
boxplot(mtcars$hp, horizontal=TRUE,
    main = "Box plot representation of engine power\n for the
'mtcars' set",
    xlab = "power(hp)")
```

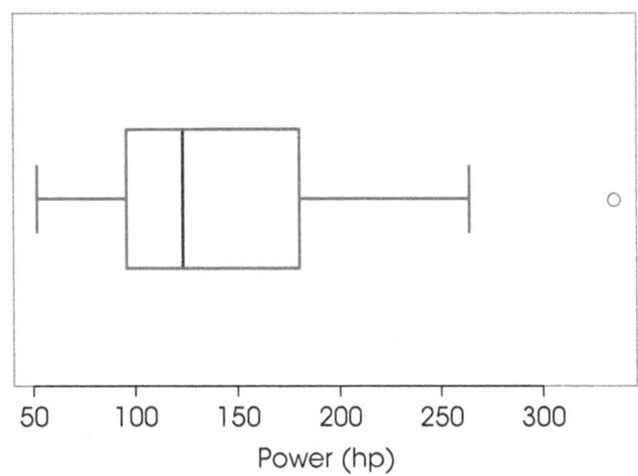

FIGURE 3.13 Example of Box Plot

Compare and contrast the graphical representation and the text representation, as provided by the `summary()` command, for example. What is the meaning of the thick vertical line in the box plot? What is the meaning of the dashed horizontal line?

3.5.2 Group Experiments

Sleep Time

Conduct a survey of the class members and record the average sleep time per day, in hours, to the nearest half-hour. Create a dot plot of the data by using the `stripchart()` function. First lookup this function and see how it works. Here is an example set of numbers. Replace the set with the numbers in your group and discuss the results.

```
# record here your data
sleep <- c(8, 6, 6.5, 8, 5.5, 6, 6, 5, 8, 6.5, 8)
# make a dot plot
stripchart(sleep, method="stack", pch = 20, cex = 3)
```

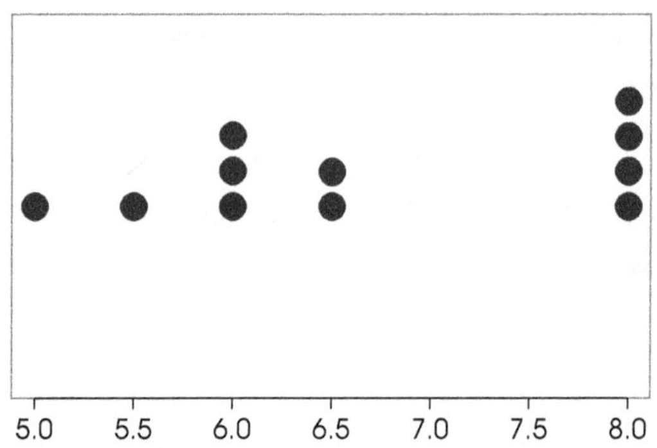

FIGURE 3.14 Example of Dot Plot

Question 1:
What observations about the data can you make that are not obvious by looking at raw data?

Question 2:
Use the methods of *descriptive statistics* that you learned in this chapter to extract few qualitative and quantitative characteristics of your data. How could you interpret the clustering?

Question 3:
What are the graphics parameters *cex* and *pch* used for?

3.5.3 Case Scenarios

FIGURE 3.15 Baseball Game

CASE SCENARIO

Home Run Derby

The Washington Nationals is a major league baseball (MLB) team based in Washington, DC. They were the 2019 World Series victors. The World Series is MLB's annual championship between the National League and American League pennant winners. The data file `Nationals Batting` contains batting data for every player on the Washington Nationals during the 2019 season. Variables include:

- Age = Age of the player
- G = Number of games played
- AB = At bats
- R = Runs scored
- H = Hits
- 2B = Doubles hit
- 3B = Triples hit
- HR = Home runs hit
- RBI = Runs batted in
- SB = Stolen bases
- CS = Caught stealing
- BB = Bases on balls/walks
- SO = Strikeouts
- PO = Position (C = Catcher, CF = Center Field, RF = Right Field, LF = Left Field, P = Pitcher, 1B = First Base, 2B = Second Base, 3B = Third Base, SS = Shortstop, IF = Infield, and UT = Utility Player)

In the game of baseball, two teams play by taking turns between being at bat and in the field. The team batting tries to hit a ball thrown by the pitcher for the team in the field. If the player hits the ball, the player tries to score a point (a run) by running and touching all four bases in the field without the team in the field tagging any players on the bases with the ball.

QR Code Sidebar 3.6

https://DataAnalysisUsingR.com/datasets/nationals_batting.dat

1. Which variables are quantitative?
2. Which variables are qualitative?
3. The person who plays the position of pitcher often does not take a turn being a batter, and when they do, the results are typically not good. To account for that, remove the pitchers from the data set. Then calculate the mean and median number of home runs. Are these numbers the same? If not, why? Which number is a better measure of central tendency for these data?
4. Which player has the most home runs? Which player has the least? Redo for players with more than 100 ABs.
5. Determine the variance and standard deviation for the number of home runs for the 2019 Washington Nationals season. Be sure to provide the appropriate units of measurement for each.
6. Who is the youngest player on the team? Who is the oldest?
7. Make a histogram of the number of times a player hit a double (2B). What does the histogram show?
8. Make a graphical display of the positions for the team. What does your graph tell you about the makeup of the Washington Nationals baseball team?

Use these questions as a self-assessment checklist for this chapter:

1. Do you know how to design a statistical study?
2. Do you know various ways to scientifically collect data?
3. Do you know how to construct a statistical graph that best represents your data?
4. Do you know three measures for describing data?
5. Do you know how to perform basic functions in R such as simulating data, calculating summary statistics, and constructing graphs.

References

Ateweberhan, M., Rougier, A., & Rakotomahazo, C. (2015). Influence of environmental factors and farming technique on growth and health of farmed *Kappaphycus alvarezii* (cottonii) in south-west Madagascar. *Journal of Applied Phycology, 27*, 923–934. https://doi.org/10.1007/s10811-014-0378-3

Lohr, S. L., & Brick, J. M. (2017). Roosevelt predicted to win: Revisiting the 1936 Literary Digest poll. *Statistics, Politics, and Policy, 8*(1), 65–84. https://doi.org/10.1515/spp-2016-0006

Machado, F. R., Cavalcanti, A. B., Bozza, F., Angus, D. C., Ferreira, E. M., Carrara, F., Lubarino, J., Salomao, R., & Pontes de Azevedo, L. C. (2015). Epidemiology of sepsis in Brazilian ICUs: A nationwide stratified sample. *Intensive Care Medicine Experimental*, 3(Suppl 1), A642. http://www.icm-experimental.com/content/3/S1/A642

Sondhi, R., Chhibber, K., & Parikh, S. (2016). Insight: A confounding variable in therapy for patients with mood disorders. *Journal of Depression and Anxiety, 5*(4), 1–3. https://doi.org/10.4172/2167-1044.1000250

Figure Credits

Fig. 3.1: Copyright © 2020 by Po Hao Hsu. Reprinted with permission.
Fig. 3.2: Copyright © Unsplash/chuttersnap.
Fig. 3.3: Copyright © 2020 by Konstantinos Argyroglou. Reprinted with permission.
Fig. 3.4: Copyright © 2019 by Melpomeni Kalliri. Reprinted with permission.
Fig. 3.5: Copyright © Unsplash/Brooke Lark.
Fig. 3.6: Copyright © Unsplash/Jair Lázaro.
Fig. 3.7: Copyright © Unsplash/Mr. Cup/Fabien Barral.
Fig. 3.8: Copyright © Unsplash/Ulysses pcl.
Fig. 3.15: Copyright © Unsplash/Joshua Peacock.

CHAPTER

4

Probability

CHAPTER OUTLINE

CHAPTER OBJECTIVES

After completing this chapter, you will have established the foundation to:

1. Understand the fundamentals of probability.
2. Understand when to apply the addition rule.
3. Understand when to apply the multiplication rule.
4. Learn counting techniques.
5. Learn how to use R and RStudio for counting techniques and to find probabilities.

The probability of an event is the number of ways an event can happen divided by the total number of possible outcomes. Therefore, probabilities are based on counting principles. When learning the fundamentals of probability, it is essential to understand the counting rules presented in this chapter. For example, to determine the number of ways to climb 5 steps by taking at most 2 steps at a time. Let O represent taking 1 step and let T represent taking two steps at once. The possibilities are OOOOO (taking only 1 step at a time for all 5 steps), OOOT (taking 1 step for the first 3 steps, then taking 2 steps at once), OOTO (taking 1 step for the first 2 steps, taking 2 steps at once, then taking 1 step), and so on. In total, there will be 8 ways to climb 5 steps by taking at most 2 steps at a time. Hence, the probability of taking 1 step on the first 2 steps in this scenario is 3/8 because there are 3 ways to take 1 step on the first 2 steps and 8 ways to climb 5 steps by taking at most 2 steps at a time. In this chapter you will learn how to apply such rules of probability to these as well as common real-life experiences.

FIGURE 4.1 How Many Different Ways Exist for Climbing the Stairs?

Chapter Vocabulary

- A probability is the likelihood that something will occur.
- The outcome of a probability experiment is the result of a single trial.
- The set of all outcomes of a probability experiment is called the sample space.
- An event is a subset of a sample space.
- The theoretical probability of an event E is the number of outcomes in event E divided by the total number of possible outcomes.
- The empirical probability is the frequency of an event E divided by the total frequency.
- According to the law of large numbers as an experiment is repeated over and over, the empirical probability of an event approaches the theoretical probability of the event.
- Subjective probability is based on opinions, estimates, or other inexact information.
- A contingency table shows the distribution of one variable in rows and another variable in columns.
- A tree diagram is a figure that consists of connected line segments that emanate from a starting point and contains nodes throughout that indicate each possible outcome of a probability experiment.
- A compound event is any event that is the combination of two or more events.
- When events cannot happen at the same time, they are said to be mutually exclusive events.
- A Venn diagram is a diagram that shows the outcomes of an experiment.
- Two or more events are independent of each other if the probability of one event occurring has no bearing on the probability of the other event(s) occurring.
- Three or more events {A, B, C} or {A, B, C, D} are mutually independent if every pair from the three events such as {A, B}, {A, C}, {B, C}, every triple and pair from the four events such as {A, B, C}, {A, B, D}, {B, D, C}, {A, C, D}, {A, B}, {A, C}, {A, D}, {B, C}, {B, D}, {C, D}and so on are all independent.
- The multiplication rule states that if two events are independent, the probability of events *A* and *B* happening in succession is: $P(A \cap B) = P(A) * P(B)$.
- Dependent events are events that are not independent.
- A permutation is an ordered arrangement.
- The definition of factorial of n is that for any positive integer *n*, the number *n!* equals the product of all integers from *n* down to 1.
- Each distinct group of objects that can be selected without regard to order is called a combination.

4.1 Probability Fundamentals

Students in beginning statistics courses often consider probability concepts to be challenging. However, having a solid understanding of probability fundamentals makes this topic much less daunting. We will start with fundamental definitions. A probability is the likelihood that something will occur.

Probability is a branch of mathematics. In advanced statistics courses, the field of probability is also defined as a subbranch of statistics called measure theory. The purpose of probability is to measure an event on a scale from 0 to 1. Therefore, a probability is a measure on the interval [0, 1] on the real number line. In mathematics, the set of real numbers includes integers {...,−3, −2, −1, 0, 1, 2, 3, ...}, fractions, and irrational numbers such as square roots. A real number line contains points that are real numbers. Hence, intuitively the probability of an event is a measure of the likelihood of an event that results from a probability experiment.

4.1.1 Probability Experiments

A probability experiment is a series of actions that leads to unambiguous results called outcomes. As mentioned in Section 1.2, probability grew out of a gambler's dispute in 1654 France. Therefore, many games of chance use probability. Rolling a fair die is an example of a probability experiment. A coin toss is another example of a probability experiment. Each action in a probability experiment yields an outcome. The outcome or element of a probability experiment is the result of a single trial. For example, getting "heads" when tossing a fair coin is an outcome. The set of all outcomes of a probability experiment is called the sample space. In the experiment of tossing a fair coin once, the sample space is S = {H, T}, where H indicates "heads" and T indicates "tails." An event is a subset of a sample space. In the experiment of tossing a fair die once, the sample space is $S = \{1, 2, 3, 4, 5, 6\}$. A subset of the sample space is $E = \{\text{all even numbers}\} = \{2, 4, 6\}$.

There are two basic probability rules that are helpful in solving probability problems:

1. $0 \le P(E) \le 1$, where $P(E)$ is "the probability of event E"
2. $\sum P(E) = 1$

Note that $P(E) = 0$ does not mean that an event will not happen. It implies only that the event is highly unlikely to happen. Likewise, $P(E) = 1$ does not mean that an event definitely will happen. It means that it is highly likely that the event will happen. The explanation for this is based on measure theory, which is beyond the scope of this textbook. In determining probabilities, the objective is first to determine the type of probability before calculating the probability of an event.

There are three types of probability—classical or theoretical, empirical or sample-based, and subjective probability. The theoretical probability of an event E is the number of outcomes in event E divided by the total number of possible outcomes:

$$P(E) = \frac{\textit{Number of outcomes in event E}}{\textit{Total number of possible outcomes}}$$

The difference between theoretical and empirical probability is that theoretical probability assumes that certain outcomes are equally likely, while empirical probability relies on the frequency of outcomes in an actual experiment to determine the likelihood of outcomes. The empirical probability is the frequency of an event E divided by the total frequency:

$$P(E) = \frac{\textit{Frequency of event E}}{\textit{Total frequency}}$$

The frequency of an event is the number of times an element from an event occurs during an experiment. The total frequency is the total number of times an experiment is performed.

For example, suppose E = {all even numbers} when rolling a fair die. The theoretical probability of E is

$$P(E) = \frac{3}{6} = \frac{1}{2}$$

because there are three elements in the event {2, 4, 6} and a total of six possible outcomes {1, 2, 3, 4, 5, 6}.

To determine the empirical probability of E, the die needs to be rolled a repeated number of times. According to the law of large numbers, as an experiment is repeated over and over, the empirical probability of an event approaches the theoretical probability of the event.

If a die is rolled 500 times and 255 rolls result in an even number, then

$$P(E) = \frac{255}{500} = \frac{51}{100} = 0.51.$$

Example:

Suicide is the second leading worldwide cause of death for individuals 15 to 29 years old (World Health Organization, 2019). Although the majority of people who have depression do not die by suicide, having major depression increases the risk of suicide.

In Zimbabwe, a country in southern Africa, trauma from war and high unemployment rates can leave people in despair. Instead of turning to a therapist, people who feel hopeless find hope on a "Friendship Bench" where they speak to trained elderly women or mental health stakeholders.

FIGURE 4.2 Colorful Flowers

FIGURE 4.3 Friendship Bench

The Friendship Bench Project is an intervention to reduce the treatment gap of mental disorders especially in sub-Saharan Africa. The Friendship Bench has been running in three large primary care clinics in Harare Zimbabwe where eight workshops were held over a six-month period (Chibanda et al., 2016). The number of participants are in the contingency table below. A contingency table shows the distribution of one variable in rows and another variable in columns. It is useful for displaying the relationship between variables.

Number of Workshop Participants

STAKEHOLDERS	NUMBER OF PARTICIPANTS (TOTAL = 54)
Policy makers	
Health ministry	8
City health	6
University lecturer	4
Community-level workers	6
Nurse in charge	8
Direct health promoters	2
Community health workers	8
Research team	6
Psychiatrist	3
Senior psychologist	1
Psychologist	1
Project coordinator	1
Study Participants	
Research assistants	0

A randomly selected attendee is to do an interview with the media about the workshop. Determine the probability that the individual is a nurse in charge.

Answer:

There were a total of 54 workshop participants. Of the 54, eight had the title nurse in charge. Therefore, the probability that a nurse in charge is selected for the interview is:

$$P(\textit{Nurse in Charge}) = \frac{8}{54} = \frac{4}{27} \approx .1481.$$

Converting the decimal to a percent, there is a 14.81% chance that the workshop attendee that is selected to do an interview with the media about the workshop is a nurse in charge.

A subjective probability is the third type of probability. Subjective probability is based on opinions, estimates, guesses, or other inexact information. This guess typically is based on experience and evaluation of a situation. In the Friendship Bench example, an individual may state that the probability that they will attend the workshop is .90 or 90%. This value may be based on their opinion of the workshop and whether they believe it will be beneficial to attend.

4.1.2 Fundamental Counting Principle

Thus far, sample spaces were determined, and the number of elements in the sample space were counted by hand. A tree diagram is another way to determine all possible outcomes of a probability experiment. A tree diagram is a figure that consists of connected line segments that emanate from a starting point and contain nodes throughout that indicate each possible outcome of a probability experiment.

Example:

Jupiter Pizza & Waffle Co. is located in Sugar Land, Texas, USA. Jupiter specializes in California-style pizza, and it offers two types of crust = {Gluten-Free, Sourdough}, three sauces = {Spicy Tomato, Tomato, Barbecue}, and two sizes = {Medium, Large}. Use a tree diagram to determine the sample space for the kinds of pizza that can be ordered.

FIGURE 4.4 Pizza Time

Answer:

Because there are two possibilities (Gluten-Free and Sourdough) for the type of pizza dough, draw two branches from a starting point and label one GF and the other S. Then if Gluten-Free is chosen, there are three possibilities for the sauce (Spicy Tomato, Tomato, Barbecue). So, draw three branches from GF and label them ST, T, and B, respectively. Do the same for Sourdough. Follow the same procedure for the two sizes.

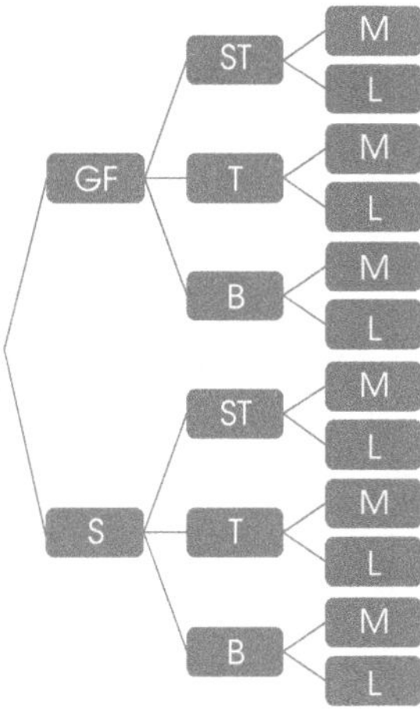

IMG 4.1

From the tree diagram, the sample space contains 12 items:

S = {(GF, ST, M), (GF, T, L), (GF, T, M), (GF, T, L), (GF, B, M), (GF, B, L), (S, ST, M), (S, ST, L), (S, T, M), (S, T, L), (S, B, M), (S, B, L)}.

In both the Jupiter Pizza example and the Friendship Bench example, the events occurred in ways that made it practical to count by hand. In some cases, an event can occur in so many different ways that it is impractical to list all outcomes. In this case, the fundamental counting principle is necessary.

The fundamental counting principle states that if event E_1 can be performed in n_1 ways and event E_2 can be performed in n_2 ways, then the number of ways the events can occur in succession is $n_1 * n_2$ ways. This can also be extended to any number of events.

Example:

Suppose the Friendship Bench workshop attendees want to form a committee. They want one member from each type of stakeholder. Recall that the stakeholders are policy makers, community-level workers, research teams, and study participants. In how many ways can the committee be formed?

Answer:

Because there are three types of policy makers, three types of community-level workers, four types of research teams, and one type of study participant, the committee can be formed in

$$3*3*4*1 = 36 \text{ ways.}$$

4.1.3 Exercises

Understanding Concepts

1. What is an outcome or element of a probability experiment?
2. What are the three types of probability?
3. What is a sample space?
4. State the law of large numbers.
5. What does a contingency table show?

True or false? In Exercises 6–11, determine whether the statement is true or false. If it is false, rewrite it as a true statement.

6. A tree diagram can be used to determine the sample space.
7. According to the law of large numbers, the number 10 is large.

8. A sample space is the set of all possible outcomes of an event.

9. The probability of obtaining a sum of 7 when rolling a pair of fair dice can be calculated in more than one way.

10. Theoretical probabilities can be determined by hand.

11. In a probability experiment, outcomes and elements have the same meaning.

Skill Building

12. Probability is a number that ranges from _____ to _____.

13. Think of a random phenomenon involving three fair coins. Explain what constitutes a trial in your experiment. Now, define the sample space.

14. A student in your class performed a simple experiment. The student kept track of how often a fellow student fell asleep during class. The probability was calculated to be 0.17. How can the professor use this information to determine the probability that no students fall asleep on a given day?

15. From your experiment in Exercise 13, create an event and derive the probability using the counting principle. Explain your answer.

16. How can a student be sure that the long-run relative frequency of an event's occurrence will approach the event's true frequency?

17. Consider a pair of fair dice, each having six sides. Each side is labeled with the numbers 1, 2, 3, 4, 5, or 6. Call the total of the two faceup numbers, X. What are all of the possible values for X and their corresponding probabilities?

18. A popular candy called M&M® contains individual pieces of chocolate candy that can come in six different colors (e.g., brown, yellow, green, red, orange, and blue). We bought a large bag and randomly filled a jar with 80 M&Ms®. There were 15 brown, 18 yellow, 15 green, 29 red, and 22 blue. Let us perform an experiment; we will draw a single M&M from the jar. What is the sample space for this experiment?

19. Consider the problem described in Exercise 18. Is drawing a blue M&M® from the jar considered a random event?

20. Consider the problem described in Exercise 18. Draw one piece of candy from the jar. Define the random variable X as the number of letters in the color of the selected candy. Now, construct a probability histogram.

Extending Concepts

21. A professor randomly selects a student to solve a problem on the board. There are 12 male students and 15 female students in the class. What is the probability of choosing a male student?

22. If one is equally likely to be born on any day of a year, what is the probability of someone being born on a Monday? Assume 365 days in a year.

23. When you roll a couple of dice, what is the probability that the sum of the face values is greater than 12?

24. The letters "p," "q," "r," "s," and "t" are used to form a five-letter password. How many passwords are possible if letters cannot be duplicated in the password?

25. A license plate contains two letters and four digits. How many unique license plates are possible?

4.2 Addition Rule

To help understand probability concepts, a student may contact their classmate, a tutor, or both a classmate and a tutor. Let "contact a classmate" be event *A*, and "contact a tutor" be event *B*. These are known as compound events because they represent a combination of two events. A compound event is any event that is the combination of two or more events.

In this section we focus on compound events of the form "*A* or *B*," which means that event *A* occurs, event *B* occurs, or both events *A* and *B* occur. The event "*A* or *B*" is written as $A \cup B$, and pronounced "*A* union *B*." The event "*A* and *B*" is written as $A \cap B$, and pronounced "*A* intersect *B*." The addition rule is one of the rules that determines the probability of compound events.

4.2.1 Using Addition Rule to Find Probabilities

In the fair die example, let event A = {roll an even number} and event B = {roll a number less than 3}. Use the addition rule:

$$P(A \cup B) = P(A) + P(B) - P(A \cap B)$$

$$P(A) = \frac{3}{6} = \frac{1}{2}$$

$$P(B) = \frac{2}{6} = \frac{1}{3}$$

$$P(A \cap B) = \frac{1}{6}$$

$$P(A \cup B) = \frac{1}{2} + \frac{1}{3} - \frac{1}{6} = \frac{2}{3}$$

There are three even numbers {2, 4, 6}. There are two numbers less than 3, {1, 2}, and there is one number that is both even and less than 3, {2} which lies in the intersection of the set of two events. Therefore, there is a 66.67 % chance of rolling an even number or rolling a number less than 3.

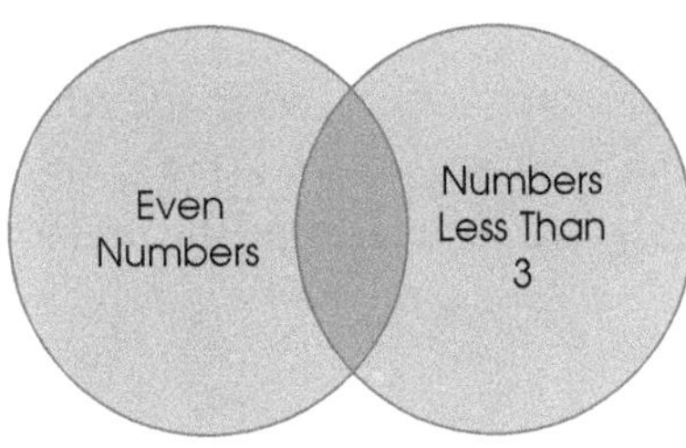

IMG 4.2

This example is illustrated with a Venn diagram, a diagram that shows the outcomes of an experiment. English mathematician John Venn invented Eulerian circles in the 1880s. He named the diagrams after Swiss mathematician Leonard Euler, who created similar diagrams in the 1700s. In 1918, Eulerian circles were referred to as Venn diagrams by U.S. academic philosopher Clarence Lewis (1918) in his book *A Survey of Symbolic Logic*.

FIGURE 4.5 John Venn (1834–1923)

4.2.2 Mutually Exclusive Events

When events cannot happen at the same time, they are called mutually exclusive events. Suppose event A = {roll an even number} and event B = {roll an odd number}. Because a roll of a die cannot yield a number that is both odd and even at the same time, events A and B are mutually exclusive. The addition rule for mutually exclusive events is

$$P(A \cup B) = P(A) + P(B).$$

If $A \cap B = \varnothing$, the probability $(A \cap B) = 0$.

Example:

Refer back to the Friendship Bench contingency table. Are nurse in charge and psychiatrist mutually exclusive?

Answer:

The events *nurse in charge* and *psychiatrist* are not mutually exclusive because a person can be a psychiatric nurse.

4.2.3 Exercises

Understanding Concepts

1. What is an event that is the combination of two or more events called?

2. When an experiment results in compound events, what does this mean?

3. Which probability rule(s) can be applied to determine the probability of compound events?

4. What is the purpose of a Venn diagram?

True or false? In Exercises 5–9, determine whether the statement is true or false. If it is false, rewrite it as a true statement.

5. Mutually exclusive events cannot happen at the same time.

6. The intersection of two mutually exclusive events is zero.

7. John Venn invented Eulerian circles in the 1800s, which were later referred to as "Venn diagrams" by Clarence Lewis in 1918.

8. Both the design of the experiment and data-collection technique may cause sampling bias.

9. An event is a subset of a sample space.

Skill Building

Use the following to answer questions 10–13:

> A box of M&Ms®, contains individual pieces of chocolate candy in six different colors (e.g., brown, yellow, green, red, orange, and blue). A jar was filled with 99 M&M®. There were 15 brown, 18 yellow, 15 green, 29 orange, and 22 blue.

10. What is the probability of drawing a yellow or green M&M® on a single draw?

11. What is the probability of not picking a blue M&M®?

FIGURE 4.6 M&Ms

12. If you are picking one M&M® and then replacing it, is the color you picked the first time mutually exclusive from the color you picked the second time?

13. Are the chances of picking any color M&M® equally likely?

Use the following to answer questions 14–16:

What is the most popular type of music? The table below lists the probability that a person selected at random will have a specific favorite genre.

FIGURE 4.7 Old School

TYPE OF MUSIC	COUNTRY	POP	CLASSICAL	RHYTHM AND BLUES	ROCK
Probability	.12	.37	.10	.15	.16

14. Do the probabilities in the above table constitute a valid probability distribution? Please explain. If not, what can be done to resolve any problems?

15. Using the possibly modified probabilities from Exercise 14, find the probability that someone prefers country, rock, or pop genres of music.

16. If two people are randomly selected, are their favorite musical genres mutually exclusive? Please explain.

17. Let us assume you do a taste test on campus to find out the most enjoyed pizza toppings. You find out that the probability students enjoy pepperoni on their pizza is 0.63, the probability students enjoy mushrooms on their pizza is 0.35, and the probability students enjoy both pepperoni and mushrooms is 0.76. Are these enjoyed toppings mutually exclusive? Please explain.

Use the following to answer questions 18–20:

> Eating nutritional meals and exercising are important steps in maintaining a strong healthy body. Suppose 60% of students eat proper nutritious meals daily, and 20% exercise regularly. Also, there is a 25% chance that a student does both.

18. Find the probability that students eat proper nutritious meals or exercises, but not both.

19. Find the probability that a randomly selected student does not exercise.

20. Find the probability that a student does not exercise and does not eat proper, nutritious meals.

Extending Concepts

21. When choosing a card at random from a deck of cards, the events of getting a diamond or a 6 are mutually exclusive. True or false?

22. When choosing a card at random from a deck of cards, what is the probability of getting a diamond or a 6?

23. The probability of event A is $P(A) = 0.4$, and the probability of event B is $P(B) = 0.25$. If the probability of A and B is 0.13, what is the probability of choosing A or B?

24. A student conducts an experiment and discovers that three events can occur with probability 0.3, 0.4, and 0.5. The student reasons that the probability of obtaining any of these results should be the sum of their probabilities, which is 1.2. Is this result plausible? Explain.

25. The probability that I am selected to solve a problem on the board today is 0.2. What is the probability that I will not be selected?

4.3 Conditional Probability and Multiplication Rule

When using the addition rule, it is important to know whether events are mutually exclusive. Analogously, when using the multiplication rule, it is important to know whether events are independent. Although the mutually exclusivity property and the independence property are quite different, it can be difficult to distinguish them in reality.

If the occurrence of one event prevents the occurrence of other events, then the events are mutually exclusive and cannot happen at the same time. If the occurrence of one event does not prevent the other events from occurring, then the event may or may not be independent. The events would be independent only if the occurrence of one event does not change the probability that the other event occurs.

4.3.1 Independent Events and Conditional Probability

Two or more events are independent of each other if the probability of one event occurring has no bearing on the probability of the other event occurring. When this extends to more than two events, they are referred to as mutually independent events. Dependent events are events that are not independent. If two events A and B are dependent, the conditional probability of an event B happening given event A occurs is $P(B \mid A)$ is read "the probability of B given A." This is determined by:

$$P(B \mid A) = \frac{P(B \cap A)}{P(A)} = \frac{P(A \cap B)}{P(A)},$$

provided $P(A) \neq 0$. If the events are independent, then

$$P(B \mid A) = P(B),$$

which can be used to show whether two events are independent or dependent.

OB/GYN: First Line of Defense in Fighting Breast Cancer

Dr. Michael Hold, MD, FACOG (Fellow of the American Congress of Obstetricians and Gynecologists), practices in Houston, Texas. According to Dr. Hold, monthly breast self-exams along with routine visits to a well-qualified obstetrician/gynecologist are crucial to early diagnosis and treatment of breast cancer. Inflammatory breast cancer (IBC) is a rare and aggressive malignancy (Hester et al., 2021). However, it is often initially misdiagnosed because of its similarity to benign breast pathologies, such as breast abscesses. Patients with IBC initially seek care from an obstetrician/gynecologist or primary care physician, not an oncologist, because early symptoms are similar to an insect bite or rash. Imperative to a correct diagnosis is a well-qualified, aggressive physician, such as Dr. Hold. Upon cancer diagnosis, Dr. Hold promptly refers patients to an oncologist.

IMG 4.3 Michael Hold, MD, Fellow of the American Congress of Obstetricians and Gynecologists

The annual incidence of female breast cancer in the United States in 2020 was 275,000 (Hester et al., 2021). Of women diagnosed with breast cancer in the United States in 2020, there were an estimated 13,750 diagnosed with IBC. Determine the probability that a randomly selected woman was diagnosed with breast cancer, and she was diagnosed with having IBC. The entire female population in the United States in 2020 was approximately 166 million.

Answer:

Let *A* be the event that in 2020 a woman in the United States was diagnosed with breast cancer. Let *B* be the event that in 2020 a woman in the United States was diagnosed with having IBC.

The probability that a woman was diagnosed with breast cancer and it was IBC is:

$$P(A \text{ and } B) = P(A) * P(B|A) = (275{,}000/166{,}000{,}000) * (13{,}750/275{,}000) = 8.2831 \times 10^{-8}$$

Therefore, the probability that a randomly selected woman in the United States who was diagnosed with breast cancer was also diagnosed with having IBC is approximately 8.2831×10^{-8}.

When sampling with replacement, the draws are independent. If sampling is done without replacement, the draws are dependent. Consider the following example.

Example:

A student is constructing a colorful statistics study guide, and he keeps his marker in a box containing S = {1 green, 2 yellow, 3 blue, 4 red} colored markers. Sampling is done without replacement. What is the probability of selecting a blue marker given that the first selection was a yellow marker?

Answer:

This is a conditional probability because it is computed with the knowledge of additional information. The additional knowledge is that the first marker selected was yellow. There are two yellow markers out of a total 10 markers. Therefore, the probability of selecting a yellow marker is $\frac{2}{10}$. Since the next marker is selected without replacing the first marker, there are only nine markers left in the box. The probability of the compound event of selecting a yellow marker then selecting a blue marker, is $\left(\frac{2}{10}\right)\left(\frac{3}{9}\right) = \frac{6}{90} = \frac{1}{15} = .0667$. Therefore, there is approximately a 6.67% chance of selecting a blue marker given that the first marker selected was a yellow marker.

Determining probabilities for independent and dependent events are also demonstrated in the following example.

Example:

Between 1933 and 1945, Nazi Germany and its allies established more than 44,000 camps and other incarceration sites (Heřmanová & Abrhám, 2015). The exhibition *To Survive—Voices from Ravensbrück,* at the Museum of Cultural History in Sweden, is a collection of small objects secretly and illegally created by women in the Ravensbrück concentration camp as acts of resistance against their inhuman conditions (Tinning, 2016). Ravensbrück was a concentration camp built exclusively for women. It was designed to terrorize, brutalize, humiliate, torture, and murder women and their children. From 1939–1945, an estimated 132,000 women were imprisoned there. Only 15,000 are estimated to have survived.

From 1942 onward, a diverse group of women from 27 countries were incarcerated at Ravensbrück. The largest group was Polish (30%); next, Russian and Ukrainian (21%); followed by German and Austrian (18%); Hungarian, including Roma and Sinti Gypsies (8%); French (7%); Belgian, Swedish, and Danish women as well as 12 British women (Hore, 2019).

Given that a woman was imprisoned at Ravensbrück, what is the probability that she was British?

Answer:

This is a conditional probability because it is computed with the knowledge of additional information. The additional information is that the woman was imprisoned at Ravensbrück instead of one of the other more than 44,000 camps. Let *B* be the event the woman is British, and *A* the event the woman is at Ravensbrück. Because there were approximately 132,000 women at Ravensbrück, the conditional probability that a woman was British is

$$P(B \mid A) = \frac{12}{132{,}000} = .0000909$$

4.3.2 Using Multiplication Rule to Find Probabilities

The multiplication rule can be used to find the probability of two or more events that occur in sequence. For example, if you roll a die and toss a coin, you can determine the probability of getting a five on the die and a "head" on the coin. The multiplication rule states that if two events are independent then the probability of events *A* and *B* happening in succession is:

$$P(A \cap B) = P(A) * P(B).$$

Because rolling a die and tossing a coin are independent events, the probability of getting a five and then getting a "heads" is $P(A \cap B) = P(A) * P(B) = \frac{1}{6} * \frac{1}{2} = \frac{1}{12}$. Therefore, there is an 8.33% chance of obtaining a five on a die, then obtaining a "head" on the flip of a coin.

In the case of dependent events,

$$P(A \cap B) = P(B \mid A) * P(A)\cdot$$

Example:

In the Ravensbrück example, if the written personal stories of two women were selected at random to place in the museum exhibit, what is the probability that the women were Polish and French women? Assume that the women did not have dual citizenship.

Answer:

Let A be the event a woman is Polish and B the event a woman is French. Under the assumption of the women not having dual citizenship, the events are independent. The probability that a Polish and a French woman are selected is $P(A \cap B) = P(A) * P(B) = (.30)(.07) = 0.021$. Therefore, there is a 2.1% chance that two randomly selected women are Polish and French.

4.3.3 Exercises

Understanding Concepts

1. Suppose one event is rolling a die, and another event is tossing a fair coin. Are the two events independent? Explain your answer.

2. Suppose you sample one card from a deck of cards, do not replace the first card, then sample another card. Are the two events independent? Explain your answer.

3. Which probability rule can be used to find the probability of two events occurring in sequence?

True or false? In Exercises 4–6, determine whether the statement is true or false. If it is false, rewrite it as a true statement.

4. Mutually independent events are also called "mutually exclusive events."

5. Venn diagrams can easily display independent events.

6. Dependent events are events that are not independent.

Skill Building

7. Can knowledge of the outcome of event B change the probability of event A? If so, how?

8. Suppose there are two events, A and B, with associated probabilities $P(A) = .2$, $P(B) = .5$, and $P(B|A) = .8$. Are events A and B independent events? How do you know?

9. Using the information provided in Exercise 8, determine the probability that both events, *A* and *B*, occur.

10. Suppose the probability that event *A* occurs is .1, the probability that event *B* occurs is .5, and the probability that both events *A* and *B* occurs is .3. What is the conditional probability that event *B* occurs given that event *A* occurs?

11. Newly enrolled college student Jason wants to join a fraternity. Jason researches and visits three different fraternities. Jason would like to get a feel for his prospects. Therefore, one afternoon he comes up with the probabilities of getting an offer letter from the fraternities. Let the events *A*, *B*, and *C* be defined as follows:

    A = Jason is accepted into the Alpha house.
    B = Jason is accepted into the Beta house.
    C = Jason is accepted into the Chi house.
    Jason enlists the help of some seniors, and they come up with the following probabilities:

PREDICTED PROBABILITIES						
A	*B*	*C*	*A and B*	*A and C*	*B and C*	*A and B and C*
0.7	0.8	0.4	0.3	0.15	0.1	0.05

    Construct a Venn diagram to represent these predicted probabilities.

    Using the table and diagram from question 11, answer questions 12–15.

12. Calculate the probability that Jason is accepted to at least one of the fraternity houses.

13. What is the probability that Jason is presented with an offer from both the Alpha and Beta houses, but not the Chi house?

14. What is the probability that Jason is invited to any two of the houses but not all three?

15. Jason wants to make sure that he has a probability of no less than .99 of getting an offer. What calculation does Jason need to perform? Based on the results, does Jason need to apply to more fraternity houses?

16. Determine if each of the following groups of events are independent:
    a. The grade on your final exam and the grade on your midterm exam
    b. The value rolled on two unbiased dice
    c. The amount of time your cell phone battery lasts each day
    d. The amount of food you eat for breakfast, lunch, and dinner

Use the following to answer questions 17–21:

How are age and music preference related? Researchers surveyed 550 people about their favorite musical genre, and the results are presented in the contingency table below:

	OVER THE AGE OF 50	UNDER THE AGE OF 50	TOTAL
Country	60	50	110
Classical	80	70	150
Pop	104	186	290
TOTAL	244	306	550

17. What is the probability that someone likes pop music?

18. What is the probability that someone likes country music?

19. What is the probability that someone likes country or pop music?

20. What is the conditional probability that someone likes pop music given that they are over the age of 50?

21. Are liking pop music and being over the age of 50 independent events?

Extending Concepts

According to meteorological records for our county, the probability that rain is predicted in a given day is 0.2. The probability that it rained on a day rain was predicted is 0.9. The probability that it rained on a day when rain was not predicted is 0.3.

22. What is the probability that rain is predicted and it does rain on a given day?

23. What is the probability that rain is NOT predicted and it does rain on a given day?

24. What is the probability that it does rain on any randomly selected day?

25. What is the probability that rain is NOT predicted and it does NOT rain?

26. What is the probability that the prediction is correct on a randomly chosen day?

4.4 Counting

Many topics in this textbook are presented as a gentle introduction to a larger discipline in statistics and mathematics, such as counting. Counting is a part of combinatorics, a branch of mathematics that deals with how discrete objects combine with one another and the probabilities of these outcomes. Anything that is separated from something else is a discrete object. For instance, cars, pianos, and animals (unless they are conjoined) are all examples of discrete objects.

Combinatorics is important in statistics because it provides rules for determining the number of possible outcomes without doing a hand count. We have already discussed the fundamental counting principle. We will now discuss two more rules for counting, starting with permutations.

4.4.1 Permutations

A permutation is an ordered arrangement. To count the number of permutations means to count the number of distinct ways a group of items can be ordered.

The notation for the number of permutations of n objects is $n!$ pronounced "n factorial." The definition of n factorial is for any positive integer n, the number $n!$ equals the product of all integers from n down to 1:

$$n! = n(n-1)(n-2)\ldots(2)(1),$$

and 0! = 1 by definition. Table 1 in Appendix A lists the factorials for numbers up to 30.

The number of permutations of r objects selected from a group of n objects is pronounced "n permute r" and is defined by

$$_nP_r = n(n-1)\ldots(n-r+1) = \frac{n!}{(n-r)!}.$$

Example:

A student's statistics study guide is composed of four sections S = {Vocabulary, Directions, Formulas, Examples}. The student prefers to use color index cards to construct his study guide. The student has decided to study all for four sections each day, but he will change which sections he studies first, second, third, and fourth every day. For example, on Monday he studies Formulas, Vocabulary, Directions, and Examples in that order. How many days will pass before the student repeats the order in which he has studied each section of his study guide?

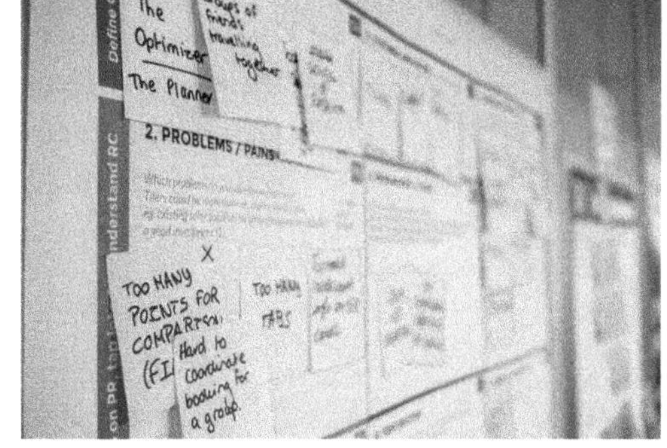

FIGURE 4.8 Study Guide

Answer:

Because the order in which the student studies each of the four sections of this study guide is important to him, this is a permutation. On Day 1, the student may choose to study the sections in the following order, Day 1 = {Formulas, Vocabulary, Directions, Examples}. On Day 2, the student may choose to study in the following order, Day 2 = {Vocabulary, Formulas, Directions, Examples}, and so on.

Because the study guide contains four sections, $n! = 4! = 24$ days will pass before the student repeats the order in which he studies each section of his study guide.

Example:

Refer to the study guide example above. In how many ways can the student determine the first two sections he will study each day?

Answer:

The number of permutations of two sections chosen from the four total sections is

$$_4P_2 = 4(4-1)_{\dots}(2-2+1) = \frac{4!}{(4-2)!} = \frac{4!}{2!} = \frac{4*3*2!}{2!} = 12 \text{ ways.}$$

For example, on Day 1, the student studies the following two sections first, Day 1 = {Formulas, Vocabulary}. On Day 2, the student starts by studying in the following order, Day 2 = {Vocabulary, Formulas}, Day 3 = {Directions, Formulas}, and so on for 12 days.

4.4.2 Combinations

In some instances when choosing a set of objects from a larger set, the ordering of the chosen objects does not matter. The only thing that matters is which objects are chosen. Each distinct group of objects that can be selected without regard to order is called a combination. The number of combinations of r objects chosen from a group of n objects is

$$_nC_r = \binom{n}{r} = \frac{n!}{r!(n-r)!},$$

which is pronounced "n choose r."

Suppose there is a set of letters S = {A, B, C}. In the case where order is important and two objects are chosen, the number of permutations is $_3P_2 = 6$. That is, {A, B}, {B, A}, {A, C}, {C, A}, {B, C}, and {C, A}.

However, order is not important in determining the number of combinations. Therefore the three combinations are {A, B} ⇔ {B, A}, {B, C} ⇔ {C, B} and {A, C} ⇔ {C, A}.

Because order is important in determining the number of permutations and order is not important when determining the number of combinations, the relationship between permutations and combinations is:

$$ {}_nP_r = {}_nC_r * r! $$

4.4.3 Exercises

Understanding Concepts

1. In statistics, what is a mathematical technique that determines the number of distinct groups that can be selected without regard to order?

2. What is a permutation?

3. To compute a combination, which values are needed?

4. What is the mathematical relationship between a permutation and a combination?

5. What is a major difference between a permutation and a combination?

True or false? In Exercises 6–7, determine whether the statement is true or false. If it is false, rewrite it as a true statement.

6. A permutation is greater than or equal to a combination.

7. Order is important when determining a combination.

Skill Building

8. A four-student prize committee to select the teacher of the year will be chosen randomly. One member will be selected to represent each grade level (freshman, sophomore, junior, and senior). If there are eight freshmen, six sophomores, 11 juniors, and two seniors eligible for the committee. How many possible committees could be formed?

9. SweetFrog® is a popular frozen yogurt store, and you have just won its free mystery dessert! The dessert will be created based on your selections. There are three different categories. Category 1 is cup or cone. Category 2 is one of their 20 yogurt flavors, and Category 3 is one of their six topping options. How many different delicious dessert options can you create?

10. There are 19 departments (e.g., music, history, math, physics, performing arts, religion, English, biology, chemistry, American studies, etc.) in the College of Arts and Sciences at a particular university. Each department has two degree programs, namely a bachelor of arts and a bachelor of science. Students must select one degree from one department in order to graduate. How many different choices are possible?

11. The warden at a local prison is trying to calculate how many distinct license plates he can have his prisoners make if the first three spots are distinct letters and the last four are distinct numbers? Calculate the total for the warden. Now compare that to the total if the letters, and numbers do NOT have to be distinct.

12. The Washington Nationals are a major league baseball (MLB) team based out of Washington, DC. In the game of baseball, two teams play by taking turns between being at bat and out in the field. A line-up is the designated order in which a team's nine batters will bat. How many distinct line-ups can be created by the National's manager?

FIGURE 4.9 Washington, DC, USA

13. Partial requirements to complete a degree from a private university in Washington, D.C., include a student needing to take 10 courses that are considered general education courses. These courses have no prerequisites. Two courses are in mathematics (MA1, MA2), two in science (SC1, SC2), two in social science (SS1, SS2), two in literature (LI1,

LI2), and two in performing arts (PA1, PA2). How many possible arrangements are there to take the courses?

14. Use the information in Exercise 13. Suppose a student wants to take two of the general education classes from the same field (e.g., M1 and M2) each of the next five semesters. How many possible arrangements are there to take the courses?

15. Use the information in Exercise 13. Suppose the student wants to complete the general education requirements in two semesters by taking five courses each semester, one course from each group. How many different arrangements are possible?

16. How many different permutations are possible from the letters that make up the word STATISTICS? In this case, the same letters are identical. That is $S_1T_1A_1T_2I_1S_2T_3I_2C_1S_3$ and $S_3T_1A_1T_2I_2S_1T_3I_1C_1S_1$ are considered the same arrangement.

17. What are the main differences between permutations and combinations?

18. Morse code is an encoded alphabet using dots and dashes to represent characters. For example, the letter A is represented by • _. If a letter can be a combination of 1, 2, 3, or 4 dot/dash combinations, can every letter of the English alphabet be represented? What if the digits are included?

19. There are 25 faculty members eligible to receive one of three distinct awards from the Provost for best teaching. How many possible combinations of winners are there?

20. Many websites require the use of a password for security. Examples include bank accounts, social media accounts, and shopping sites. Many websites require a strong password selection to avoid potential hackers from being able to use software easily to guess your password. If your password contains only six letters, how many different password combinations are there? (Note: Each letter could be used more than once.) A password would be much stronger and secure if you were forced to use eight characters. Of those eight characters, one must be a letter and one must be a number between 0–9. How many different password combinations exist for this scenario?

Extending Concepts

21. A student has to match four names of basketball players from a list of six pictures. She is shown a random sequence of six pictures of those players. What is the probability that she identifies all four players correctly? Explain your answer.

22. A deck of cards has 4 aces, 4 kings, and 44 other cards. What is the probability of having 2 aces and 2 kings, in any order, when 4 cards are extracted randomly from the deck?

23. How many solutions are there to the equation "A + B + C = 5" if A, B, and C are nonnegative integers?

24. In how many ways can nine books be arranged on a shelf?

25. In how many ways can nine books be arranged on a shelf if a particular book must be the fifth book on the shelf?

4.5 R and RStudio

4.5.1 Programming Assignments

Exercise 4.1

The best way to explore elementary probability concepts with R is by using the package `prob` written by G. Jay Kerns (http://prob.r-forge.r-project.org). This package offers several convenient functions that represent classical texbook examples illustrating the theory of probability. With a simple command, you can simulate coin tossing, die rolling, playing cards, selecting from urns with balls of different colors, and even the game of roulette.

Chances are that this package did not come installed by default with your R distribution. The command `install.packages("prob")` will first ask you to select a CRAN mirror, then download this package, and all prerequisites, in a special folder hosting all of your packages. The CRAN software is the same at all mirror locations, so your choice does not matter, except it should be a server in geographic proximity so that internet traffic is minimized. Once on your computer, the software will be compiled, prepared, and set up for your environment, which might take a while. Now the package is installed in your hard drive, but this does not mean you can use it right away. If you want to use it in an R session, you have to activate it by calling or invoking the function `library` with the argument `prob`, like this:

```
library(prob)

## Loading required package: combinate
## Attaching package: 'combinat'
## The following object is masked from 'package:utils'
## combn
## Loading required package: fAsianOptions
## Loading required package: timeDate
## Loading required package: timeSeries
## Loading required package: fBasics
## Loading required package: fOptions
## Attaching package: 'prob'
## The following objects are masked from 'package:base':
## intersect, setdiff, union
```

Note that functions of some packages, such as the `base` package, are loaded by default and do not need activation. This is why you might get a warning saying, "The following objects are masked from ... package," meaning that new functions are replacing previously loaded functions that happen to have the same name, so the old functions are not available anymore, at least not in a simple way. The package `combinat` is required by `prob` and is automatically installed and activated whenever we need `prob`.

Like with any package, you can orient yourself and find documentation about `prob` with function `help(package="prob")`. Do that and learn about what this package can do for you.

Exercise 4.2

A sample space in R is represented by a *data frame*, in which each row corresponds to a possible outcome of the experiment. For example, consider the random experiment of tossing a coin. The outcomes are head (H) and tail (T). The sample space in this case has only two elements, and is obtained with function `tosscoin()`:

```
tosscoin(1)
```

```
## toss1
## 1 H
## 2 T
```

The argument 1 corresponds with tossing just a coin, but the same function will create the sample space for tossing, in principle, any number of coins. How many outcomes do we obtain for tossing three coins with `tosscoin(3)`? How about 10 coins or 20? Would using 30 coins be a reasonable use of this function?

Try looking at the sample space for other experiments such as `cards()` or `rolldie(2)`.

Exercise 4.3

A sample space, as obtained by using functions `tosscoin()` or `rolldie()`, is a simple enumeration of all outcomes expected in an experiment. The probability space is obtained by adding a new column to the sample space data frame. This column is a vector of numbers representing the probability for each element of the sample space. The probability theory gives no prescription about these numbers except they are all positive and sum up to unity, which equals one. In practice, probabilities are assigned to each element in the sample space based on some theoretical assumptions or simply as an expression of the subjective degree of belief of the experimenter, who, for example, would have no reason to believe that a die would not be fair.

Build the probability space for rolling a die by assuming the equally likely model that asserts that every outcome has the same probability. Thus, if a sample has n outcomes, the probability vector p would have n identical entries $1/n$.

```
p <- rep(1/6, times = 6)
probspace(rolldie(1), p)
```

```
## X1 probs
## 1 1 0.1666667
## 2 2 0.1666667
## 3 3 0.1666667
## 4 4 0.1666667
## 5 5 0.1666667
## 6 6 0.1666667
```

What happens if, by mistake, you make `p = rep(1/5, times = 6)`? Run the example again, and explain the results.

Exercise 4.4

An event is a subset or a collection of outcomes from the sample space. The function `subset(S, cond)` selects outcomes from *S* that satisfy condition *cond*.

Here are the events for which the sum of faces from throwing a couple of dice is exactly 7:

```
Z = probspace(rolldie(2), rep(1, times=36))
subset(Z, X1+X2 == 7)
```

```
## X1 X2 probs
## 6 6 1 0.02777778
## 11 5 2 0.02777778
## 16 4 3 0.02777778
## 21 3 4 0.02777778
## 26 2 5 0.02777778
## 31 1 6 0.02777778
```

Note that here we assigned the number 1 as the probability for all 36 outcomes. This works correctly because the package rescales all probabilities before use, such that they sum up to one. In this case the probabilities used in calculations are all equal to 1/36. The condition for the sum of faces uses the symbol `==` because the use of `=` would mean an assignment operation, which can create some confusion. It is exactly this reason the preferred way to assign a value to a variable in *R* is *x* `<- 3.14` or even `3.14 -> x`.

The function `subset(cards(), rank %in% 7:9)` lists all cards in a set that have the value 7, 8, or 9. Try this function and make sure this assumption is correct. Here the logical condition uses the function `%in%` and the list of consecutive integers `7:9`. The function `%in%` helps to learn whether each value of one vector lies somewhere inside another vector. Try this example:

```
x <- 8:12
y <- 1:10
x %in% y
```

the result is a vector with five elements, the same as *x*.

Exercise 4.5

Can a computer be used to simulate experiments with random results? Anyone who has once played computer games would say "of course." But this is not so clear since we build, use, and trust computers because of their ability to invariably produce the same result when presented with identical inputs. Computers are deterministic by design. The random numbers generators, available in any programing language, including R, are functions that produce a sequence of *random-looking* numbers. The sequence will be the same every time it is started from a given seed number. So it is not really random.

The function `sim()` from package `prob` uses random numbers to select outcomes from a sample space repeatedly, providing a way to *simulate* the system under investigation. Here is an example:

```
S = tosscoin(2, makespace = TRUE)
sims = sim(S, ntrials = 10000)
empirical(sims)
```

```
## toss1 toss2 probs
## 1 H H 0.2402
## 2 T H 0.2530
## 3 H T 0.2485
## 4 T T 0.2583
```

In this simulation, two coins are tossed 10,000 times. The results are accumulated in the list `sims`. The function `empirical()` tallies up the results and calculates the experimental probabilities, which we expect to be not much different from the *theoretical probabilities.* We also expect that for even more trials, the agreement should improve. Run the experiment several more times with increasingly more trials, and discuss the results. How many more trials are necessary to obtain one more digit in the agreement between theoretical and experimental probabilities?

Exercise 4.6

In Exercise 4.4 we explored ways in which we can identify events from a sample space. The probability associated with an event is the sum of all probabilities of the outcomes out of which that event is made. This is accomplished with the `prob()` function.

In the code below, we have *S* the probability space for drawing a card from a well shuffled standard deck of playing cards. Events *A* and *B* are defined by selecting outcomes that are either "Diamond" or have number 5, 6, or 7, and function `Prob()` calculates the associated probabilities:

```
S = cards(makespace = TRUE)
A = subset(S, suit == "Diamond")
B = subset(S, rank %in% 5:7)
Prob(A)
```

```
## [1] 0.25
```

```
Prob(S, suit == "Heart")

## [1] 0.25
```

The last call of `Prob` shows how this function can be used directly on a probability space, without detaching an event. Calculate `Prob(B)`, and `Prob(S)`. Are the results what you expected?

Given events A and B, it is often useful to manipulate them using set operations. For example, the union of $A \cup B$ corresponds to the *A or B* compound event, while $A \cap B$ corresponds to the *A and B* compound event. Let us verify the addition rule for the events from the playing cards experiment.

```
Prob(union(A,B))

## [1] 0.4230769

Prob(A) + Prob(B) - Prob(intersect(A,B))

## [1] 0.4230769
```

Exercise 4.7

Follow the code in Exercise 4.6 and obtain the event A and B that are both subsets of the sample space S. The conditional probability of the event A given event B is simply looking only to those outcomes of event A that happen to also be outcomes of event B, as if the subset B replaces the sample space S. This is different from the intersection $A \cap B$ because the probability for it refers to the whole sample space S, while the conditional probability refers only to the subset B. We can easily verify the multiplication rule for conditional probabilities. For example:

```
Prob(intersect(A, B))

## [1] 0.05769231

Prob(A) * Prob(B, given = A)

## [1] 0.05769231
```

Exercise 4.8

Use functions `perm()`, `factorial()`, and `chose()` to explore the different ways of counting combinations of a list of letters, say

```
L <- c("L", "I", "S", "T")
```

The function `perm()` is included in the library `mixtools`, so you need to install and activate it before use. Display all possible permutations and show that the number of permutations is equal to the factorial of the length of the list. Use the function `choose()` to calculate the number of ways one can select two elements from the list, with replacement, when the order of the letters counts.

The function nsamp() from the package prob calculates the size of the sample space for an urn experiment under various sampling scenarios, without actually building the sample space. This is advantageous for problems where the sample space may be too large to fit in the computer memory, or it might take a long time to build. This can come up more often than you think. Try some R code to flip a coin 30 times to find how many times you have a streak of five heads "HHHHH" in the experiment. If you are not careful, this simple problem could take a very long time. The sample space for this case is too large to be stored in computer memory. Instead, you can use the function "sample" to randomly generate trials of 30 flips, repeat it, say, 1,000 times, and count the number of times your a trial has a five-heads streak. Use the function paste to collapse the list of characters to a string, and use the function grepl to test whether the substring "HHHHH" is part of a given string.

Exercise 4.9

One of the most fundamental types of random experiments is sampling from urns. Imagine a bag that contains a bunch of distinguishable objects inside, colored balls, for example. Even if two or more balls have the same color, they can be still distinguished in some other ways, by labels, for example. Several kinds of experiments are possible. We can extract two or three balls and ask for the probability of them being of the same color. We can take all the balls out of the urn at once, or we could select a ball, take a look, and put it back, such that we might get it again the next time we extract. We say that we sample without or with *replacement*, respectively. Another variant is to count the extracted balls without actually caring in which *order* they were selected. This also can be done by looking at the balls one by one, and putting them back in the bag. Many other experiments can be thought as a special case of a sampling from urn experiment. For example, rolling a six-face die is equivalent to selecting a ball from an urn with six elements labeled from 1 to 6.

The function that deals with this kind of experiment is urnsamples(), which has four arguments: *x*, a vector with the content of the urn; *size* of the sample to be extracted from the urn; a Boolean *replace* to indicate whether the sampling is done with or without replacement; and a Boolean *ordered* to indicate whether the order of the elements of the sample is important or not when counting the outcomes. A Boolean variable is a variable that has two possible values, typically indicating "true" or "false."

Consider an urn with 11 balls inside, seven of which are white and four of which are black. What is the probability of selecting three white balls successively from the urn? This probability that the first ball is white and the second one is white and the third one is also white should be

$\frac{7}{11} \times \frac{6}{10} \times \frac{5}{9} \approx 0.2121212$. Let's see how we simulate this experiment in R:

```
L <- rep(c("white", "black"), times = c(7, 4))
M <- urnsamples(L, size = 3, replace = FALSE, ordered = TRUE)
N <- probspace(M)
Q1 <- subset(N, X1 == 'white')
```

```
Q2 <- subset(Q1, X2 == 'white')
Q3 <- subset(Q2, X3 == 'white')
prob(Q3)

## [1] 0.2121212
```

What is the probability of having the first and the last ball white and the second one black? Verify the results by using the multiplication rule.

Exercise 4.10

What is the probability to select twice, in succession, an ace from a full deck of 52 well shuffled standard playing cards? For this problem, we define two events: A = the first card drawn is an ace, and B = the second card drawn is an ace. The probability of A is 4/52 because there are four aces in the deck. The probability of B is more complicated because it depends on what was the first card drawn. If the first card was an ace, then the probability of B is 3/51, because there are only three aces left in a deck that now has 51 cards, but if the first card is not an ace, then the probability of B is 4/51.

Let us try to model this situation with the R package `prob`. First we get a sample space L with function `cards()`. Internally, L is a dataframe with two columns: `rank` and `suit`. These factors have 13 and 4 levels, respectively. Next we sample two cards from L by using the urn model without replacement. The function `urnsample()` returns a list M with all possible pairs of rows from L. Check that there are `chose(52,2)` such possible combinations. Finally, we associate equal probabilities to M to obtain the probability space N and obtain the solution of the problem using the function `prob()`:

```
L <- cards()
M <- urnsamples(L, size = 2, replace=FALSE, ordered=FALSE)
N <- probspace(M, probs = rep(1/choose(52,2), times=choose(52,2)))
Prob(N, all(rank == "A"))

## [1] 0.004524887
```

In this code, the set M contains all combinations of two cards from the deck, extracted without replacement, regardless of their order. The size of M is therefore the number "52 chose 2" = $\frac{52!}{50!\,2!}$. The probability for each combination, which is one over this number, is associated to each combination by using the function `rep` to create a vector with a repeated value. Here we used the function `all()` from the *base* package, which returns true only when all elements from a vector are true. The result should be identical to the product of probabilities

$$P(A \text{ and } B) = \frac{4}{52} \times \frac{3}{51} = 0.0045249.$$

Calculate the conditional probability of the event B given A in two ways: first by using the multiplication rule and second by working with subsets of M.

4.5.2 Group Experiments

The Battle of Factorials

The factorial of a number $n! = n(n-1)(n-2)...(2)(1)$ has a very simple and direct mathematical definition. However, its implementation in a calculator or computer can be tricky, and could lead to surprising results, and possible errors that can be hard to spot. The main reason for this difficulty is that the factorial could be a very, very long number.

Question 1:
Tabulate the required number of digits to represent $n!$ for moderate n up to $n = 10$. What do you observe? Discuss in the group ways to extrapolate this to find the number of digits for 100!.

Question 2:
As a product of integers, the factorial is obviously also an integer number. In a computer, integer numbers are represented using either 32 or 64 bits. This means that the maximum integer that can be assigned to a variable is 2^{63} (one bit is reserved to encode the sign). How much is 2^{63}, and how does it compare with *factorial*(19) and with *factorial*(20)?

Question 3:
There is nothing obviously different between *factorial*(19) and *factorial*(20). To see the difference, obtain in R the results for the following calculations:

```
x = factorial(18); y = x + 1; 1/(y - x)
x = factorial(19); y = x + 1; 1/(y - x)
```

You would expect the result of both calculations to be 1. What result do you obtain? Can you explain it?

Question4:
What is the difference between R functions `factorial` and `lfactorial`?

Question 5:
Write an R program to print a table of the first 200 factorials and find the maximum n for which *factorial*(n) can still be calculated. Explain this result in terms of the maximum floating-point number that can be represented in a computer. A floating point number is a positive or negative whole number that contains a decimal point.

Question 6:
Are calculators better for obtaining factorials? Run a competition to establish whose calculator can get the greatest factorial. If you know Python or Mathematica, write a program to try finding the greatest factorials in those programming languages.

4.5.3 Case Scenarios

FIGURE 4.10 Game Night

CASE SCENARIO

Game Night

It is a cold and raining Saturday night, and none of your friends want to go out; therefore, you suggest a game night. The games include Yahtzee, Battleship, Monopoly and Texas Hold 'em Poker.

Monopoly is a game in which players roll two six-sided dice to move around a game board, buying and trading properties and developing houses and hotels.

Yahtzee is a game in which players roll five dice to create special combinations. The dice can be rolled up to three times in order to create the different scoring combinations.

Battleship is a war-themed board game in which two opposing players attempt to locate the other's ships that have been placed secretly on a ruled grid.

Texas Hold 'em Poker is a popular variation of traditional poker. Each player is given two hold cards at the beginning, then possibly up to an additional three rounds of community cards are disseminated. The rounds are called the flop, the turn, and the river.

Now it's time to see your probability winning game night!

Monopoly

1. Imagine that you are close to two of the most coveted properties on the Monopoly board, Park Place and Boardwalk. You need a six or an eight to land on one of them. What is the probability that you get one of these prized locations?
2. The board also contains a jail. As in real life, there are multiple reasons one would end up in jail. For example, in Monopoly if you roll three consecutive doubles, you immediately are sent to jail. Calculate the probability of this occurrence starting at the beginning of your roll. Now, fast-forward and you have already rolled back-to-back doubles. What is the chance of rolling a third consecutive double?

Yahtzee

1. One of the various scoring combinations in Yahtzee is called a large straight. A large straight requires that all five dice be in consecutive order, that is, 1–5 or 2–6. You need a large straight for the win and you only have one roll left. What is the probability of rolling a large straight in a single toss of the dice?
2. The game is coming down to the end, and you still need a Yahtzee (all five dice the same) to win the game. After your second roll you have a single matching pair with all other dice different. You have to decide if you should keep the pair and roll the remaining three dice one more time or reroll all five dice. What decision do you make, and why?

Battleship

1. The game board is a grid, with the columns labeled A–J and the rows numbered 1–10. Each player has their own board. In this slightly modified version, each player secretly places all 10 of their ships on the board. Each ship occupies a single grid point. What is the probability of randomly striking one of your opponent's ships on your first attempt? How about a hit in your first three attempts?
2. Now imagine that you were able to get a hit on your first three attempts. However, you miss on your fourth guess. Your opponent now gets a chance to attack. Keeping in mind your early success, what is your opponent's chance to sink one of your ships on their first attempt?
3. Does the probability of a success or failure change as the game progresses? If so, how and why?

Texas Hold 'em Poker

1. In Texas Hold 'em Poker, each player is dealt two cards facedown, from a standard 52-card playing deck, to start the hand. What are the chances that you are dealt two aces?
2. A flush is another poker hand. A flush occurs when the player has at least five cards of the same suit. Recall that in a standard 52-card deck, there are four suits, each having 13 different ranks for (2, 3, 4, 5, 6, 7, 8, 9, 10, J, Q, K, A). Imagine you were dealt two hearts in your hand to start, and then the flop (the first three community cards) comes

out with two more hearts and one club. That means, two more community cards will be dealt, one during the turn and then the last one, called "the river." You have to decide whether to keep playing. Calculate the probability that you complete a flush. In other words, calculate the probability that at least one remaining card (out of the two) will be a heart.

Use these questions as a self-assessment checklist for this chapter:

1. Do you understand the fundamental rules of probability?
2. Do you know how to apply the addition rule?
3. Do you know how to apply the multiplication rule?
4. Do you understand the counting techniques?
5. Do you know how to program R to determine probability values using counting techniques?

References

Chibanda D., Verhey, R., Munetsi, E., Cowan, F., & Lund, C. (2016). Using a theory driven approach to develop and evaluate a complex mental health intervention: The Friendship Bench project in Zimbabwe, *International Journal of Mental Health Systems, 10(16)*, 1–9. https://doi.org/10.1186/s13033-016-0050-1

Heřmanová, E., & Abrhám, J. (2015). Holocaust tourism as a part of the dark tourism. *Czech Journal of Social Sciences Business and Economics*, 4(1), 16–34. https://doi.org./10.24984/cjssbe.2015.4.1.2

Hore, P. (2019). *Saving British and American women at Ravensbrück*. The History Press.

Lewis, C. I. (1918). *A survey of symbolic logic*. University of California Press.

Sagan, B. E. (2020). *Combinatorics: The Art of Counting*. American Mathematical Society.

Tinning, K. (2016). To survive Ravensbrück: Considerations on museum pedagogy and the passing on of Holocaust remembrance. *Museum & Society, 14*(2), 338–353. https://doi.org/10.29311/mas.v14i2.647

World Health Organization (2019). *Suicide in the world: Global health estimates*. World Health Organization. https://www.who.int/publications/i/item/suicide-in-the-world

Figure Credits

Fig. 4.1: Copyright © 2020 by Melpomeni Kalliri. Reprinted with permission.
Fig. 4.2: Copyright © 2020 by Melpomeni Kalliri. Reprinted with permission.
Fig. 4.3: Copyright © Unsplash/Eye for Ebony.
Fig. 4.4: Copyright © 2013 Depositphotos/smuayc.
Fig. 4.5: Source: https://commons.wikimedia.org/wiki/File:John_Venn_2.jpg.
Fig. 4.6: Copyright © Unsplash/Robert Anasch.
Fig. 4.7: Copyright © Unsplash/Natalie Cardona.
Fig. 4.8: Copyright © Unsplash/Daria Nepriakhina.
Fig. 4.9: Copyright © Unsplash/Ridwan Meah.
Fig. 4.10: Copyright © Unsplash/Travel LocalLV.

PART III

Discrete and Continuous Probability Distributions

CHAPTER

5

CHAPTER OUTLINE

5.1 Random Variables
5.2 Probability Distributions
5.3 Mean and Variance of a Discrete Random Variable
5.4 Specific Discrete Distributions
5.5 R and RStudio

CHAPTER OBJECTIVES

Upon completion of this chapter, you will be able to do the following:

1. Understand the relationship between a sample space and a random variable.
2. Understand the relationship between a random variable and a probability distribution.
3. Determine the mean and variance of a discrete random variable.
4. Recognize two common discrete distributions.
5. Use R and RStudio to determine geometric and Poisson probabilities.

Probability Distributions

Random variables can be discrete or continuous. For example, a fair coin is tossed twice, and the sample space is S = {HH, HT, TT, TH}. The discrete random variable X represents the number of heads, and X(HH) = 2, X(HT) = 1, X(TT) = 0, and X(TH) = 1. The probability distribution of X is called a binomial, which is discrete. A commonly used continuous distribution is the normal distribution. Figure 5.1 below depicts a normal distribution, which will be further explored in Chapter 7. In Chapter 5, you will learn about the relationship between a sample space, a random variable, and the probability distribution of a

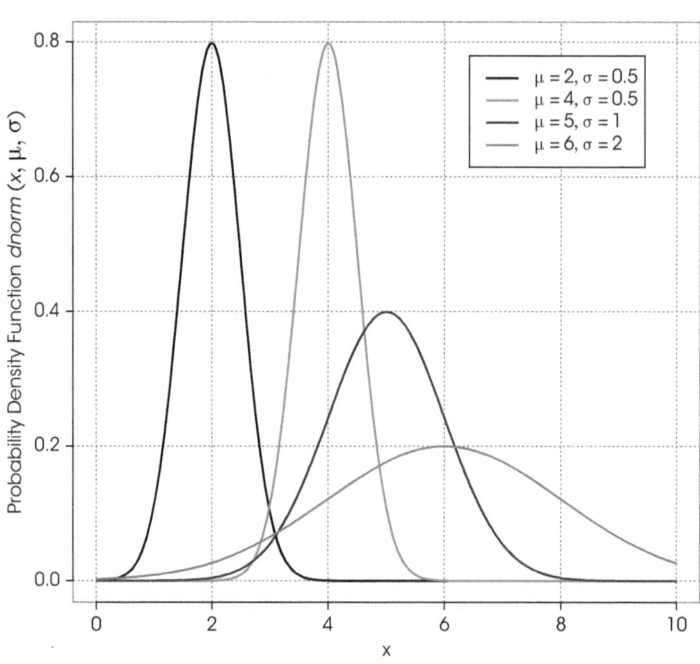

FIGURE 5.1 Normal Distribution Graph

random variable. Understanding this relationship helps you to make decisions in inferential statistics.

Chapter Vocabulary

- A random variable is a function whose domain is the sample space and whose range is the real line.
- The support of a random variable is the set of values that the random variable can take.
- A random variable is discrete if it has a finite or countable number of possible outcomes that can be listed.
- A random variable is continuous if it has an uncountable number of possible outcomes, which is represented by an interval on the real line.
- Countable means there is a one-to-one correspondence with the set of counting numbers {1, 2, 3, ...}.
- The distribution of a random variable tells which values a random variable can take on and how often it takes on those values.
- A discrete probability distribution specifies the probability for each possible value of the corresponding discrete random variable.
- The expected value of a random variable is its mean.
- The mean of a discrete random variable is given by $\mu = \Sigma xP(x)$.
- Given that all conditions of a geometric distribution are satisfied, a geometric random variable represents the trial number of the first success. A geometric random variable is a special case of negative binomial random variable.
- A negative binomial random variable represents the trial number of the rth success (where r ranges between 1 and the number of trials).
- Given that all conditions of a Poisson distribution are satisfied, a Poisson random variable represents the number of occurrences in an interval of time, area, or volume.
- A continuous uniform distribution of numbers between 0 and 1 is the probability distribution of random number selection from this continuous interval.

5.1 Random Variables

Many real-life decisions in biology, psychology, business, and so on are made by assigning probabilities to all possible outcomes of a particular situation. For example, a bank's science and technology lender specializes in obtaining loan approvals for business start-ups that specialize in science and technology. The lender can compute the probability that they will get zero, one, two, three, or more loans approved in a month.

Recall the coin-tossing experiment discussed earlier where the sample space was S = {HH, HT, TH, TT}. A random variable X can be associated with this experiment. A random variable is a function whose domain is a sample space and whose range is the real line. The support of a random variable is the set of values that the random variable can take. A random variable may be discrete or continuous.

5.1.1 Discrete Random Variables

A random variable is discrete if it has a finite or countable number of possible outcomes that can be listed. Countable means there is a one-to-one correspondence with the set of counting numbers {1, 2, 3, ...}. In the coin-tossing experiment, the random variable is discrete because there are a finite number of possible outcomes. Typically, a capital letter represents a random variable and a lowercase letter indicates the realized values of the random variable.

Example:

In the coin-toss example, let the random variable X represent the number of "heads" when tossing a fair coin twice. Determine all of the possible values of X.

Answer:

Recall that the sample space is S = {HH, HT, TH, TT}. Because a random variable is a function whose domain is the sample space and whose range is a real line, $f(x)$ in math is analogous to X(HH) in statistics. In this experiment, because X represents the number of heads and the number of heads in the sample space element HH equals 2, X(HH) = 2. This is typically written as $X = 2$. Likewise, the other values are X(HT) = 1, X(TH) = 1, and X(TT) = 0. Therefore, the possible values of X are 0, 1, and 2.

Example:

A senior executive at a bank has worked over 25 years in commercial finance and banking. Over an 8-year period, the executive closed and funded over $300 million in debt financing commitments for technology firms. In commercial banking, typically one deal is negotiated each month. Let the random variable X represent the number of deals that were successfully closed in the past 3 months. In banking, the phrase "successfully close a deal" means to "fund a loan." What is the sample space? What is the support of the random variable?

FIGURE 5.2 Senior Executive in Commercial Finance and Banking

Answer:

The sample space is the set of all possible outcomes. Let F represent a loan being funded and N represent a loan not being funded. Then FFF means that all loans were funded in the past three months. FNN means a loan was funded in month 1, but not funded in month 2 or 3, and so on. The sample space is:

S = {FFF, FNN, NFN, NNF, NNN, NFF, FNF, FFN}.

The random variable X represents the number of loans that were funded in the past 3 months. Since a random variable is a function whose domain is the sample space and whose range is the real line, X(FFF) = 3, X(FNN) = 1, X(NFN) = 1, and so on. This is typically written as $X = 3$, $X = 1$, and $X = 1$. Therefore, the support is the set of numbers {0, 1, 2, 3}, indicating the number of deals that were possibly funded in the past 3 months. These are the values the random variable can take on.

5.1.2 Continuous Random Variables

Continuous random variables cannot be counted, but they can be measured. A random variable is continuous if it has an uncountable number of possible outcomes, which is represented by an interval on the real line. These random variables can take on an infinite number of values including decimal and fractional values. Examples of continuous random variables include weight, height, time, and so on.

Determining whether a random variable is discrete or continuous is the first step of determining the probability of a random variable. It is also necessary for determining the mean, variance, and standard deviation of a random variable.

Example:

San Diego, California, USA, is known for its beautiful weather year-round (Centurioni et al., 2017). On one typical day in May 2020, the high was 69 degrees Fahrenheit, and the low was 63 degrees Fahrenheit. Is temperature a discrete or continuous random variable?

Answer:

In that 24-hour period, the temperature passed through every possible number from 63 to 69. The random variable temperature can assume any value between 63 and 69, such as 64.0007, 68.4759, and so on, which can be represented by an interval on the real line. Therefore, the random variable is continuous.

FIGURE 5.3 San Diego, California, USA

Example:

Ocean Beach is approximately 7 miles (1.6093 km) from downtown San Diego. An Ocean Beach lifeguard has very sensitive skin, so she wears only Lancôme® sunscreen on her face. She prefers the 30-milliliter size. Let the random variable X represent the amount (in ml) of sunscreen left in her container at the end of the day. What is the support of the random variable? Is the random variable amount of suncreen discrete or continuous?

Answer:

The support of a random variable is the set of values that the random variable can take. Because the sunscreen container is 30 milliliters, the support of the random variable X (in milliliters) is $[0, 30]$. Because the support represents an interval on the real line, the random variable is continuous.

FIGURE 5.4 Downtown San Diego, California, USA

5.1.3 Exercises

Understanding Concepts

1. Name two types of probability distributions.

2. What is a major difference between a discrete and a continuous random variable?

3. In a probability experiment, a fair die is rolled once. Suppose X represents a number on the face of a die. Is X discrete or continuous? Explain your answer.

True or false? In Exercises 4–6, determine whether the statement is true or false. It if is false, rewrite it as a true statement.

4. A random variable is the same as the distribution of a random variable.

5. A random variable is a function whose range is a sample space.

6. A random variable is a number.

Skill Building

7. In your own words, explain why random variables are important to statistics and probability.

8. What are the differences between continuous and discrete random variables?

9. Would you consider the temperature outside a discrete random variable? Why or why not?

10. Suppose a piggy bank contains 100 coins (25 pennies, 25 dimes, 25 nickels, and 25 quarters). Let the random variable X represent the total value of five randomly selected coins. Is X a discrete or continuous random variable?

11. What are the properties of a continuous distribution?

12. What are the properties of a discrete distribution?

13. Give an example of a discrete and a continuous random variable.

14. Give examples of three different discrete random variables.

15. Give examples of three different continuous random variables.

16. Can you describe a random variable Y that is both discrete and continuous?

17. Suppose you have a data set and define the random variable X as the number of students at your university with the same last name. What type of random variable is this?

18. Give two examples of variables that are not random.

19. What are the major differences between discrete and continuous random variables?

20. In each of the following situations, indicate whether the random variable is discrete or continuous:

    a. The number of Twitter followers for each student in your statistics class
    b. The amount of rainfall in 2022 in each U.S. state
    c. The amount of time it takes each student in your statistics class to travel to campus
    d. The number of text messages students on a college campus received today
    e. The GPA of the first-year students at your college

Extending Concepts

21. Is the sum of face values when rolling two dice a random variable? Explain your answer.

22. If you answered "yes" to the previous question, what kind of random variable is that: discrete or continuous? Explain your answer.

23. Is the age of a student selected at random from a class a discrete or continuous random variable? Explain your answer.

24. Is the eye color of a person selected at random from a class a discrete random variable? Explain your answer.

25. What is the support of the random variable represented by the sum of face values in rolling two dice?

26. What is the support of a random variable that represents the weights of students selected at random from a class where the students' weights range from 100 to 250 pounds?

5.2 Probability Distributions

A probability distribution is analogous to a family name. Some well-known family names in China are Chiang, Soong, Kung, and Chen. Some well-known family names in the United States are Kennedy, Obama, Bush, and Hilton. In fact, there are family notables in countries worldwide. Whereas a family name does not always describe an individual, the distribution of a random variable describes the random variable.

The distribution of a random variable tells which values a random variable can take on and how often it takes on those values. In doing so, a probability distribution describes a population because when items are sampled from a population, the value observed is the value of a random variable. Probability distributions are represented in several ways such as graphs, tables, and mathematical formulas. A probability distribution may be either discrete or continuous. Discrete random variables have discrete distributions, and continuous random variables have continuous distributions.

5.2.1 Discrete Probability Distributions

A discrete probability distribution specifies the probability for each possible value of the corresponding random variable. If $P(x)$ is a probability distribution of a discrete random variable, then it must satisfy two properties:

1. $0 \leq P(x) \leq 1$, for every x
2. $\sum P(x) = 1$

That is, each $P(x)$ lies in the interval $[0, 1]$, and the sum of the probabilities equals 1.

5.2.2 Constructing a Discrete Distribution

Constructing a discrete random variable's probability distribution can be explained in the following two steps:

1. Determine the probability of each possible outcome of the random variable.
2. Place the random variable along with its corresponding probability in either a vertical or a horizontal table.

Example:

Benford's law states that the leading digit 1 appears more frequently than the digit 9. Benford's law is used by the U.S. Internal Revenue Service to detect tax fraud. It has also been proposed as a useful way to examine the financial accuracy of nonprofit financial reports (Qu et al., 2020).

Suppose the random variable X represents the digits between 1 and 9 inclusive. Probabilities assigned by Benford's law are given as illustrated in the following discrete probability distribution:

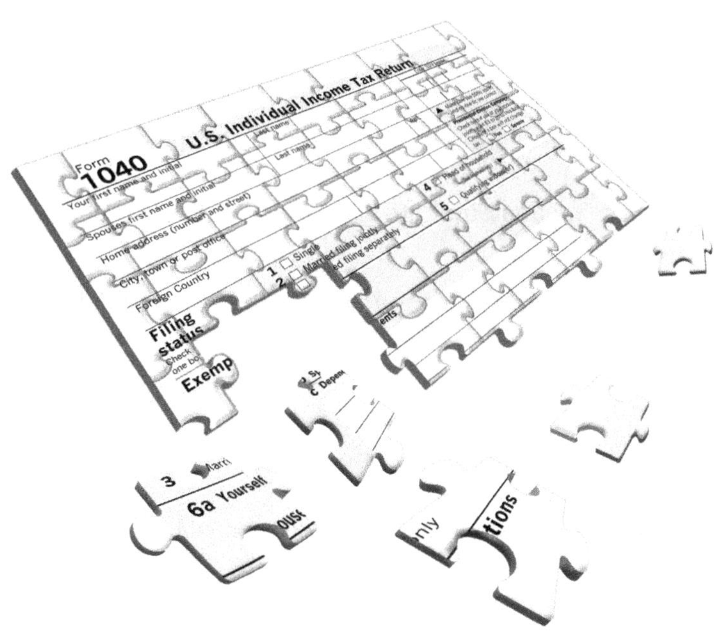

FIGURE 5.5 Income Tax Return Puzzle, USA

x	1	2	3	4	5	6	7	8	9
P(x)	0.301	0.176	0.125	0.097	0.079	0.067	0.058	0.051	0.046

Verify that the table represents a discrete probability distribution.

Answer:

The two properties that have to be satisfied is for each x, $P(x)$ is a number between 0 and 1, and the sum of the probabilities equals 1. Observe that $P(x)$ is in the interval $[0,1]$ for each x. Next, sum all probabilities: $\sum P(x) = 1$. Therefore, the table represents a discrete probability distribution.

5.2.3 Exercises

Understanding Concepts

1. Name three ways to represent a discrete probability distribution.
2. Which properties must a probability distribution satisfy?
3. How would you verify a discrete probability distribution?

4. The random variable X represents the number of small-business owners in an incubator program. Does X have a discrete or continuous probability distribution? Explain your answer.

5. The random variable X represents the amount of water left in a 16-ounce (474 ml) bottle. Is the distribution of X discrete or continuous? Explain your answer.

6. What does the word "random" indicate in the phrase "random variable"?

True or false? In Exercises 7–11, determine whether the statement is true or false. If it is false, rewrite it as a true statement.

7. A discrete random variable can have a continuous probability distribution.

8. A probability distribution is also referred to as a "distribution."

9. A discrete probability distribution cannot be represented by a graph.

10. A continuous probability distribution can be represented by a graph.

11. The values of a continuous probability distribution cannot be represented in a table.

Skill Building

12. For discrete random variables, what type of display is used to show the probability distribution? What provides the probability for a specific outcome?

Use the following to answer questions 13–15:

> Let us define an experiment in which a fair coin is tossed three times. Let the random variable X represent the number of times the coin lands on tails in the three flips.

13. What is the probability that two tails are observed?

14. Construct a complete discrete probability distribution for X.

15. Verify that all necessary properties are satisfied.

Do the following tables in questions 16–18 represent valid discrete probability distributions? If so, state why. If not, make the necessary adjustments.

16.

X	12	19	23
$P(x)$	0.2	0.3	0.5

17.

X	0	2	4	6
$P(X)$	0.11	0.34	0.17	0.21

18.

X	12.4	13.2	15.9
$P(X)$	0.49	0.37	0.25

Extending Concepts

19. Build the distribution table for the discrete random variable "the sum of face values when rolling two dice."

20. Can a continuous distribution have values greater than 1? Explain your answer.

21. Describe the probability distribution given by the sum of a hand of five cards randomly picked from a deck of 52 cards. Is this a continuous or discrete variable? Explain your answer.

22. For the random variable in the previous question, what are the smallest and largest values of the random variable?

23. Is the height times age of a person a continuous random variable for people randomly selected from a group? Explain your answer.

24. The difference between the arm span and height for a person randomly selected from a group can be positive or negative. Is this difference a random variable? Explain your answer.

5.3 Mean and Variance of a Discrete Random Variable

It is useful to represent the distribution of a discrete random variable using a table because this information can then be used to calculate the mean and variance of the random variable.

5.3.1 Mean

The mean of a random variable is what we would expect to observe over many repeated trials of an experiment. That is, the expected value of a random variable is its mean. The mean of a discrete random variable is computed by multiplying the value of each realized value of the random variable by its corresponding probability. The mean of a discrete random variable is given by

$$\mu = \Sigma x P(x).$$

Example:

Use Benford's law to determine the digit the U.S. Internal Revenue Service (IRS) would expect to see in amounts on a legitimate tax return (Berger & Hill, 2015).

Answer:

According to Benford's law, digits and their corresponding probabilities are:

x	1	2	3	4	5	6	7	8	9
P(x)	0.301	0.176	0.125	0.097	0.079	0.067	0.058	0.051	0.046

Let the random variable X represent the digits between 1 and 9. The digit the IRS would expect to see in amounts on a legitimate tax return is computed using the formula

$$\mu = \Sigma x P(x).$$

Therefore, μ = (1)(0.301) + (2)(0.176) + 3(0.125) + ... + (9)(0.046)
= 3.441.

Rounding to the nearest whole number, the IRS would expect to see the digit 3.

5.3.2 Variance

The variance of a discrete random variable X utilizes the expected value. The variance of X is the expected value of X^2 minus the expected value of X quantity squared:

$$\begin{aligned}\sigma^2 &= E[X^2] - (E[X])^2 \\ &= E[X^2] - \mu^2.\end{aligned}$$

Various formulas are used to determine the variance of a random variable. Determining the variance of a data set was initially discussed in Chapter 3. The formulation used in Chapter 3 to compute the population variance and sample variance, respectively, for a data set,

$$\sigma^2 = \frac{\Sigma(x-\mu)^2}{N} \text{ and } s^2 = \frac{\Sigma(x-\bar{x})^2}{n-1},$$

cannot be used when the population and sample sizes are infinite.

Therefore, the variance of a discrete probability distribution is found by multiplying the square of each outcome by its corresponding probability, summing the products, and then subtracting the square of the mean as illustrated in the following example.

Example:

Use Benford's law to determine the variance and standard deviation of the digits the U.S. Internal Revenue Service (IRS) observes in amounts on a legitimate tax return (Berger & Hill, 2015).

Answer:

Let the random variable X represent a digit between 1 and 9. Use the random variable's probability distribution to organize the terms in a table, and then use the formula:

$$\sigma^2 = E[X^2] - \mu^2$$

x	1	2	3	4	5	6	7	8	9
x^2	1	4	9	16	25	36	49	64	81
$P(x)$	0.301	0.176	0.125	0.097	0.079	0.067	0.058	0.051	0.046
$x^2\,P(x)$	0.301	0.704	1.125	1.552	1.975	2.412	2.842	3.264	3.726

Hence, the variance of the random variable X is

$$\begin{aligned} \sigma^2 &= E[X^2] - \mu^2 \\ &= \sum x^2 P(x) - \left(\sum xP(x)\right)^2 \\ &= [(1)(0.301) + (4)(.176) + \ldots + (9)(0.046)] - (3.441)^2 \\ &= 17.901 - 11.840481 \\ &= 6.060519. \end{aligned}$$

The standard deviation is the positive square root of the variance.

$$\sigma = \sqrt{6.060519} \approx 2.4618$$

This means that most of the digits on a legitimate tax return differ from the mean by no more than 2.4618 units.

5.3.3 Exercises

Understanding Concepts

1. What is the difference between the mean of a random variable and the expected value of a random variable?
2. What is standard notation in the field of statistics for the population mean?
3. What is standard notation in the field of statistics for the sample mean?
4. What does the mean of the random variable of a probability distribution describe?
5. Does the mean or variance provide information about how the outcomes of a probability experiment vary? Explain your answer.

True or false? In Exercises 6–10, determine whether the statement is true or false. If it is false, rewrite it as a true statement.

6. The variance of a random variable is an expected value.
7. In the field of statistics, standard notation for the population variance is represented by the Greek letter σ.
8. The mean of the distribution of a discrete random variable is always positive.
9. The variance of the distribution of a discrete random variable is always positive.
10. The standard deviation of the distribution of a discrete random variable is always positive.

Skill Building

Use the following to answer questions 11–15:

Assume the distribution of a random variable Y is defined in the table below:

y	0	1	2	3
$P(y)$	0	.6	.1	.3

11. Is the distribution a valid probability model? Explain why or why not.
12. Does the probability model describe a continuous or discrete random variable?
13. Compute the mean of this probability distribution.

14. What is the variance of this probability distribution?

15. Calculate the variance and the standard deviation of the probability distribution.

Use the following to answer questions 16–19:

> Construct your own valid probability model that describes a discrete random variable X. Assume the random variable X can take on six distinct values. The random variable X should have an expected value of 12.

16. Fill in the table below to show the values and probabilities for your model.

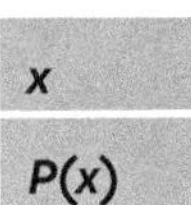

x						
P(x)						

17. How do you know that you constructed a valid probability distribution?

18. What is the variance of your probability distribution?

19. What is the standard deviation of your probability distribution?

Extending Concepts

20. Can the expected value of the square of a random variable be smaller than the square of the expectation value of that variable?

21. What does it mean for a random variable to have 0 variance?

22. When flipping a coin, we define a random variable with value 0 as "heads" and value 1 as "tails." What is the expected value for this random variable?

23. What is the variance for the random variable in Exercise 22 ?

24. What is the standard deviation for the random variable in Exercise 22?

25. Six dogs at a kennel have the following ages (in years): 1,2,2,1,3,3. What is the value of the variance of the age of the dogs in this population? Write the number and include the unit of measure for this number.

5.4 Specific Discrete Distributions

As mentioned earlier in this chapter, the distribution of a random variable is analogous to a family name. The "family names" discussed in this section are "geometric" and "Poisson."

5.4.1 Geometric Distribution

A random variable always represents some number. Specifically, a random variable describes which numerical values a distribution takes on and how often it takes on those values. A geometric random variable represents the trial number of the first success. A geometric random variable is a special case of a negative binomial random variable. A negative binomial random variable represents the trial number of the rth success, where r is a number between 1 and the number of trials.

Alternatively, a negative binomial random variable can be defined as the number of failures, k, that occur in a sequence of Bernoulli trials before a target of r number of successes is reached. The geometric distribution is included as the $r = 1$ case. See Table 3 in Appendix A for an example of a negative binomial random variable table. Random variables such as a geometric random variable have many applications to actions repeated in real life. For example, when an action is repeated until a success occurs, the action may be represented by a geometric distribution.

A geometric distribution is a discrete probability distribution of a random variable X that satisfies the following conditions:

- A trial is repeated until a success occurs.
- The repeated trials are independent of each other.
- The probability of success p is the same from trial to trial.
- The random variable X represents the trial number of the first success.

The probability that the first success will occur on trial number x is:

$$P(X = x) = pq^{x-1} \text{ for } x = 1, 2, ...,$$

where p represents the probability of success, and $q = p - 1$ represents the probability of failure. Probabilities for a few geometric distributions are listed in the first section of Table 3 in Appendix A, corresponding to the $n = 1$ case. This is because the geometric distribution is actually a particular case of a more general distribution called the "negative binomial distribution," which counts the number of trials until obtaining n successes.

Example:

An information technology company gives a 1-year warranty on its printers. Historically, 2% of this company's printers have required service under this warranty. Determine the probability that the first claim under this warranty is the third printer sold (Warranty Week, 2016).

Answer:

In this example, a "trial" is a new printer sale to a customer. A "success" is a warranty claim on the printer that was sold to a customer. The random variable X represents the trial number that resulted in the first claim under the warranty. The random variable $X = 3$ implies that the third customer was the first to file a warranty. The probability is:

$$P(X = x) = pq^{x-1}$$
$$P(X = 3) = (.02)(.98)^{3-1}$$
$$= .0192.$$

Therefore, there is a 1.92% chance that the first claim under this warranty is the third printer sold.

5.4.2 Poisson Distribution

Both the geometric and the Poisson distributions can be used quite effectively to model discrete data (Pradhan & Kundu, 2016). The Poisson distribution was formulated by Simeon D. Poisson in the early 1800s. However, it received little attention until 1907 when statistician W. S. Gosset found real applications for it (Altenbach, 2020). Gosset also formulated the *t*-distribution, which will be discussed in several later chapters of this textbook.

A Poisson distribution is a discrete probability distribution of a random variable *X* that satisfies the following conditions:

FIGURE 5.6 Simeon D. Poisson (1781–1840)

- The experiment consists of counting the number of times *x* an event occurs in a given interval. The interval can be an interval of time, area, or volume.
- The probability of the event occurring is the same for each interval.
- The number of occurrences in one interval is independent of the number of occurrences in other intervals.

The probability of the number of occurrences in an interval of time, area or volume is

$$P(X = x) = \frac{\mu^x e^{-\mu}}{x!} \quad \text{for} \quad x = 0, 1, 2, \ldots,$$

where *e* is the natural number approximately equal to 2.71828, and μ is the mean number of occurrences per interval unit. Tables 4A and 4B in Appendix A list probabilities for the Poisson distribution.

Example:

FIGURE 5.7 Jamestown, South Carolina, USA

Hell Hole is an actual place located in Jamestown, South Carolina, USA. Hell Hole is off Highway 45. There are many stories about how Hell Hole got its name. However, wonderful people live in Hell Hole as attested to by the first author of this textbook. In Jamestown and the surrounding areas, Hell Hole is well known for its annual Hell Hole Swamp Festival.

At only 1 square mile (1.609 square km), Jamestown is one of the smallest towns in South Carolina. Despite its small population, an average of 8,000 vehicles pass through Jamestown every day (Rindge, 2018). What is the probability that 2,000 vehicles pass through Jamestown on a given day?

Answer:

Let the random variable X represent the number of vehicles that pass through Jamestown (in thousands of vehicles) on a given day, then $X = 2$. The probability that $X = 2$ is:

$$P(X = x) = \frac{\mu^x e^{-\mu}}{x!}$$

$$P(X = 2) = \frac{8^2 e^{-8}}{2!}$$

$$= \frac{\mu^x e^{-\mu}}{x!}$$

$$= .005367.$$

Therefore, there is a .5367% chance that 2,000 cars pass through on a given day. Because this is less than a 1% chance, it must have been a cold day in Hell Hole.

5.4.3 Exercises

Understanding Concepts

1. If you must send several text messages before your ex responds, which distribution can you use to represent this situation? Explain your answer.

2. If you charge your smartphone while driving an average of five times a week, which distribution can you use to determine the probability that you will charge your smartphone two times in any given week? Explain your answer.

3. Why is the word "Poisson" capitalized and "geometric" not capitalized in reference to random variables and distributions?

True or false? In Exercises 4–5, determine whether the statement is true or false. If it is false, rewrite it as a true statement.

4. A negative binomial distribution is a special case of a binomial distribution.

5. Theoretically, a success may never occur in a geometric distribution. Therefore, the geometric distribution is a continuous distribution.

Skill Building

6. Is the geometric distribution discrete or continuous?

7. Is the Poisson distribution discrete or continuous?

8. Suppose you flip a coin 10 times and count the number of times the coin lands on heads. Is this a setting that would allow the use of a Poisson distribution?

9. Netflix™ is a popular streaming service that allows you to watch movies and TV shows for a subscription fee. Suppose you count the number of episodes each student in your class watched last night of any show. Would this be a setting appropriate for the Poisson distribution? Explain why or why not.

10. Give an example of a data set that could be modeled using a Poisson distribution.

11. Suppose a couple would like to start having children. Let the random variable X represent the number of children they have until the first girl. Is this a setting for a geometric distribution? Explain why or why not.

12. Give an example of a data set that could be modeled using the geometric distribution.

Use the following to answer questions 13–15.

We are going to use the Poisson distribution to model the number of customers at a popular fast-food chain restaurant. Suppose the mean number of people at the restaurant is 98 during any given hour.

13. What is the probability that there will be over 100 customers at the restaurant from 5 p.m. to 6 p.m. today?

14. What is the probability that there will be exactly 10 customers at the restaurant for the hour starting at 1 p.m.?

15. What is the variance for this distribution?

Use the following to answer questions 16–18.

The University of Maryland has approximately 40,000 students from all over the world. As a new student on campus, you are interested in meeting students from your home town of Paris, France. Suppose that when you meet someone, the probability that they are from Paris is 0.04. Utilize the geometric distribution to answer the questions below.

16. What is the probability of success, p, and the probability of failure, q, for this distribution?

17. What is the probability that you have to ask 20 random students on campus where they are from before you find a student who is from Paris?

18. What is the mean and variance of this distribution?

19. Stephen Curry, a member of the Golden State Warriors professional U.S. basketball team, has one of the three best free throw shooting percentages of all time. Using the fact that his free throw shooting percent is 90.56%, calculate the probability that it takes more than 10 shots before Curry would miss a free throw.

20. Babe Ruth, known as The Sultan of Swat, is often referred to as the greatest baseball player of all time. Ruth was known for hitting home runs. He had a career home run percent of 8.5%. Design an appropriate probability model, and then calculate (a) the expected number of at bats to hit a homerun and (b) the probability that Ruth goes more than 15 at bats in a row without a home run.

Extending Concepts

21. You notice that there are 400 typos in the first 200 pages of a book. What is the probability of finding no typos on one of the first 200 pages of the book?

22. If your chance of winning at a slot machine is 0.01, what is the probability of winning after trying 100 times and failing the first 99 trials?

23. Your school's basketball team has a 39% chance of winning any given game. What is the probability that they do not win their first game of the season until the seventh game?

24. A call center receives four calls per minute, on average. Assuming the calls are independent and equally probable, make a table for the distribution of calls per minute from 0 to 10.

25. Use the table from Exercise 24 to determine the chance that there will be no calls in one minute. How probable is it that there will be 10 calls in one minute?

26. Use the table from Exercise 24 to determine the mean and the variance for the distribution of calls.

5.5 R and RStudio

5.5.1 Programming Assignments

Exercise 5.1

The package `prob` can be used to construct sample spaces, find subsets, define probability spaces, and simulate experiments. Sometimes you might be interested in calculating numerical quantities associated with the experiment. This can be done with function `addrv()`, which extends the probability space with another column that is calculated according to a formula. For example, imagine that we roll a four-sided die three times, and let us define a random variable $U = X1 - X2 + X3$, where Xi ($i = 1, 2,$ and 3) is the face value of each die. What is the minimum and the maximum value that U can take? What would be the probability for U to be greater than six?

```
library(prob)
S <- rolldie(3, nsides =4, makespace = TRUE)
S <- addrv(S, U = X1 - X2 + X3)
Prob(S, U > 6)
```

```
## [1] 0.015625
```

Model an experiment where you roll two dice, and you are interested in the sum of the face numbers.

Exercise 5.2

For the experiment in the previous exercise, what is the most probable sum of the faces we can obtain by rolling a regular die twice? Use the function `marginal()` to consolidate rows in the sample space that have the same value for a given random variable. The function which.max() finds the index corresponding to the maximum value in a vector. What if the die is not fair, and one face is slightly more probable than all other faces that are equally probable? Make a plausible assumption.

Exercise 5.3

Calculate the mean, variance, and standard deviation for the sum of faces when rolling a die three times. The function weighted.mean() should help you.

Exercise 5.4

There are more than a dozen discrete probability distributions in R. For each distribution, four different functions are available:

- The function that calculates the probability for the corresponding value of the random variable starts with letter "d."
- The function that calculates the cumulative probability, which is the probability that the random variable gets a value less than a given value. This function effectively gives the sum of probabilities up to a given point. Such a function starts with letter "q."
- The function that calculates the quantile for the distribution is a value in the range of the random variable for which the cumulative probability has a given value. For example, the median is the quantile function calculated at 0.5. This is effectively the inverse of a function that starts with "q." Such a function starts with the letter "p."
- The function that generates a vector of random numbers distributed according to the given distribution starts with the letter "r."

For example, for the geometric distribution, we have dgeom(), pgeom(), qgeom(), and rgeom().

Make a data frame of probabilities for a geometric distribution with the probability of success 0.4, and the numbers of trials n = *0, 1, 2, ... 10*.

Exercise 5.5

Make a plot that shows in the same graph the probability distribution for a geometric distribution with p = *0.5*, for a Poisson distribution with $\lambda = 0.5$, and for a Poisson distribution with $\lambda = 2$, for the random variable with values between 0 and 8. Use crosses for the geometric distribution and blue and red lines for the Poisson distributions.

Exercise 5.6

An average of about 12 cars per minute cross a bridge. Use the function dpois() to find the probability of having 17 or more cars crossing the bridge in a given minute. Hint: Make a vector with the probability of having n cars crossing the bridge with n = *17:30*. The probability of more than 30 cars is so low that it can be neglected. Can you prove that?

Exercise 5.7

Answer the question for the previous exercise by using the cumulative distribution function ppois().

Exercise 5.8

A geometric distribution represents the number of failures in a sequence of Bernoulli trials before success occurs. Use the function `rgeom` to generate 100 random geometric numbers with 0.25 success probability. Use the function `factor()` to identify the categories (unique appearances) in the list and then the function `table()` to count the frequencies corresponding to each factor and to form a contingency table. Add another row to the table with the corresponding expected theoretical value for the given frequencies. You first have to transform the contingency table to a data frame, and then add the extra column like this: "G["expected"] = Ex" where "G" is the data frame and "Ex" is the vector of expected value. This vector is obtained by multiplying the formula for the geometric distribution in Section 5.4.1 with the sample size.

Exercise 5.9

A continuous uniform distribution of numbers between 0 and 1 is the probability distribution of random number selection from this continuous interval. Because there is an infinite number of possibilities in the sample space, all numbers in the continuous interval $0 \leq x \leq 1$ can possibly result as an outcome of the experiment with equal probability. Therefore, it does not make sense to talk about the probability of a given outcome, but the probability of the outcome to be within a given subinterval. The R functions that deal with the uniform distribution end with `*unif()`. Use the function `runif()` to obtain 100 uniformly distributed numbers and function `hist()` to verify that the numbers have the same frequency. Why are the frequencies for different intervals not equal? Repeat the experiment with 10,000 trials. Did the situation improve?

Exercise 5.10

Simulate an experiment in which the outcome is uniformly distributed between 1 and 3. Use the function `runif()` to obtain 1,000 results. Calculate the mean value, variance, and standard deviation. Are these in agreement with your expectation?

Exercise 5.11

Plot the probability distribution function for a uniform distribution of numbers between 1 and 5 by using the probability distribution function `dunif()`. We first choose a grid of 200 points between 0 and 6, plot the distribution function with a red line and shade the area under the curve by using the function `polygon()`. Note in the code below how we use an anonymous function (function without name) to get the vector of theoretical values for the probability distribution function $y = P(x)$, which in this case is simply 0.25 for x between 1 and 5, and 0 otherwise.

```
x=seq(0,6,length=200)
y = sapply(x, function(n) dunif(n, min=1, max = 5))
plot(x,y,type="l",xlim=c(0,6),ylim=c(0,0.5),lwd=2,col="red",ylab="p")
polygon(x,y,col="lightgray",border=NA)
```

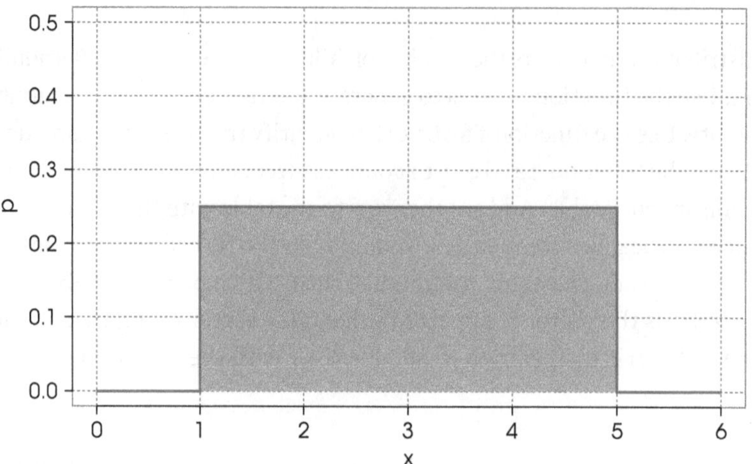

FIGURE 5.8 Probability Density Function of Uniform Distribution

How much is the area under the shaded region?

Suppose that you would like to find the probability that the random variable *X* is less than or equal to 2. Modify the code to shade the region under the density function to the left, include 2, and then calculate the area and compare it with the result of function `punif()`.

5.5.2 Group Experiments

The Birthday Paradox

In a classroom of only 23 people there is a 50% chance that at least two people have their birthday on the same day. In a room of 75 people, the probability for at least two people with matching birthday is 99.9%!

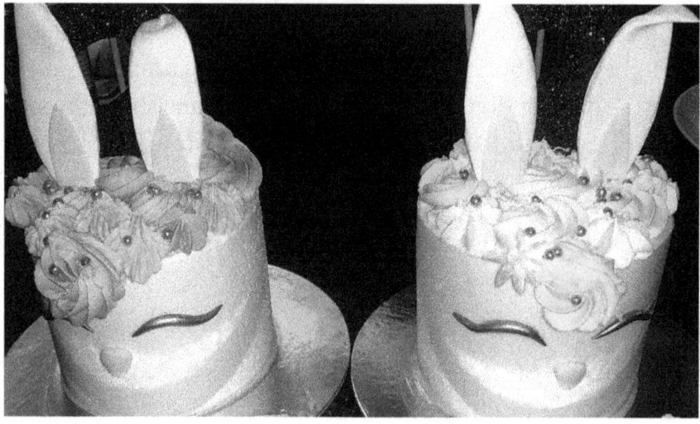

FIGURE 5.9 The Birthday Paradox

If you find this hard to believe, you are not alone. The goal of this exercise is to collect as much data on dates of birth as you can and analyze them. First, collect the date of birth of all students in your class on a piece of paper on which each student records their month and day of birth. Second, do the same with all other classes that you attend. Ask the professor's permission, and make sure you do not record the same student twice. Write all your data in a file. Make groups of records of 24, 30, and 35, and find the experimental probability of having a matching birthday.

To model this experiment and obtain a theoretical probability we first must make some assumptions. We assume that all years are `N = 365` days long, that no day is special in any way, and that the probability that anyone has any given day as a birthday is the same and equals `p = 1/365`.

The question here is to find how many times the birthday matches for two, three, or more people out of a group of `n` people. The easiest way is to actually look at the complementary event, because *P*(*at least two birthdays are the same in a group of n*) = 1 − *P*(*all birthdays are different in a group of n*). Let us see how to determine this probability. But first let us shorten the notation and write the equation for those probabilities as `p(n) = 1 - q(n)`.

One idea would be to use the `prob` library in R. With the function `urnsamples` we can simulate the extraction of balls from an urn. Here we would have 365 labeled balls, corresponding to the days in a year, and extracting `n` times without replacement. The order of the extracted numbers is not important. Next, we would need to build a probability space for this situation. Try this approach. What difficulties do you encounter? Is there a way to get around them?

Let us try a different approach. If my friend and I make up the group, then the probability that we have different birthdays is $\frac{364}{365}$, because there are 364 ways in which my friend can have a birthday different than mine. How about a group of three friends? The probability of my friend and I not having the same birthday remains $\frac{364}{365}$, but there remains only 363 ways in which the third friend would not have the same birthday as the other friend or I. Therefore $q(3) = \frac{364}{365} \times \frac{363}{365}$. It is pretty clear that we can extend this reasoning to get

$$q(n) = \frac{365-1}{365} \times \frac{365-2}{365} \ldots \times \frac{365-(n-1)}{365}.$$

The product of numbers in this formula is not particularly difficult to compute, but it can be a little awkward and is not particularly illuminating. The trick to getting something easier is to remember that for small x we have approximately that $e^x \approx 1 + x$. All numbers in the product are of the form $1 - \frac{S}{N} \approx e^{-s/N}$. Therefore we have the second form:

$$q(n) \approx \exp(-(1+2+\cdots n-1)/N) = \exp\left[-\frac{n(n-1)}{2N}\right].$$

Use the following code to understand this "paradox":

```
N = 365
x <- 1:40
y <- sapply(x, function(n) 1 - prod((N - (1:n-1))/N))
z <- 1 - exp( - x*(x-1)/2/N)
```

```
plot(x,y, col="blue", ylim=c(0,1), ylab="prob", xlab="n")
lines(x,z, col="orange", lwd=2, panel.first = grid())
```

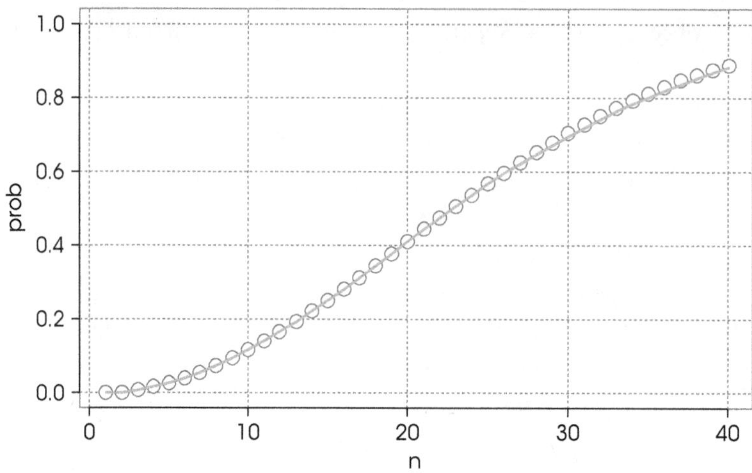

FIGURE 5.10 The Birthday Paradox Graph

The function `sapply()` returns a vector with an element obtained from the application of a function to each element of an original vector. For each n, this function calculates the product $q(n)$. The exponential approximation of $q(n)$ is easier to obtain because we can use vector operations. For example, $x * x$ is an element-by-element multiplication of a vector x. The result is another vector with the same length. We plot the result of $q(n)$ with blue symbols, set the limits on the vertical axis between 0 and 1, and label the axes. On the same graph, we plot the exponential approximation with orange lines, and add grid lines.

From this graph, you can see that for a group of $n = 23$ students, there is about 0.5 probability of birthday coincidence.

Question 1:
Compare the results of your experiment with the theoretical expectation. Do the results make sense?

Question 2:
What was the difficulty when using the function `urnsamples()` from the `prob` package?

Question 3:
Verify that $e^x \approx 1 + x$ by making three vectors: one with numbers from 0 to 1 in steps of 0.01, a second one with exact evaluation of the exponential for each element of the first vector, and the third vector with approximation. Make a data frame with these three vectors. Up to what value is the approximation good enough? What do you mean by good enough?

Question 4:
For how many students in a class is there a 90% probability of finding at least two students with the same birthday?

Question 5:
How would the birthday paradox change in a leap year? It is known that more babies are born during the late summer months and the beginning of any given week. Discuss the reasons, and how would this complicate the calculation.

Question 6:
The distribution of birthdays among days of a year is not uniform. Would this complication increase or decrease the probability of finding at least two students with the same birthday in a class of 23 students?

Question 7:
Plot the number of people who were born between 1969 and 1980 on any given day of the year. A public data set collected by the U.S. Centers for Disease Control and Prevention (CDC), publicly available from the CDC's website, is accessible in a comma separated value (CSV) file named *natality.csv*. Import the data into R with the function `read.csv()`, plot it, and discuss the features of the data.

QR Code Sidebar 5.1

https://DataAnalysisUsingR.com/datasets/natality.csv

Question 8:
What is the minimum number of students needed in class so that there is at least a 50% percent probability that at least two students are born in the same week?

Question 9:
What is the minimum number of students needed in class so that there is at least a 50% percent probability that at least two students are born in the same month?

5.5.3 Case Scenarios

CASE SCENARIO

Kansas City

FIGURE 5.11 U.S. Football

The Kansas City Chiefs are a U.S. football team based in Kansas City, Missouri. There are 32 U.S. football teams that make up the National Football League (NFL). The Super Bowl is the annual championship game that determines the best team in the NFL. In 2020, the 54th Super Bowl was played in Miami, Florida, between the Kansas City Chiefs and the San Francisco 49ers, an NFL team based in California. The Chiefs defeated the 49ers by a score of 31–20 to become the 2020 Super Bowl champions.

The city of Kansas City hosted a parade to celebrate the Chief's victory. Approximately 500,000 people live in Kansas City, Missouri, and many attended the parade. The parade was so popular because it was only the second time the Chiefs had won the championship title, the last time being 50 years ago. Let us assume the probability that a Kansas City resident did not attend the parade is .25

1. You and your friends decide to go to a popular downtown hangout spot in the Power and Light District in Kansas City. You want to see if you can find someone who did not attend the parade. What is the distribution of the random variable? What is the probability you have to ask exactly 10 random people before you find someone who did not attend the parade?
2. What is the probability that you would have to ask more than five people before you found one who did not attend the parade?
3. What is the probability that someone attended the parade?
4. What is the expected number of people you would have to ask before you found one who did not attend the parade?
5. Suppose the average number of parade goers that visited the Super Bowl trophy display was 20,000 per hour. What is the probability that there were more than 30,000 visitors at the trophy display from 1 p.m.–2 p.m.?

CASE SCENARIO

Tacos

FIGURE 5.12 Tacos

A popular meal in many parts of the world is tacos. We asked a large group of college students how many tacos they prefer to eat in one meal. The random variable X represents the number of tacos. The distribution is shown in the table below.

x	0	1	2	3	4	More than 4
$P(x)$	.1	.20	.31	.29	.10	?

1. Is the above distribution discrete or continuous? Explain.
2. The category "more than 4" is missing a probability. What must the probability be for this to be a valid probability distribution?
3. What is the probability that someone prefers to eat two tacos?
4. What is the probability that someone prefers to eat fewer than three tacos?
5. What is the expected number of tacos that someone prefers?
6. What is the standard deviation and variance for the expected number of tacos that someone prefers?

Use these questions as a self-assessment checklist for this chapter:

1. Do you understand the relationship between a sample space and a random variable?
2. Do you understand the relationship between a random variable and a probability distribution?
3. Do you know the definition of discrete random variable?
4. Can you determine the mean and variance of a discrete random variable?
5. Can you name the discrete probability distributions presented in this chapter?
6. Do you know how to use R to determine probabilities for the geometric and Poisson distributions?

References

Altenbach H. (2020). Poisson, Siméon Denis. In H. Altenbach, & A. Öchsner (Eds.) *Encyclopedia of continuum mechanics*. Springer. https://doi.org/10.1007/978-3-662-53605-6_125-1

Berger, A., & Hill, T. (2015). *An introduction to Benford's law.* Princeton University Press.

Centurioni, L., Horányi, A., Cardinali, C., Charpentier, C., & Lumpkin, R. (2017). A global ocean observing system for measuring sea level atmospheric pressure: Effects and impacts on numerical weather prediction. *Bulletin of the American Meteorological Society, 98*(2), 231–238. https://doi.org/10.1175/BAMS-D-15-00080.1

Pradhan, B., & Kundu, D. (2016). A choice between Poisson and geometric distributions. *Journal of the Indian Society for Probability and Statistics, 17*, 11–123. https://doi.org/10.1007/s41096-016-0008-2

Qu, H., Steinberg, R., & Burger, R. (2020). Abiding by the law? Using Benford's law to examine the accuracy of nonprofit financial reports. *Nonprofit and Voluntary Sector Quarterly, 49*(3), 548–570. https://doi.org/10.1177/0899764019881510

Rindge, B. (2018, October 27). Sacrifice required but worthwhile to live in 1 of SC's smallest towns, *Post and Courier.* https://www.postandcourier.com/news/sacrifice-required-but-worthwhile-to-live-in-1-of-scs-smallest-towns/article_343f95c2-d60f-11e8-8bc0-87f3abe2feb0.html

Warranty Week. (2016, February 18). *HP's warranty accounting.* https://www.warrantyweek.com/archive/ww20160218.html

Figure Credits

Fig. 5.2: Copyright © 2012 by William R. Griesinger. Reprinted with permission.
Fig. 5.3: Copyright © Unsplash/MontyLov.
Fig. 5.4: Copyright © Unsplash/Lital Levy.
Fig. 5.5: Copyright © 2018 Depositphotos/robgoebel1@gmail.com.
Fig. 5.6: Source: https://commons.wikimedia.org/wiki/File:Simeon_Poisson.jpg.
Fig. 5.7: Source: https://commons.wikimedia.org/wiki/File:Jamestown,_South_Carolina_Hell_Hole_Swamp_Festival.jpg.
Fig. 5.9: Copyright © 2019 by Melpomeni Kalliri. Reprinted with permission.
Fig. 5.11: Copyright © Unsplash/Muyuan Ma.
Fig. 5.12: Copyright © Unsplash/Chad Montano.

CHAPTER

6

CHAPTER OUTLINE

6.1 Binomial Random Variables

6.2 Determining Binomial Probabilities

6.3 Mean, Variance, and Standard Deviation of a Binomial Random Variable

6.4 R and RStudio

CHAPTER OBJECTIVES

After completing this chapter, you will be equipped to do the following:

1. Recognize a binomial random variable.
2. Determine a binomial probability.
3. Determine the mean and variance of a binomial random variable.
4. Use R and RStudio to determine Bernoulli probabilities, binomial probabilities, binomial mean, binomial variance, and graph of a binomial random variable.

Binomial Probability Distributions

There are many probability experiments that result in one of two possible outcomes, labeled as either a success or failure. Such experiments are called Bernoulli trials. When a basketball player shoots a free throw, he or she makes the basket or does not. Each free throw attempt is an example of a Bernoulli trial. A binomial probability distribution models the number of successes in repeated Bernoulli trials. Figure 6.1 depicts three different binomial probability

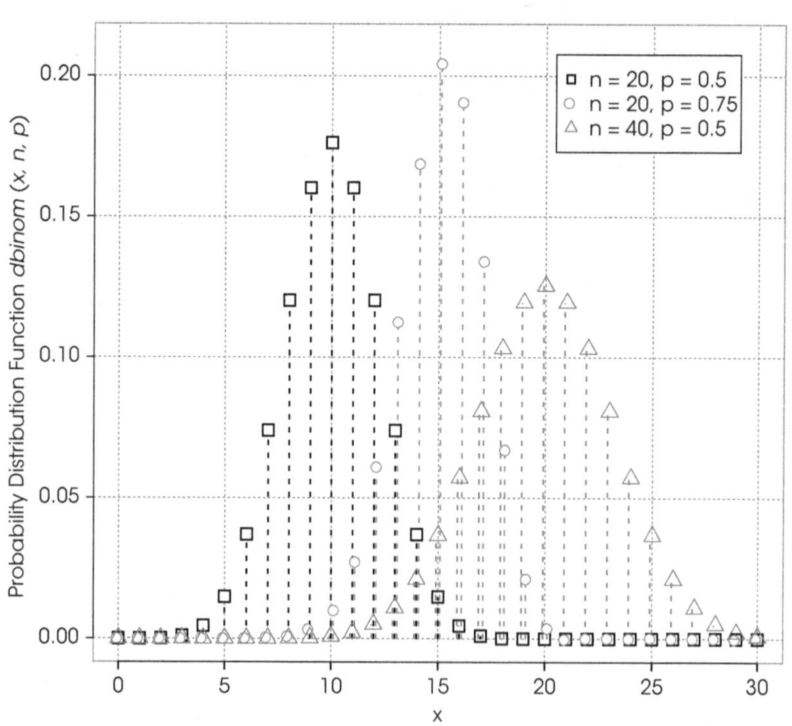

FIGURE 6.1 Binomial Distribution Graph

distributions represented by black squares, red circles, and blue triangles. The black squares represent a binomial probability distribution with $n = 20$ Bernoulli trials and probability of success $p = 0.5$. The height of each black square represents the probability of success of the random variable X, which is along the horizontal axis. In this chapter you will learn how to recognize when a random variable has a binomial distribution. You will also learn how to determine probabilities of a random variable that has a binomial distribution.

Chapter Vocabulary

- A Bernoulli trial is an experiment that results in one of two possible outcomes.
- In a binomial experiment, the random variable X represents the number of successes in n Bernoulli trials.
- A binomial probability is the probability that a binomial experiment results in x successes.
- The mean of a binomial random variable is determined by multiplying the number of trials n by the probability of success p.
- The variance of a binomial random variable is a product of the number of trials n, the probability of success p, and the probability of failure q.

6.1 Binomial Random Variables

Many types of probability problems have only two possible outcomes or can be reduced to two outcomes. In the coin-toss example, the coin lands on either heads or tails. In a true-false question on an exam, the question can be answered in one of two ways, true or false. When a baby is born in a hospital, its gender is typically labeled as either a male or a female.

Situations that can be reduced to two possible outcomes include a medical treatment that can be either effective or ineffective or a person's cholesterol level because it can either be normal or abnormal. Such outcomes and situations are Bernoulli trials.

6.1.1 Bernoulli Trials

A Bernoulli trial is an experiment that results in one of two possible outcomes. One outcome is classified "success" and the other "failure." The term "success" is not necessarily something that is desirable. It instead indicates an item of interest in the study.

A random variable associated with such an experiment is called a *Bernoulli random variable*. The probability function of a Bernoulli random variable X is

$$P(X = x) = p^x (1 - p)^{1-x} \text{ for } \quad x = 0, 1,$$

where p represents the probability of "success." The Bernoulli random variable X equals either 0 or 1. The number zero indicates that the trial resulted in a failure, and one indicates that the trial resulted in a success.

Example:

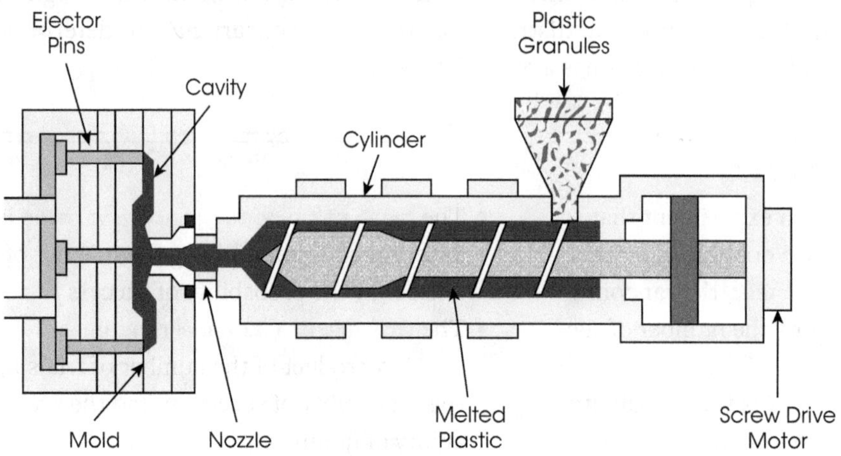

FIGURE 6.2 The Injection Molding Process

Injection molding is a manufacturing process for producing parts by injecting molten material into a mold. For example, molding technology is used to produce a typical laptop keyboard. Injection molding can be optimized to obtain better quality products by using statistical methodologies to reduce the number of defects (Rajendra et al., 2019). Can a defective item be considered to be a "success"?

Answer:

In any process, a defect can be an item of interest. Therefore, observing a defect can be considered a "success" in the injection molding process. In engineering applications, a defective item is typically considered to be a "success" because identification of defectives is typically of interest.

Example:

In the injection molding example above, the random variable X represents whether an item is defective or nondefective. What is the sample space? What is the support of the random variable?

Answer:

The sample space is the set of all possible outcomes, $S = \{\text{Defective, Nondefective}\}$. The random variable is a function whose domain is the sample space and whose range is the real line. Therefore $X(\text{Defective}) = 1$ and $X(\text{Nondefective}) = 0$, and the support is $\{0, 1\}$. Of note, if nondefective were the item of interest, then $X(\text{Nondefective}) = 1$ and $X(\text{Defective}) = 0$.

When referring to the Bernoulli distribution, the name "Bernoulli" is always capitalized because Bernoulli is a last name. Bernoulli trials were formulated by Swiss mathematician Jacob Bernoulli. He was one of several prominent mathematicians from the Bernoulli family (Debnath & Basu, 2015).

FIGURE 6.3 Jacob Bernoulli (1654–1705)

In a succession of Bernoulli trials, one is typically more interested in the total number of successes. The probability of observing exactly x successes in n independent Bernoulli trials is a *binomial probability.*

6.1.2 Binomial Experiments

There are many probability experiments for which the results of each trial can be reduced to two outcomes, success and failure, and then the number of successes can be tabulated. In other words, there are many probability experiments for which the results of Bernoulli trials can be tabulated. In a binomial experiment, the random variable X represents the number of successes in n Bernoulli trials.

A binomial experiment must satisfy these conditions:

- The experiment has a fixed number of Bernoulli trials.
- There are only two possible outcomes of interest for each trial. Each outcome can be classified as a success or a failure.
- The probability of success is the same for each trial.
- The random variable X represents the number of successful trials.

Example:

Infants born to mothers who contracted COVID-19 while pregnant were tested for antibodies (Schwartz, 2020). A researcher is interested in determining the number of infants out of 38 who have tested positive for having COVID-19 antibodies. There were no inconclusive results, the tests were independent of each other, and the probability of testing positive was the same for each infant. Let the random variable X represent the number of infants who have tested positive for COVID-19 antibodies. Is X a binomial random variable? Why or why not?

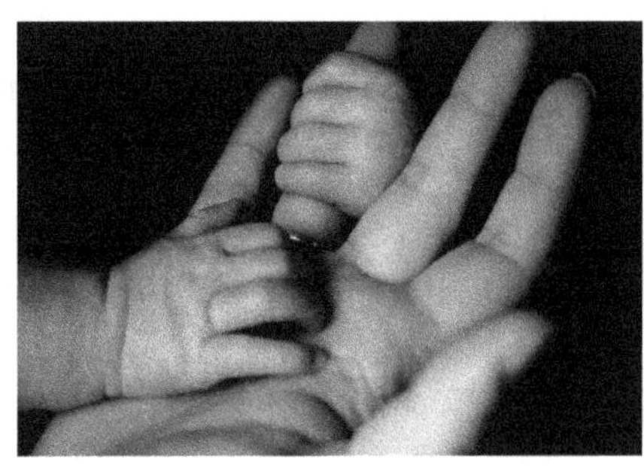

FIGURE 6.4 Newborn Care During COVID-19

Answer:

A binomial random variable represents the number of successes in n Bernoulli trials. In this example, a Bernoulli "trial" is a COVID-19 antibodies test on an infant born to a mother who had contracted COVID-19 while pregnant. A "success" is an infant who has tested positive for antibodies. The Bernoulli random variable has only two possible outcomes, either $Y = 1$ indicating that an infant has tested positive for antibodies, or $Y = 0$ indicating otherwise. There are no inconclusive results. The binomial random variable X indicates the number of successes in n Bernoulli trials, that is, the total number of infants out of a total of $n = 38$ who tested positive for having COVID-19 antibodies. The probability of an infant testing positive is the same for each infant. Additionally, the trials are independent of each other. Because all of the conditions of a binomial random variable are satisfied, X represents a binomial random variable.

6.1.3 Exercises

Understanding Concepts

1. Suppose the random variable X has a Bernoulli distribution. What are the possible values of X?

2. What is the relationship between a binomial random variable and a Bernoulli random variable?

3. A coin is tossed five times. If it lands on heads, it is considered a success. Suppose the coin lands on tails during a toss. What is the distribution of X?

4. A coin is tossed five times. The two possible outcomes are H, representing heads, and T, representing tails. Can a tree diagram be used to determine the sample space? Recall tree diagrams were discussed in Section 4.1.2, and sample spaces were defined in Section 4.1.1.

5. What does a success indicate in a binomial distribution?

True or false? In Exercises 6–10, determine whether the statement is true or false. If it is false, rewrite it as a true statement.

6. A Bernoulli random variable is a discrete random variable.

7. "Binomial" should always be capitalized because it represents a person's last name.

8. A binomial trial is an experiment that results in one of two possible outcomes.

9. In a Bernoulli experiment, the random variable X represents the number of successes in n binomial trials.

10. The range of a binomial random variable is the real line.

Skill Building

11. Explain in your own words what a Bernoulli trial is.

12. How many possible outcomes are there in a Bernoulli trial?

13. Which of the following situations can be represented as a Bernoulli trial? Explain why or why not.

    a. The event that Mike's Facebook post gets a like.

    b. Brian rolls a die and records the value.

c. Whether it rains on Tuesday.

d. During an NFL game, the event that Patrick Mahomes throws a touchdown pass.

14. Choose one of the Bernoulli trials from Exercise 13 and expand it into a binomial experiment. Be sure to explain why it classifies as a binomial experiment.

15. Modify one of the situations in Exercise 13 that was not a Bernoulli trial to make it a binomial experiment.

16. Create a binomial experiment using two fair coins.

17. Consider the number of text messages you receive in a 1-hour period. Could this be a Bernoulli experiment? Explain why or why not.

18. Which of the following are not conditions for a binomial experiment?

a. There must be two or more possible outcomes.

b. The observations are independent.

c. The probability of success is fixed throughout the experiment.

d. The experiment can consist of an unlimited number of events.

19. Modify the following scenario to make it a valid binomial experiment: Researchers in Spain report that this divorce rate is 65%. You survey between 200–300 people in Spain and ask them if they are married, single, divorced, or separated.

FIGURE 6.5 Old Street in Cataluña, Tarragona, Spain .

20. Explain why the following scenario is not a binomial trial: A six-person committee is being formed to select the next speaker for the university graduation ceremony. There are 600 students who qualify for the committee. Students who have leadership experience are given higher priority to be on the committee than other students. Let X represent the students selected to be on the committee.

FIGURE 6.6 Graduation Ceremony Moments, New Haven, Connecticut, USA

Extending Concepts

21. You roll a die five times and need to get at least three fours to win the game. Is this a Bernoulli trial? Explain your answer.

22. We deal five cards from a deck and get one spade and one king. Is this a Bernoulli trial? Explain your answer.

23. In an experiment a student observes the success or the failure when repeating the experiment 10 times. The result of one experiment depends on the results of the previous one. Are these examples of Bernoulli trials? Is this a Bernoulli experiment? Explain your answer.

24. Is flipping a coin that is known to be tainted (not fair) a number of times a binomial experiment? Explain your answer.

25. A student in a class can pass or fail an exam. Can the number of students who failed be considered a binomial experiment? Explain your answer.

6.2 Determining Binomial Probabilities

There are several ways to determine the probability of x successes in n trials of a binomial experiment. We will illustrate finding binomial probabilities using a binomial probability formula, a binomial table, and with software using R.

6.2.1 Binomial Probability Formula

The binomial formula uses the counting rule for combinations that was introduced in Chapter 4. There are $\binom{n}{x}$ ways to get x success from n trials without regard to order. Each probability of success p can occur x times and each probability of failure $(1 - p) = q$ can occur $n - x$ times. Using the fundamental counting rule from Chapter 4 yields the binomial formula

$$P(x) = \binom{n}{x} p^x q^{n-x} \quad for \quad x = 0, 1, 2, ...$$

A binomial probability is the probability that a binomial experiment results in x successes.

Example:

Born in McClellanville, South Carolina, in 1924, Eugenia P. Deas, or "Sister Days" as the locals lovingly call her, draws upon the rich heritage of her Gullah culture for her storytelling (SCETV, n.d., para. 1). Deas received the statewide Jean Laney Harris Folk Heritage Award in 2005 (SCETV, para. 1). Gullah is an English-based creole language still spoken by both African Americans and whites in the Charleston, South Carolina, area and a few other regions in the southeast. Gullah Geechees are direct descendants of African Americans who were enslaved for generations in the southern United States. Unfortunately, the Gullah language is dying. Researchers wanted to investigate the prevalence of peer-reviewed publications about Gullah (Ghahramani et al., 2020). A total of 109 peer-reviewed publications about Gullah were identified using the Web of Science database. Approximately 40% of the peer-reviewed publications concentrated on health science, while the remaining 60% were centered on the social sciences. A random sample of 12 publications are selected. What is the probability that exactly eight of the publications focus on the social sciences?

FIGURE 6.7 Mrs. Eugenia P. Deas (1924–)

Answer:

A Bernoulli trial in this example is the act of selecting a publication from the peer-reviewed publications. There are $n = 12$ trials. A "success" is selecting a publication that focuses on the social sciences. The probability of success is

$p = .60$. The random variable X represents the number of publications out of 12 that center on the social sciences. The probability that eight publications focus on the social sciences is computed as follows:

$$P(x) = \binom{n}{x} p^x q^{n-x}$$

$$P(8) = \binom{12}{8} (.60)^8 (.40)^{12-8}$$

$$= (495)\ (.60)^8 (.40)^{12-8}$$

$$\approx .2128.$$

Therefore, there is approximately a 21.28% chance that eight of the 12 publications will concentrate on the social sciences.

6.2.2 Binomial Table

Finding binomial probabilities using the binomial probability formula is helpful for gaining insight into exactly how binomial probabilities are determined. However, this process can be made easier by using a binomial probability table. Before computers were readily available, tables, paper, and pencil were the only ways to compute such probabilities.

Even with the advent of hand-held calculators and computing software, all capable of easily computing binomial probabilities, tables are still a fast and easy way to determine binomial probabilities. Table 2 in Appendix A lists binomial probabilities for selected values of n and p. Table 2 is constructed such that the first column represents the binomial random variable $X = k$, the number of successes in n Bernoulli trials. The first row of the Table 2 contains p, the probability of success of each Bernoulli trial. Each value in the body of Table 2 represents the binomial probability $P(X = k)$ for the corresponding binomial parameters p and n. The values in the body of Table 2 can also be calculated by the binomial probability formula, the probability mass function (pmf), presented in Section 6.2.1, as well as by the R function `dbinom(k,n,p)`.

Note that in this textbook, the values in the body of Table 2 represent the binomial probabilities $P(X = k)$. However, in some textbooks, the values in the body of a binomial probability table represent the cumulative probabilities, $P(X \leq x)$. To discern which probability is presented in any binomial table, use the key presented in the table. The R function `dbinom(k,n,p)` in the header of Table 2 indicates the body of the table contains the values for this function. Books that do not contain R functions, as this is the first elementary statistics book that focuses on R, will have a key indicating either $P(X = x)$ or $P(X \leq x)$.

Example:

Refer to the Gullah example in Section 6.2.1 where a random sample of 12 publications are selected, and 60% of the publications about Gullah that were identified using the Web of Science database concentrated on the social sciences. Use a binomial table to determine the probability that exactly eight of the publications concentrate on the social sciences.

Answer:

Since a random sample of 12 publications is selected, there are $n = 12$ trials. A "success" is selecting a publication that focuses on the social sciences. The probability of success is $p = .60$ because 60% of the publications about Gullah that were identified using the Web of Science database concentrated on the social sciences. The random variable X represents the number of articles that center on the social sciences. The probability that exactly eight publications concentrated on the social sciences is found in Table 2. First locate $p = 0.6$ in the first row of the header. The next step is to locate the group of probabilities corresponding to the parameter $n = 12$. This is the fourth group on the second page of the binomial table. Finally, follow the column corresponding to $p = 0.6$ down to the eighth row in the fourth group to the value 0.213. The answer is

$$P(X = 8) = 0.213.$$

6.2.3 Using R

Binomial tables are useful, but contain only a limited selection of values for n and p. Probabilities involving values not in the table must be computed by hand or with software such as R.

As with other probability distributions that are available in R, there are four general functions that help us work with the binomial distribution. The functions start with either **"d," "p," "q,"** or **"r"** letters followed by the word "**binom**." By convention, `d`-functions are used to obtain the density of probabilities, `p`-functions are for cumulative probabilities, `q`-functions are for getting the quantiles, and `r`-functions are used to generate random samples distributed according to a given distribution.

dbinom()

This function gives the probability for a value, or a vector of values. The name of the function starts with `d` because, in general, this function refers to the density of probability for a given distribution. This function is used as `dbinom(x, n, p)` with the three arguments in this order:

1. "x" is the number of successes for which we are interested in obtaining the probability. This can also be a vector, in which case, the function returns a vector of probabilities for each element in this vector.
2. "n" is the size, or the number of Bernoulli trials, in the distribution.
3. "p" is the probability for success in one trial.

The calculation in dbinom() makes sense only when x is an element of the sample space of the binomial distribution, $0 \leq x \leq n$. Otherwise, the result is 0.

For example, the probability of getting a head seven times when tossing a fair coin 30 times is:

```
dbinom(7, 30, 0.5)

## [1] 0.001895986
```

Arguments in R functions are identified by their position in the arguments list or by using the associated keyword followed by the equal sign "=," in which case, their order is not important. This way of invoking the function works as well:

```
dbinom(7, prob=0.5, size=30)

## [1] 0.001895986
```

Suppose we are interested in knowing the probability of getting between a head 10 to 20 times in 40 coin tosses. To determine that, we first calculate the probability for a vector of values, and then we use the addition rule for independent events to get the result, all in one neat expression of chained functions.

```
sum(dbinom(seq(from=10, to=20, by=1), 40, prob=0.5))

## [1] 0.5623456
```

pbinom()

This function gives the cumulative probability of a binomial event. It is used in the same way, with three arguments as pbinom(x, n, p), except that the result returned is the probability of having x or less successes in n Bernoulli trials with probability p for each.

The result for the last example could have been obtained as the difference of two cumulative probabilities as:

```
pbinom(20, 40, 0.5) - pbinom(9, 40, 0.5)

## [1] 0.5623456
```

Example:

Refer to the Gullah example in Section 6.2.1. Use R to determine the probability that exactly eight of the articles concentrate on the social sciences.

Answer:

We can directly calculate the probability with `dbinom()`, or subtract two cumulative probabilities and print the results using function the `cat()`, which is short for *concatenate.*

```
exact = dbinom(8, 12, 0.6)
less_than_8 = pbinom(8, 12, 0.6)
less_than_7 = pbinom(7, 12, 0.6)
cat("Exactly 8 articles:", exact)

## Exactly 8 articles: 0.2128409
cat("\nOr by using cumulative prob's:",
  less_than_8, " - ", less_than_7, "=", less_than_8 - less_than_7)

##
## Or by using cumulative prob's: 0.7746627 - 0.5618218 = 0.2128409
```

6.2.4 Exercises

Understanding Concepts

1. Name three ways to determine probabilities of a binomial random variable.
2. In a binomial distribution, can one of the trials influence other trials? Explain your answer.
3. What are the parameters of a binomial distribution?
4. What is the definition of a probability mass function of a random variable X?

True or false? In Exercises 5–8, determine whether the statement is true or false. If it is false, rewrite it as a true statement.

5. If the number of trials equals one, then a binomial formula is the same as a Bernoulli formula.
6. A binomial table cannot be calculated by hand.
7. A binomial distribution can also represent the number of failures.
8. In R there are four functions that determine probabilities associated with a binomial distribution.

Skill Building

9. Is the binomial distribution continuous or discrete?

10. Calculate the value of 4!. Show your work.

11. How do you compute the probabilities for a binomial distribution?

12. True or false? The possible values of the random variables for a binomial distribution could range between -1,000,000 to 1,000,000.

13. The World Health Organization published a report in March 2020 (Ioannidis, 2020) that said the mortality rate for people with COVID-19 was 3.4%. In a random sample of 25 infected people, what is the probability that more than five people die?

14. Chris enjoys listening to YouTube music, which suggests songs he might like. He estimates that 80% of the suggested songs he truly likes. If Chris listens to 20 suggested songs, what are the chances that he truly likes them all?

15. About 54% of Europeans are said to know more than one language. You sample 45 people and find that 21 of them know more than one language. What is the portion of people in this population who know more than one language? What is the sample proportion of people who know more than one language?

16. What is the distribution that can be used to describe the scenario in Exercise 15? Be sure to include the parameters for the distribution.

17. Using the information in Exercises 15 and 16, compute the probability that 10 people know more than one language.

18. Suppose we have a binomial experiment. Let X be a binomial random variable that can be modeled using the binomial distribution, with a probability of success $p = 0.5$ and $n = 20$ trials. Compute the probability that $X = 4$.

19. Write out the binomial formula to compute $P(X \leq 2)$.

20. In 2018, Harvard University posted on its website that its acceptance rate was 5.2% to get into this prestigious university. You use social media to survey 200 students who applied to Harvard who have similar academic achievements to your own. What is the probability that 15 students were accepted to Harvard?

FIGURE 6.8 Arnold Arboretum of Harvard University, Arborway, Boston, Massachusetts, USA

Extending Concepts

21. In a Bernoulli trial, the probability of success is p and the probability of failure is q. In an experiment, each Bernoulli trial is repeated three times. Determine the probabilities of having 0, 1, 2, and 3 success for this experiment and show that the sum of the probabilities equals 1.

22. A quality control engineer in a factory found that the first batch of 100 cell phones contained five defective phones. If the first batch is representative of the quality of cell phones in the entire factory, determine the probability that the next batch of 100 phones also contains five defective phones?

23. How many possible outcomes are possible in a binomial experiment that consist of 5,000 Bernoulli trials? Explain your answer.

24. Describe an example of using the R function `rbinom` to simulate an experiment.

6.3 Mean, Variance, and Standard Deviation of a Binomial Random Variable

As mentioned earlier, a binomial random variable has many real-life applications. Its mean, variance, and standard deviation have many real-life applications as well. For example, researchers have developed a new method of classifying a tumor as malignant or nonmalignant. The methodology uses magnetic resonance imaging (MRI) and improves upon previous methods by using the binomial mean, variance, and standard deviation to improve thresholding (Sharif et al., 2018). Thresholding is a technique that divides an MRI into various regions by comparing each pixel value to a predefined threshold value.

Because a binomial distribution is a discrete distribution, the mean and variance can be determined by organizing the random variable X along with its corresponding probabilities $P(X = x)$ in a table, and then using the same formulas for the mean variance as discussed in Section 5.3. However, there is an easier way, the binomial mean formula.

6.3.1 Binomial Mean Formula

The properties of a binomial distribution enable utilization of simple formulas. The number of trials and the probability of success are the parameters that uniquely define a binomial distribution. The mean of a binomial random variable is determined by multiplying the number of trials n by the probability of success p:

$$\mu = np.$$

Example:

Refer to the Gullah example in Section 6.2.1. Use the formula for the mean of the binomial random variable to find the mean number of publications that concentrate on the social sciences.

Answer:

There are $n = 8$ trials. A "success" is selecting an article that focuses on the social sciences. The probability of success is $p = .60$. The random variable X represents the number of publications that focus on the social sciences.

$$\begin{aligned}\mu &= np \\ &= (8)(.60) \\ &= 4.8\end{aligned}$$

Therefore, on average 4.8 or approximately five publications will focus on the social sciences.

6.3.2 Binomial Variance and Standard Deviation

The variance of a random variable is a numerical measure of spread that represents the average squared distance from the mean of the random variable. The variance of a binomial random variable is a product of the number of trials n, the probability of success p, and the probability of failure q.

$$\sigma^2 = npq$$

The standard deviation is the positive square root of the variance. It is a measure of how spread out a set of numbers is from the mean.

$$\sigma = \sqrt{npq}$$

Example:

Refer to the Gullah example in Section 6.2.1. Use the formulas for the variance and standard deviation of a binomial random variable to find the standard deviation of the number of publications that concentrate on the social sciences.

Answer:

There are $n = 8$ trials. A "success" is selecting an article that focuses on the social sciences. The probability of success is $p = .60$. The random variable X represents the number of publications that focus on the social sciences. The standard deviation is the positive square root of the variance.

$$\sigma = \sqrt{npq} = \sqrt{(8)(.60)(.40)} \approx 1.3856$$

This means that the number of publications that focus on the social sciences differ from the mean by no more than 1.3856 units.

6.3.3 Binomial Distribution Graph

We can use R to obtain a graphical representation of the binomial distribution. The example below builds a 2 x 2 array showing the outcome distribution for a binomial experiment with eight Bernoulli trials, and their corresponding probabilities.

```
n = 8; x = 0:n; par(mfrow=c(2,2), mar=c(2,2,2,2))
barplot(dbinom(x, n, 0.1), names=x, main = "Binomial
p = 0.1", ylim=c(0,0.45))
barplot(dbinom(x, n, 0.2), names=x, main = "Binomial
p = 0.2", ylim=c(0,0.45))
barplot(dbinom(x, n, 0.5), names=x, main = "Binomial
p = 0.5", ylim=c(0,0.45))
barplot(dbinom(x, n, 0.9), names=x, main = "Binomial
p = 0.9", ylim=c(0,0.45))
```

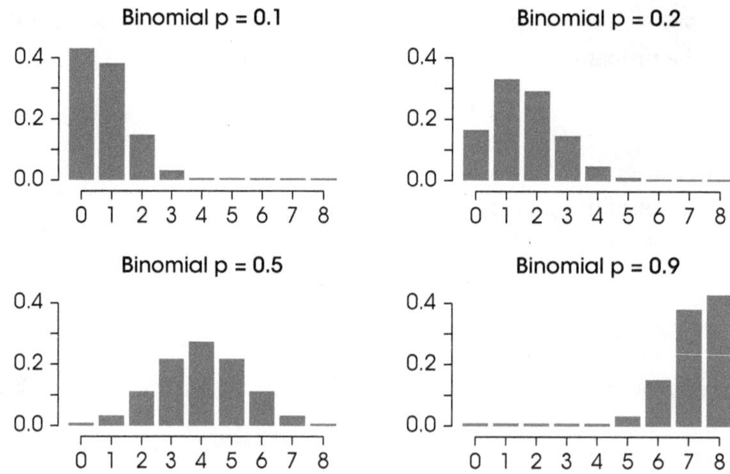

FIGURE 6.9 Histograms of Binomial Distributions

Note that $n = 8$ in each histogram in Figure 6.9. Hence $1/n = .125$. As you can see, the shape of the distribution changes. In general, for small probabilities, say $p < \frac{1}{n}$, the distribution is decreasing pretty fast, meaning that it is very likely to get zero or one success, but the probability to have two, three, or more successful outcomes is progressively smaller. This is illustrated in the top left graph of Figure 6.9 where $p = 0.1$. For larger probabilities, the distributions have a mode larger than zero, as depicted in the histograms of Figure 6.9 where $p = 0.2$, $p = 0.5$, and $p = 0.9$. There is a non-zero probability value most likely to be obtained in the experiment, which is shown as a maximum in the three of the four distributions in Figure 6.9. The experiment with probability 0.5 (bottom left histogram), like in tossing a fair coin, has a symmetric distribution because you can interchange the meanings of success and failure—the numbers will not change. Experiments with larger probabilities, $p > 0.5$, have increasing shape (see the bottom right histogram in Figure 6.9).

In this example, we set the graphical parameters with the function `par`, to set a 2 x 2 array of subplots and margins around each subplot equal to the equivalent of two lines of text. Each subsequent call of graphic functions fill slots in the array in a row-wise fashion. To call a function means to have R run or execute a set of commands.

6.3.4 Exercises

Understanding Concepts

1. What is the difference between the standard deviation of a binomial random variable and the variance of a binomial random variable?

2. Use the formula for expected value of a discrete random variable to derive the mean of a binomial random variable.

3. Suppose the number of trials of a binomial random variable X is $n = 6$, and the probability of failure of each trial is $q = 0.40$. Determine the mean μ of the binomial random variable.

4. Suppose the probability of failure of each trial of a Bernoulli experiment is $q = .40$. Determine the probability of success for each trial of a binomial experiment.

5. Suppose that X is a binomial random variable, and the probability of success of each corresponding Bernoulli trial is $p = 0.05$. Describe the shape of the histogram of the binomial distribution.

6. Is it possible to determine the variance of a binomial distribution by hand using the formula for expected value discussed in Section 5.3.2: $\sigma^2 = \mathrm{E}[X^2] - (\mathrm{E}[X])^2$?

True or false? In Exercises 7–12, determine whether the statement is true or false. If it is false, rewrite it as a true statement.

7. The variance of a binomial random variable is never negative.

8. The standard deviation of a binomial random variable is never negative.

9. In the formula for the mean of a binomial random variable, the variable n is standard notation that represents the sample size.

10. A histogram is one of many ways to graph a binomial distribution.

11. A binomial distribution can be graphed using the same types of graphs used in any continuous distribution.

12. The mean, variance, and standard deviation of a binomial random variable can all be equal in certain cases.

Skill Building

13. Let the random variable X be defined as a success if the university cafeteria is selling sushi today and a failure if not. On any given day, the probability that there will be sushi is 25%. Calculate the mean and variance of X. Explain in words what those values represent.

14. U.S. professional tennis player Andy Roddick has a career ace percentage of 15.52%. Suppose Roddick plays a tennis match in which he served 157 times. Calculate the expected number of aces.

15. Calculus is a math class required for science and math majors. Many students find the course quite difficult. In fact, at one university, approximately 11% of the students do not pass the class on the first attempt. In a class of 50 students, how many would you expect to pass the class? What is the standard deviation?

16. For small sample sizes, n, and small probabilities of success, p, is the graph of the binomial distribution typically skewed or symmetric? Graph an example of this distribution.

17. For large sample sizes, n, and probability, p, of success near 0.5, is the graph of the binomial distribution typically skewed or symmetric? Draw an example of this distribution.

18. Let X be a binomial random variable with parameters $n = 20$, $p = 0.2$. Compute the standard deviation, mean, and variance of X.

19. A university is considering building a new on-campus residence hall for students. Typically, 80% of college students prefer to live on campus. What is the expected number of students that prefer to live on campus if the university has 6,000 students? What is the variance?

20. The notation that the random variable X is distributed as a binomial random variable with parameters n and p is $X \sim B(n, p)$. Suppose the mean of X *is 30*. Which of the following distributions are the possible distribution for X? If your response is choice a, b, or c, derive your answer. If your response is choice d, derive the correct answer.

    a. $B(4, .5)$

    b. $B(10, 3)$

    c. $B(200, .15)$

    d. None of the above

Extending Concepts

21. A quality control engineer in a factory found that the first batch of 100 cell phones contained five defective phones. If the first batch is representative of the quality of cell phones in the entire factory, determine How many phones are expected to be defective in a batch of 200 phones?

22. What is the standard deviation for the number of defective phones in Exercise 21?

23. The probability of success in a Bernoulli trial is 1%. How many times n does the trial need to be repeated so that the expected value of the number of successes in the Bernoulli trials is equal to the standard deviation of the number of successes in the Bernoulli trials .

24. The probability distribution for X = number of heads in four coin tosses is given by $P(X=0) = 1/16$ and $P(X=1) = 4/16$. What is the probability of getting four heads?

25. A die is rolled 10 times and the number of times a six is rolled is recorded. Is this a binomial experiment? Explain your answer.

6.4 R and RStudio

6.4.1 Programming Assignments

Exercise 6.1

A baseball player has a 0.232 batting average. In one game, he gets nine at bats. In baseball, an "at bat" is when a player gets a turn at batting. Use R function `dbinom()` to calculate the probability he will get exactly eight hits in the game.

Exercise 6.2

A baseball player has a 0.342 batting average. In one game, she gets 16 at bats. Use the R function `rbinom()` to simulate her batting in 1,000 hypothetical games. Use this data to calculate the probability she will get at least 10 hits in the game.

FIGURE 6.10 Is It Probable?

Exercise 6.3

A baseball player has a 0.363 batting average. In one game, he gets 12 at bats. Use the R function `pbinom()` to calculate the probability he will get at least eight hits in the game.

Exercise 6.4

A student takes a 15-question, multiple-choice exam with possible answers a, b, c, and d for each question, and makes an arbitrary guess for all answers. Use function `pbinom()` to calculate the probability of guessing at least nine questions, but no more than 11.

Exercise 6.5

With the package `prob`, we can simulate the extractions of balls of different colors from an urn, with or without replacement. For what situation, with or without replacement, can we model the experiment by a binomial distribution? Construct an example, and show by direct calculation that using the function `dprob()` gives the same result as the one derived from using the `urnsample()` function.

Exercise 6.6

The function below draws the theoretical histogram for repeated trials of a given binomial experiment by using a bar plot with the height of each bar equal to the probability associated with a given outcome. This function requires `n`, the number of trials, and `p`, the success probability for each elementary process. The function also accepts optional arguments that are passed to the bar plot function.

```
gbinom <- function(n, p, ...)
{
# plots a relative frequency histogram of the binomial distribution
     k <- 0:n
     probs <- dbinom(k, n, p)
     names(probs) <- as.character(0:n)
     barplot(probs, ...)
}
```

Modify the function so that the space between bars is reduced to 0. Also experiment with the color of bars. Use `help(colors)` or `colors()` to see what colors R knows by name.

Exercise 6.7

In an experiment, 10 cards are extracted from a well-shuffled 52-card deck and the number of face cards are counted. Use the function from the previous exercise to represent the probabilities for obtaining different numbers of face cards as a histogram that uses orange bars with no separation between bars. This experiment can be done with or without replacement. Which way can be best modeled as a binomial distribution?

Exercise 6.8

First, set up the plot window to hold four plots using par(`mfrow=c(2,2)`). Then, plot the binomial densities for the following values of n and p:

N	P
20	1/2
20	1/4
20	3/4
20	9/10

Where is the mode located in each case? What is the relationship between the mode and the values of n and p?

Exercise 6.9

For a random variable X with a `binomial(20, 1/2)` distribution, find the following probabilities:

1. $P(X < 8)$
2. $P(X > 12)$
3. $P(8 < X < 12)$

Exercise 6.10

A certain binomial experiment consists of counting the number of successes in six trials when we know that the success rate is 30%. Simulate this experiment by taking 1,000 samples using the "generator" function `rbinom()`. Write a program that generates a figure similar to the one shown here. Calculate and contrast the theoretical and experimental means and standard deviations for this experiment. Comment on the quality of agreement between the theoretical and experimental means. Repeat the experiment and this analysis with 4,000 samples. Does the agreement between the theoretical and experimental means improve?

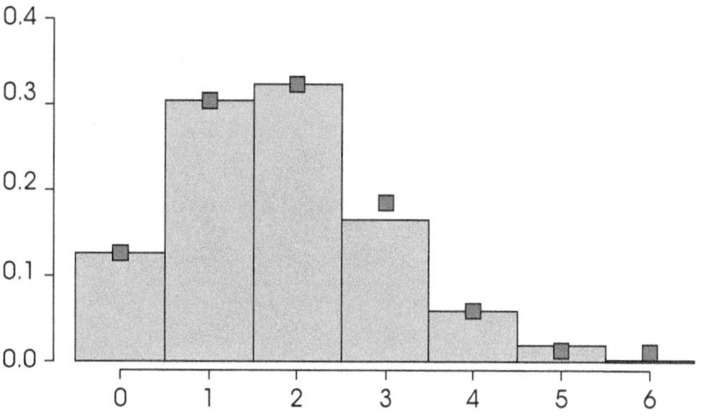

FIGURE 6.11 Histogram

6.4.2 Group Experiments

Blood Type

Do you know your blood type? In this experiment you will collect the blood type information from all students in the class, tabulate it, and compare it with some theoretical expectations.

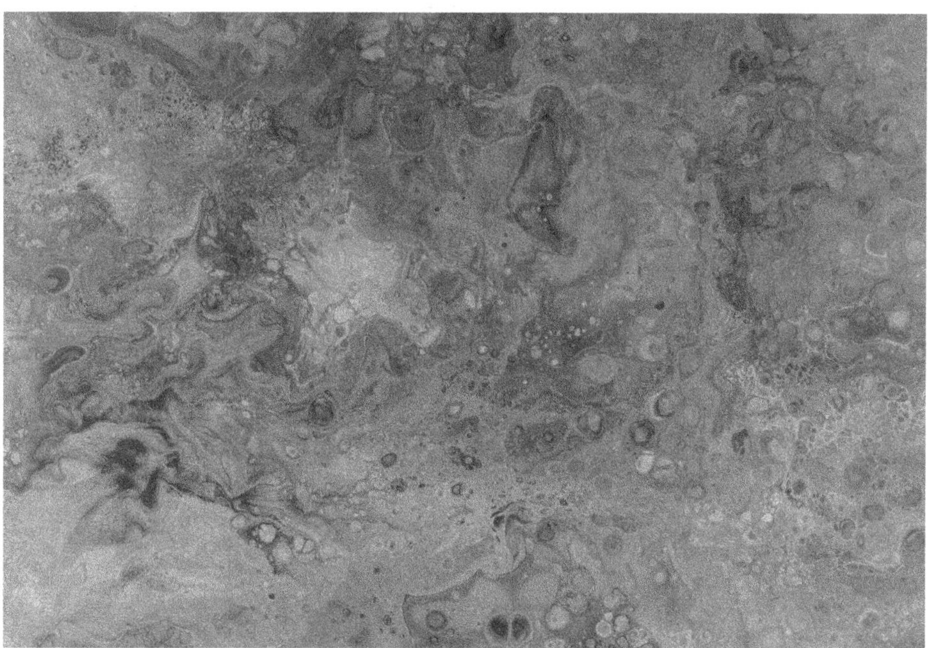

FIGURE 6.12 Do You Know Your Blood Type?

Two different antigens, A antigen and B antigen, can be present on the surface of red blood cells. A person can have only antigen A, only antigen B, both antigens, or neither A nor B. This determines someone's blood type: A, B, AB, or O. People can accept blood donation only if it comes from somebody with the same blood type or from somebody with type O, except AB type individuals, who can receive any of the blood types.

Research and find the average frequencies for each blood type in the United States, and model the experiment with a binomial distribution for each blood type. For example, for experiment *A*, each student can be labeled in a binary way as has *A* or does not have *A*, like head and tail in a fair coin-tossing experiment. A fair coin toss is one that uses a coin that has one head and one tail which are equally likely to occur. The random variable is the number of students with blood type *A* and has a sample space from 0 to the number of students. Find the probability for each outcome. Repeat the analysis for each blood type. In this experiment, Rh positive and Rh negative blood are considered together. For instance, blood type A in this experiment represents both A-positive and A-negative blood.

Question 1:
Make a plot showing the probability distribution for each blood type.

Question 2:
Describe and contrast the shape of probability distributions for each blood type.

Question 3:
Make a bar plot showing the expected number of students in your class for each blood type.

Question 4:
Compare the results of your experiment with the theoretical expectation. Do the results make sense?

Question 5:
A binomial distribution involves the assumptions that trials are independent (extract a ball from an urn with replacement). Explain how and why this experiment can about blood type be treated as a binomial distribution.

Question 6:
What is the most probable outcome for your experiment, for each blood type?

Question 7:
What is the expected outcome for your experiment, for each blood type?

Question 8:
What is the standard deviation for outcomes for your experiment, for each blood type?

Question 9:
Ask your professor and record their blood type. Given the known blood compatibility, what is the theoretical average number of students in the class who can donate blood to your professor?

Question 10:
Ask your professor and record their blood type. Given the known blood compatibility, what is the theoretical average number of students who can receive blood from your professor?

6.4.3 Case Scenarios

CASE SCENARIO COVID-19

FIGURE 6.13 Stay-at-Home

In 2019, due to COVID-19, many countries began to experience one of the worst global pandemics. COVID-19 is a recently discovered, highly infectious disease that is thought to be spread person-to-person by saliva or nose discharge from someone who is infected. The first human cases of COVID-19 were reported by officials in Wuhan City, China, in December 2019. By April 14, 2021, there were 138,828,234 confirmed cases, 2,985,467 deaths, and 111,610,416 recoveries globally. Concerns surrounding this highly infectious disease caused many nations to implement mandatory "stay-at-home" orders that prevented citizens from leaving their homes, except for necessities such as groceries and medicines. The stay-at-home orders were implemented with the hopes of slowing the spread of the disease and preventing greater numbers of deaths. They lasted several weeks.

Source: World Health Organization https://www.who.int/

1. Can the event of whether or not someone tested positive for COVID-19 be a Bernoulli trial? Explain.
2. What was the global death rate from COVID-19 as of July 31, 2022?
3. What is the probability that no one will die from COVID-19 out of 695 infected patients at a local hospital?
4. What is the probability that at least 10 patients will die from COVID-19 out of the 695 infected patients?

5. What is the expected number of people who will die globally from the COVID-19 by the end of the year that you are doing this case scenario? What is the variance? Think about what additional information you may need to answer this question correctly.
6. Use the internet to find out how many people have died globally from the COVID-19 disease by the time you read this case scenario. Does this number fall within the range that was expected?

CASE SCENARIO

Surgical Site Infections

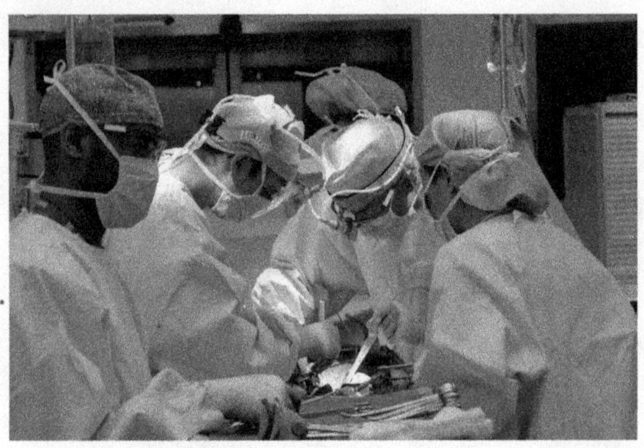

FIGURE 6.14 Surgical Site Infections

According to a recent paper [LaBove (2016)]:

> Prophylactic antibiotic administration is one of the many recommended guidelines to prevent surgical site infections (SSIs). In general, administering preventive antibiotics within 60 minutes of a surgical incision has been shown to be an effective means of reducing health-care or hospital-acquired infections. The types of infections that are seen in plastic surgery are grouped into *superficial* versus *deep* incisional, because intracavity is rarely encountered. Both infections may occur within 30 days of the operation.
>
> A 2011 analysis of readmissions to hospitals after outpatient cosmetic surgery from the National Surgical Quality Improvement Program database showed a 0.90% readmission rate, of which 19.23% of patients had superficial SSIs and 15.38% had deep SSIs. Historically, the National Surgical Infection Prevention Project reported a 55.7% compliance rate of prophylactic antibiotics within the recommended one hour after incision timeframe.

Researchers from Georgetown University and American University in Washington, DC, studied SSIs. They focused on the role of antibiotic prophylaxis guidelines in reducing SSIs to show that regardless of surgical setting, the same SSI prevention measures can be implemented with similar high compliance and low infection rates. The purpose of this project was to analyze whether compliance with guidelines is possible at an office-based surgery site and to compare national compliance rates to those of the office-based surgery site. They summarized the data in the following table.

	LOCAL HOSPITAL	LOCAL OFFICE-BASED SURGERY SITE
Total number of surgeries	11,373	277
Total number of SSIs	27	1

1. The researchers consider this a Bernoulli trial. Are they correct in that assessment? Explain.
2. What is the proportion of infections at the office-based surgical site and the local hospital? Which one has the better SSIs rate?

3. If 200 surgeries were performed in a given year at the local hospital and at the office-based surgical site, what are the expected number of SSIs at each?
4. What is the probability of less than five SSIs at each?
5. The one patient with the SSI in the office-based surgical site is a patient who was at high risk for infection because it was the patient's sixth rhinoplasty surgery. How would your answers to questions 2–4 change if this person were removed from the study?

Use these questions as a self-assessment checklist for this chapter:

1. Do you know the assumptions of a binomial distribution?
2. Do you know how to determine binomial probabilities using the binomial formula, binomial table, and R?
3. Do you know how to calculate the mean, variance, and standard deviation of a binomial random variable both by hand and using R?

References

Debnath, L., & Basu, K. (2015). A short history of probability theory and its applications. *International Journal of Mathematical Education in Science and Technology, 46*(1), 13–39. https://doi.org/10.1080/0020739X.2014.936975

Ghahramani, L., McArdle, K., & Fatorić, S. (2020). Minority community resilience and cultural heritage preservation: A case study of the Gullah Geechee community. *Sustainability, 12*(6), 2266. https://doi.org/10.3390/su12062266

Ioannidis, J. P. A. (2021). Infection fatality rate of COVID-19 inferred from seroprevalence data. *Bulletin of the World Health Organization, 99*(1), 19–33.

LaBove, G., Davison, S. P., & Jackson, M. (2016). Compliance of perioperative antibiotic dosing and surgical site infection rate in office-based elective surgery. *Plastic and Reconstructive Surgery Global Open, 4*(5), e710. https://doi.org/10.1097/GOX.0000000000000704)

Rajendra, K., Vasudevan, H., & Vimal, G. (2019). Optimization of injection moulding process parameters using response surface methodology. In H. Vasudevan, V. Kouttur, & A. Raina (Eds.), *Proceedings of international conference on intelligent manufacturing and automation. Lecture notes in mechanical engineering.* Singer. https://doi.org/10.1007/978-981-13-2490-1_40

Schwartz, D. (2020). An analysis of 38 pregnant women with COVID-19, their newborn infants, and maternal-fetal transmission of SARS-CoV-2: maternal coronavirus infections and pregnancy outcomes. *Archives of Pathology & Laboratory Medicine.* Advance online publication. https://doi.org/10.5858/arpa.2020-0901-SA

Sharif, M., Tanvir, U., Munir, E. U., Yasmin, M., & Khan, M. A. (2018). Brain tumor segmentation and classification by improved binomial thresholding and multi-features selection. *Journal of Ambient Intelligence and Humanized Computing.* Advance online publication. https://doi.org/10.1007/s12652-018-1075-x

South Carolina ETV. (n.d.). *Eugenia P. Deas.* https://www.knowitall.org/series/eugenia-p-deas

Figure Credits

Fig. 6.2: Source: https://commons.wikimedia.org/wiki/File:InjectionMolding.gif.
Fig. 6.3: Source: https://commons.wikimedia.org/wiki/File:Jakob_Bernoulli.jpg.
Fig. 6.4: Copyright © Unsplash/Liv Bruce.
Fig. 6.5: Copyright © Unsplash/M. R.
Fig. 6.6: Copyright © Unsplash/Keith Luke.
Fig. 6.8: Source: https://ark.digitalcommonwealth.org/ark:/50959/8s45qw06m.
Fig. 6.10: Copyright © Unsplash/Nathaniel Yeo.
Fig. 6.12: Copyright © Unsplash/Paweł Czerwiński.
Fig. 6.13: Copyright © Unsplash/United Nations COVID-19 Response.
Fig. 6.14: Copyright © Unsplash/Natinal Cancer Institute.

CHAPTER

7

Normal Probability Distributions

CHAPTER OUTLINE

CHAPTER OBJECTIVES

Upon completion of this chapter, you will have following skills:

1. Interpret graphs of normal probability distributions.
2. Find areas under a standard normal curve.
3. Find a *z*-score given the area under the standard normal curve.
4. Transform a *z*-score to an *x*-value.
5. Use R and RStudio to simulate normal random variables and to determine normal probabilities.

Agios Sostis Beach in Greece is a quiet and uncultivated beach as depicted in Figure 7.1. Characteristics of beach deposits are important in geological and engineering investigations of shoreline processes. Most studies of beaches include samples for determining average particle size, mineral composition, and other attributes. Beach data such as average particle size, particle shape, mineral composition, moisture content, beach firmness, and other characteristics commonly follow a normal distribution (Papadopoulos, 2018). In this chapter, you will learn about normal probability distributions and how to apply their properties to real-life applications.

FIGURE 7.1 Agios Sostis, Mykonos, Greece

Chapter Vocabulary

- A normal distribution, also known as a Gaussian distribution, is a continuous probability distribution uniquely characterized by its mean μ and variance σ^2.
- A probability density function (pdf) is a function that determines the probabilities associated with a continuous random variable.
- The standard normal distribution is a normal distribution with a mean of 0 and a standard deviation of 1.
- The process of transforming a normal x-value to a z-score is called standardizing.
- A normal probability is the area under a normal curve that corresponds to the probability that a normally distributed random variable X will lie in an interval on the real line.
- Transforming data in statistics refers to modifying the data using a mathematical function.
- A sampling distribution is the probability distribution of a sample statistic that is formed when samples of size n are repeatedly taken from a population.
- The standard error of the mean is the standard deviation of the distribution of sample means taken from a population.

7.1 Normal Random Variables

As discussed in Chapters 5 and 6, discrete random variables have a finite or countable number of outcomes. Some distributions of discrete random variables include the geometric, Poisson, Bernoulli, and binomial. There are also others not discussed in this textbook. They all describe some discrete number such as a trial number, the number of occurrences, the number of successes, and so on.

A continuous random variable has an infinite number of possible values that can be represented by an interval on a real line. Values such as volume, weight, and height are occasionally rounded to the nearest whole number. However, they too are continuous random variables as they represent measured data. The distribution of one of the most commonly used continuous random variables in the field of statistics is the normal distribution.

7.1.1 Introduction to the Normal Distribution

The normal probability distribution plays a key role not only in the development of statistical theory, but also in many real data phenomena. For example, after measuring an infant, a pediatrician predicts the infant's height as an adult. This prediction relies on the fact that height is normally distributed. Unlike discrete distributions that model specific counts, the normal distribution models a myriad of continuous measurements in medicine, science, sociology, education, and many other fields.

A normal distribution, also known as a Gaussian distribution, is a continuous probability distribution uniquely characterized by its mean μ and variance σ^2. A normal distribution satisfies the following properties:

- The mean, median, and mode are equal.
- The normal distribution follows the empirical rule (68–95–99.7 rule):
  - Approximately 68% of the data lies within one standard deviation of the mean.
  - Approximately 95% of the data lies within two standard deviations of the mean.
  - Approximately 99.7% of the data lies within three standard deviations of the mean.
- The normal curve is a graph of the normal distribution.
- The total area under the normal curve equals 1.
- The normal curve approaches but never touches the x-axis.
- The graph changes concavity at one standard deviation below and above the mean.
- The normal curve is a bell-shaped curve that is symmetric about the mean.

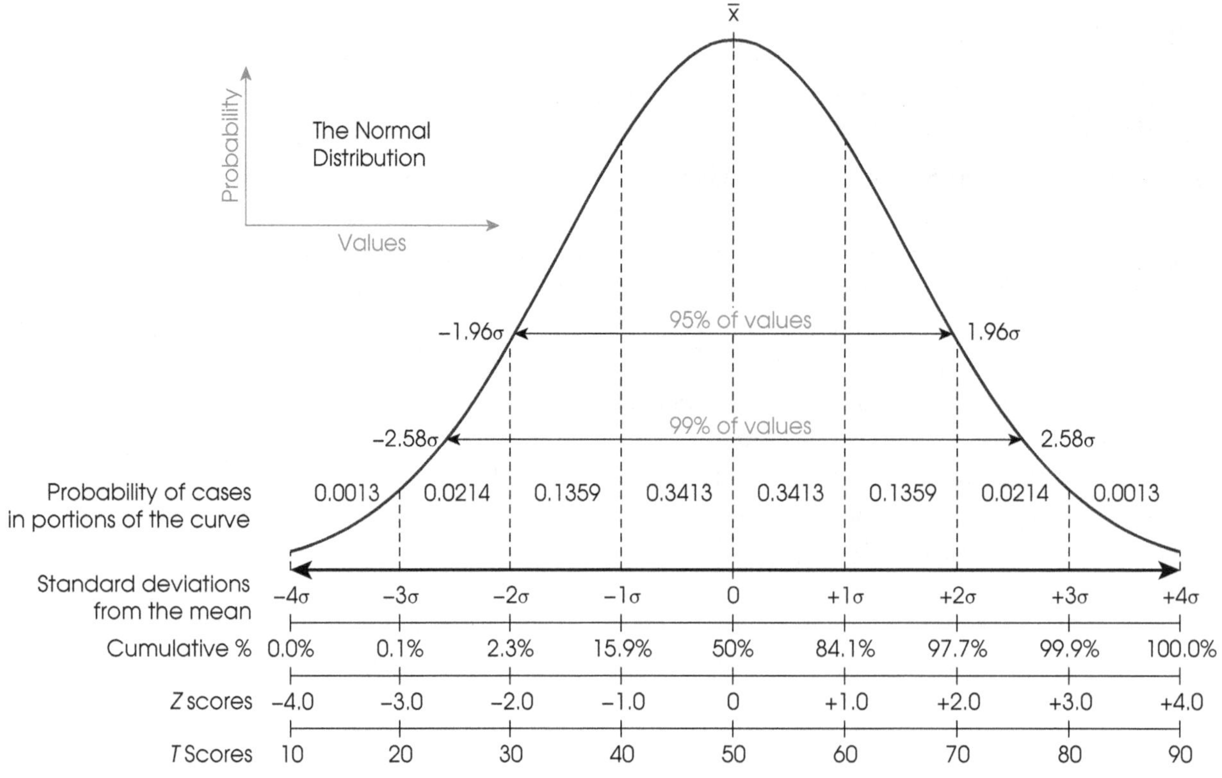

FIGURE 7.2 A Closer Look at the Normal Distribution; This Graph Also Contains Values Related to the *t*-Distribution, Which Will Be Discussed in Chapter 8.

Example:

Ceramic engineers are specialized materials engineers who work with ceramics. The three types of ceramics include earthenware, stoneware, and porcelain. Researchers use the normal distribution to model the behavior of fractures in ceramics (Zhang et al., 2018). Is the distribution of fractures in ceramics symmetric? Explain your answer.

Answer:

Because the researchers propose a normal distribution to model the behavior of fractures in ceramics, this behavior is symmetric about the mean.

FIGURE 7.3 Working With Ceramics

Continuous probability distributions can be graphed using a probability density function (pdf). The normal probability density function is

$$y = \frac{1}{\sigma\sqrt{2\pi}} e^{\frac{-(x-\mu)^2}{2\sigma^2}}.$$

The mean μ is the location of the line of symmetry and the standard deviation σ is the measure of spread of the distribution. A normal distribution can take on any mean and any positive standard deviation.

7.1.2 Introduction to the Standard Normal Distribution

Since a normal distribution can take on any mean and any positive standard deviation, there are infinitely many normal distributions. Each one has a specified mean and standard deviation.

As with the discrete distributions, using tables for determining probabilities of continuous distributions is still very common and quite handy. When working with tables, it is impossible to have an infinite number of tables. Hence, statisticians use what is called the standard normal table, which contains standardized values of a normal random variable along with corresponding probabilities.

The standard normal distribution is a normal distribution with a mean of 0 and a standard deviation of 1. The realized value x of any normal random variable X can be transformed to a standard normal random variable z using the formula

$$z = \frac{X - \mu}{\sigma}.$$

This process of transforming an x-value to a z-score is called standardizing. Probabilities in the standard normal table are sometimes presented as cumulative areas, which is the probability that the standard normal random variable z is less than or equal to some value. A standard normal distribution satisfies the following properties:

- The cumulative area increases as the z-scores increase.
- The cumulative area for $z = 0$ is 0.50.
- The cumulative area for $z = -3.50$ is close to 0.
- The cumulative area for $z = 3.50$ is close to 1.

Note that standardizing is necessary only when working with tables, and not needed when working with technology.

7.1.3 Finding Areas Under the Standard Normal Curve

Even when using software, it is helpful to sketch the standard normal curve by hand when finding areas under the curve. Finding areas under a normal curve is a two-step process, as indicated below. The second step of the process has three cases based on whether one needs to find the area to the left of z (Case I), area to the right of z (Case II), or the area between two z-scores (Case III):

Step 1: Sketch the normal curve, and shade the appropriate area.

Step 2: Find the area in the body of the standard normal table by using one of the three cases below.

Case I:

Find the area to the left of z by finding the area that corresponds to z in the standard normal table (Appendix Tables 7.A and 7.B).

Case II:

Find the area to the right of z by first finding the area that corresponds to the left of z. Next, subtract the area from 1.

Case III:

Find the area between two z-scores by finding the area corresponding to each z-score in the standard normal table. Next, subtract the smaller area from the larger area.

Example:

Determine the area to the left of $z = 1.37$.

Answer:

Start by sketching the standard normal curve. Place the value $z = 0$ on the line of symmetry. Place the value $z = 1.37$ to the right of 0. Shade the area to the left of $z = 1.37$. View the first column of Table 7B for the value 1.3, and the first row for .07. Determine where these values intersect in the body of the table. This value is 0.9139, which is the area to the left of $z = 1.37$.

7.1.4 Exercises

Understanding Concepts

1. Is a normal random variable discrete or continuous?

2. Why is the empirical rule also referred to as the 68-95-99.7 rule?

3. How is a normal random variable converted to a standard normal random variable?

4. What is the relationship among the mean, median, and mode in a normal distribution?

5. In a standard normal curve, what are the values on the horizontal axis?

True or false? In Exercises 6–10, determine whether the statement is true or false. If it is false, rewrite it as a true statement.

6. A z-score is never negative.

7. A z-score value equaled to 1 always indicates one standard deviation above the mean.

8. The normal curve approaches but never touches the horizontal axis.

9. A normal curve is a bell-shaped curve that is asymmetric about the mean.

10. It is not always necessary to standardize a normal random variable X when determining probabilities using a normal distribution table.

Skill Building

11. Is the normal distribution continuous or discrete?

12. Draw two pictures. Make one that is a normal distribution with a mean of 40 and standard deviation of 10 and another that is a normal distribution with a mean of 40 and standard deviation of 20. Explain the features of both. How are they different? How are they the same?

13. Draw two pictures. Make one that is a normal distribution with a mean of 40 and standard deviation of 10 and another that is a normal distribution with a mean of 100 and standard deviation of 10. Explain the features of both. How are they different? How are they the same?

14. Are all symmetric distributions normally distributed? If yes, explain. If not, draw a picture of a distribution that is symmetric but not a normal distribution.

15. If X is a random variable with a standard normal distribution, then X's mean is ____ and X's standard deviation is ____.

16. What are the units of measurements for standard normal random variables?

17. What is the total area under the entire standard normal curve?

18. What is the shaded area for the standard normal distribution below with $x \le 0.75$?

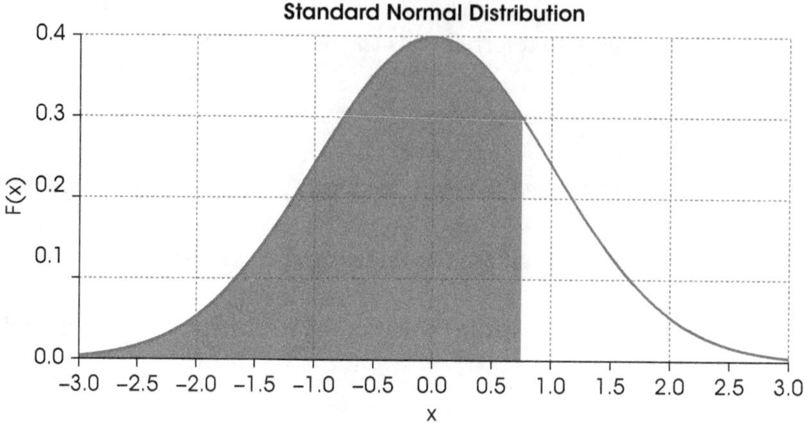

FIGURE 7.4 What Is the Area for the Standard Normal Distribution?

19. Which statement is true about the median for a normal distribution?

    a. The median is usually to the left of the mean.

    b. The median is usually to the right of the mean.

    c. The median is equal to the mean.

    d. None of the above.

20. What is the area of the shaded region in the standard normal curve below?

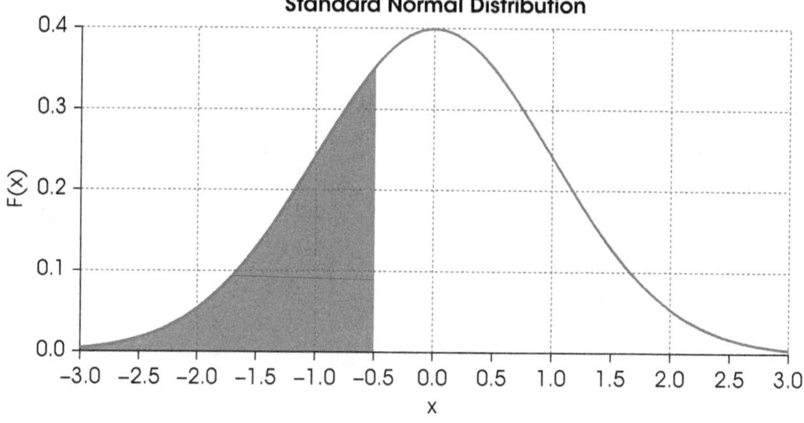

FIGURE 7.5 What Is the Area of the Shaded Region Under the Standard Normal Curve?

Extending Concepts

21. The density of a normal probability distribution is given by $C\ e^{-(x-1)^2/2}$. What is the mean of the distribution?

22. For the distribution from Exercise 21, what is the standard deviation?

23. For the distribution from Exercise 21 and Exercise 22, what is the normalization constant, C?

24. A normal distribution for a random variable is given by $\frac{1}{\sqrt{2\pi}}e^{-(x-2)^2/2}$. What transformation would make this distribution standard? You will need to define a new variable z that depends on x.

25. Find the area under the standard normal curve between $z = 1/4$ and $z = 1/2$.

7.2 Determining Normal Probabilities

The area under a normal curve corresponds to the probability that a normally distributed random variable X will lie in an interval on the real line. The area under a normal curve can also be thought of as a proportion of the population with a certain characteristic. In one application, researchers use normal probabilities to estimate the annual maximum and minimum temperature at a location (Chakrabarty & Gohain, 2015).

7.2.1 Normal Distributions and Probability

Problems involving normal distributions and probabilities are solved using the same procedures used to determine areas under a normal curve. For probabilities, the following notation is used to denote the probability of a standard normal variable z between two values a and b

$$P(a < z < b) = P(a \leq z \leq b).$$

Notice that since the normal distribution is a continuous distribution the probability of any exact z equal 0. This is because, in this case, the area would be represented by a vertical line above the value. Theoretically, vertical lines have no area. The probabilities of normal random variables can be determined from a table or by using software.

7.2.2 Determining Normal Probabilities Using Tables

Section 7.1.3 presented a step-by-step guide for finding the area under the standard normal curve. Since the area under the standard normal curve represents the probability of any normal random variable, the aforementioned steps are also used to determine normal probabilities using standard normal tables. Finding probabilities of a normal random variable X is a three-step process:

Step 1: Transform the normal random variable X to a z-score using the z-score formula presented in Section 7.1.2.

Step 2: Sketch both the normal curve and the standard normal curve, and then shade the appropriate area.

Step 3: Find the area in the body of the standard normal tables 7A and 7B in the Appendix, by using one of the three cases below.

Case I:

Find the area to the left of z by finding the area that corresponds to z in the standard normal table. This value is the probability.

Case II:

Find the area to the right of z by first finding the area that corresponds to the left of z. Next, subtract the area from 1. This value is the probability.

Case III:

Find the area between two z-scores by finding the area corresponding to each z-score in the standard normal table. Next, subtract the smaller area from the larger area. This area is the probability

Example:

Determine the probability that the standard normal variable is less than the value 1.37. That is, find $P(Z < 1.37)$.

Answer:

This is the same as finding the area to the left of $z = 1.37$. Start by sketching the standard normal curve. Place the value $z = 0$ on the line of symmetry. Place the value $z = 1.37$ to the right of 0. Shade the area to the right of $z = 1.37$. View the first column of the standard normal table for the value 1.3 and the first row of the standard normal table for .07. Determine where these values intersect in the body of the table. This value is 0.9139, which is the area to the left of $z = 1.37$. Therefore,

$$P(Z < 1.37) = 0.9139.$$

7.2.3 Determining Normal Probabilities Using R

It is remarkable that the normal distribution, described by the bell curve, or Gaussian function, is quite relevant to many situations that have very little in common with each other. For example, gambling winnings, people's height or weight, blood pressure, standardized test scores, or experimental measurement errors in the physics lab are accurately modeled by normal distributions.

All mathematical details about normal distributions are packaged in R, ready to use, through the four basic functions, available for all distributions in R. We have `dnorm()`, `pnorm()`, `qnorm()`, and `rnorm()` that help us determine the density, cumulative density, quantile, and random variate generation, respectively.

Any normal distribution is completely defined by just two parameters: `mean` and `sd` (sd in R stands for "standard deviation"). If these parameters are given as positional arguments, in this order, or as keywords, to a `*norm` type function, then that function will operate on the normal distribution specified by that *mean* and *standard deviation*. Otherwise R operates on the default standard distribution that has the `mean = 0` and `sd = 1`, with density given the function $exp(-z^2/2)\,/\,\sqrt{2\pi}$.

FIGURE 7.6 Standardized Test

dnorm()

This function gives the density of probability for the normal distribution. This function is less useful than the corresponding function for discrete distributions, because the probability of obtaining an exact given value is zero. However, the ratio between the probability of getting a value within an interval and the size of that interval has a well-defined meaning when the intervals become smaller and smaller. This process defines the density of probability for any continuous distribution, including the normal distribution.

The function `dnorm(x, m, s)` is invoked with three arguments: `x,` the value at which we need to know the density; `m`, the mean of the distribution; and `s,` the standard deviation.

```
dnorm(2, 2.0, 1.0) == 1/sqrt(2*pi)

## [1] TRUE

dnorm(1) == 1/sqrt(2*pi*exp(1))

## [1] TRUE
```

In the first example above, we obtained the density at 2, which is the same for the mean value, where the normal distribution has its maximum. In the second example, we compute the density for x=1, when mean and sd have their default values. In both cases we compared the results with what we expected mathematically. Note that the use of the `equality` test operator `==` is not safe in general for comparing floating-point numbers due to the limited representation of these numbers in a computer. A better way is to use the function `all.equal()`, which allows testing for equality within a tolerance interval (by default, 1.5e-8).

pnorm()

Most of the time we are interested in knowing the probability that a normal random variable X with mean μ and standard deviation σ is in some interval (a, b). Formally we can write this in terms of a cumulative distribution function as

$$P(a \leq X(\mu,\sigma) \leq b) = pnorm(b,\mu,\sigma) - pnorm(a,\mu,\sigma).$$

The probability that X has any value less than b is obtained when $a = \infty$ and serves as the definition for the function `pnorm()` because

$$P(-\infty \leq X(\mu,\sigma) \leq b) = pnorm(b,\mu,\sigma).$$

Of course, if we are interested in events with $X > a$ we determine that by subtracting the probability for the complementary event from the unity

$$P(a \leq X(\mu,\sigma) \leq \infty) = 1 - pnorm(a,\mu,\sigma)$$

because $pnorm(\infty,\mu,\sigma) = 1$.

For example, in the standard normal distribution, the probability that $z < -1.96$ has to be pretty small, but the probability that $z < 1.96$ will be almost one because the total area under the curve equals one. Indeed:

```
pnorm(-1.96)
```

```
## [1] 0.0249979
```

```
pnorm(1.96)
```

```
## [1] 0.9750021
```

qnorm()

This function calculates the quantile for a normal distribution, which is useful when we want to find the value of the random variable, and we have a given proportion of results with smaller values. For example, the median of a distribution is the value for which 50% of the outcomes are smaller than it. Of course, for a normal distribution, the median is the same as the mean. For example,

```
qnorm(0.5, 2.0, 3.0)
```

```
## [1] 2
```

Therefore, the `qnorm()` function is the inverse of `pnorm()` in the sense that if `pnorm(b, m, s) = x`, then `qnorm(x, m, s) = b`. For example, in reference to the examples above,

```
qnorm(0.025)
```

```
## [1] -1.959964
```

```
qnorm(0.975)
```

```
## [1] 1.959964.
```

rnorm()

Often in simulations we need to generate numbers that are distributed according to a prescribed normal distribution. For example, in a simulation of a gas, molecules move with equal probability to the left or to the right and faster if the temperature is warmer but very few of them move very fast. According to the Maxwell-Boltzmann law, their distribution is normal. The function `rnorm(n, m, s)` produces a vector of N random numbers with a normal distribution with mean m and standard deviation s.

For example, if we want to simulate the students' test grades, we can use the following code:

```
n = 1000; m = 6; s = 1
G = rnorm(n, m, s)
x = seq(3,10,length.out = 200)
hist(G, probability = TRUE, ylim=c(0,0.45), col='gray', border='white')
lines(x, dnorm(x, m, s), col='orange', lwd = 3)
```

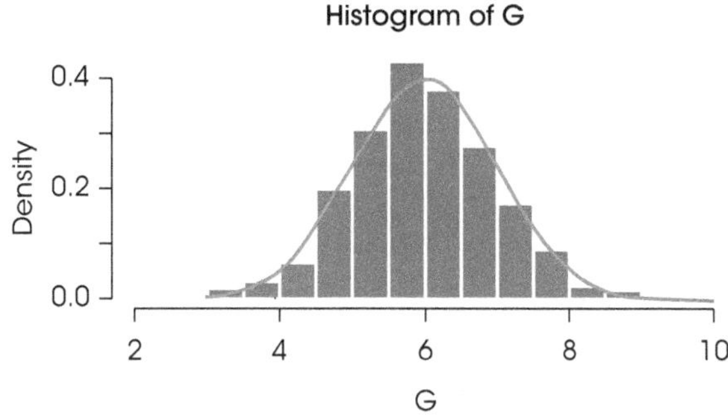

FIGURE 7.7 Histogram of Grades for Comparison

The expected density in orange was obtained by using the theoretical probability distribution function `dnorm` overlaid on the histogram of grades for comparison. Instead of showing the frequencies on the vertical axis, the `hist` function has here the option `probability = TRUE` to rescale all frequency by the sample size to estimate probabilities. Alternatively, `frequency = FALSE` produces the same result.

7.2.4 Exercises

Understanding Concepts

1. What do areas under normal curves represent?

2. What does the area under a vertical line equal?

3. Can standard normal tables be used to determine normal probabilities for random variables that are not standardized?

4. Which R function is used to determine the cumulative area of a normal random variable?

5. Can standard normal tables be used to determine probabilities associated with standardized test scores?

True or false? In Exercises 6–11, determine whether the statement is true or false. If it is false, rewrite it as a true statement.

6. Problems involving normal distributions and probabilities are solved using the same procedures as those for determining areas under a normal curve.

7. The area under the standard normal curve represents the probability of any normal random variable.

8. Determining the probability that a standard normal variable is less than a value is the same as determining the cumulative probability for that value.

9. To determine normal probabilities using R, one first needs to standardize the normal random variable.

10. Tables are never used for determining normal probabilities.

11. Normal probabilities can be computed by hand using the probability density function for a normal distribution.

Skill Building

12. What type of plot can be used to determine whether data follow the normal distribution?

13. Suppose you have data that are normally distributed with a mean of 5 and standard deviation of 2. Use the appropriate technique to compute the z-score for 2, 5, and 6.

14. The number of Twitter followers for students at a certain university is normally distributed. The mean number of followers is 2,440 with a standard deviation of 211. What is the probability that a student has more than 500 Twitter followers? What percentage of students have between 200–700 followers?

15. Students who have more than 10,000 Twitter followers can be "verified" and receive a blue check mark next to their name. Becoming verified is coveted because it means a student is popular, and their account is authentic. Using the information in Exercise 14, what is the probability that a student is verified?

16. Compute the following probabilities for a standard normal distribution:

    a. $Z > 3$
    b. $Z = 2$

c. $Z < -1$
d. $-1.5 < Z < 2.3$

17. Compute the following probabilities for a normal distribution with mean 10 and variance 4:

a. $X > 10$
b. $X < 10$
c. $X > 50$
d. $0 < X < 4$
e. $-50 < X < 10$

18. Melissa goes to her office building daily and spends, on average, four hours a day in her office with a standard deviation of one hour. What is the probability that she will spend at least three hours in her office? What is the probability that she spends less than 30 minutes in her office?

FIGURE 7.8 Daily Routine

19. Order the following statistics from smallest to largest for a normally distributed random variable: median, mean, max, min, range.

20. Give a scenario that could be appropriately modeled by a normal distribution.

Extending Concepts

21. The mean of a normal random variable x is 1 and its standard deviation is 2. Determine the probability that x lies between 0 and 3.

22. The mean of a normal random variable x is -2 and its standard deviation is 3. Determine the probability that x is positive.

23. Explain why a standard normal random variable has an equal probability of being either positive or negative.

24. What does it mean for a normal curve to be unimodal and symmetric?

25. What is the probability that a normal random variable is greater than its mean?

7.3 Normal Distributions: Determining x-Values

As illustrated in earlier sections of this chapter, the area under the normal curve can be found by transforming a normal random variable to a standard normal value z. This process can also be reversed. The z-scores and corresponding x-values can also be determined for a given area.

7.3.1 Transforming a z-Score to an x-Value

Transforming data in statistics refers to modifying the data using a mathematical function. When transforming data, every point in the data set, in addition to the scale of the variable, is modified. The purpose of this is to change the data to a more suitable form for a statistical test or method. It also offers a better interpretation of results.

For example, instead of starting with an x-value as in previous sections, suppose we start with a z-score. The formula that gives z in terms of x

$$z = \frac{x - \mu}{\sigma},$$

can be transformed to give x in terms of z. Using algebra,

$$x = \mu + z\sigma.$$

Example:

In mechanical engineering, tensile strength is a measure of the force required to pull something, such as a rope, wire, concrete, or structural beam, apart until it breaks. Tensile strength is measured in units of force per unit area such as pounds per square inch (psi) or megapascals, $f_{st,t}$ (MPa). Researchers perform an experimental study on tensile strength of concrete. They note that the mean tensile strength of concrete historically has been $\mu = 3.5$ with a standard deviation $\sigma = 1.1603$. Tensile strength is also known to have a normal distribution. Determine the actual tensile strength of the given specimens. The z-scores for a random sample of five specimens are presented in the table below (Zhao et al., 2017).

FIGURE 7.9 Battle Rope Training

SPECIMENS	z-SCORES
Specimen 1	−1.0256
Specimen 2	−0.4740
Specimen 3	1.6461
Specimen 4	−0.3964
Specimen 5	1.2755

Answer:

The *x*-value that corresponds to each standard *z*-score is calculated using the formula $x = \mu + z\sigma$. Note that $\mu = 3.5$, and $\sigma = 1.1603$ was given in the problem. Also note that *z*-scores are unitless measures.

SPECIMENS	z-SCORES	TENSILE STRENGTH (MPa)
Specimen 1	−1.0256	2.31
Specimen 2	−0.4740	2.95
Specimen 3	1.6461	5.41
Specimen 4	−0.3964	3.04
Specimen 5	1.2755	4.98

There are several interpretations:

- The *z*-scores that lie between 0 and 1 indicate tensile strengths that lie within 1 standard deviation above the mean.
- Specimens 1, 2, 3, and 4 have tensile strengths that lie within 1 standard deviation of the mean
- Based on the empirical rule, the tensile strengths lie within 1 standard deviation of the mean 68% of the time.
- Specimen 5 has a tensile strength that is 1.2755 standard deviations above the mean.

7.3.2 Determining Values Given Probabilities

A normal distribution can also be used to find specific data values for given percentages. In this case, we start with a given probability or a percentage, and then find the corresponding x-value. This also uses the transformation $x = \mu + z\sigma$. To determine values for given probabilities, we use the following steps:

Step 1:

Draw a normal curve, and shade the desired area that represents the probability, proportion, or percentile.

Step 2:

Look in the body of the standard normal table for the desired probability, proportion, or percentile.

Step 3:

Determine the z-score from the table that corresponds to the desired area.

Step 4:

Determine x using the formula $x = \mu + z\sigma$.

Example:

Physical training is a common practice for most law enforcement academies. Recruits need to be both physically and mentally prepared for their vocation. The PT500 is a battery of several general fitness tests used in law enforcement training. Variables that comprise the test are push-ups, pull-ups, mountain climbing, and running. All variables are normally distributed. On the mountain-climbing portion of the test, the population mean score including male and female recruits is $\mu = 58.67$ with a standard deviation of $\sigma = 8.49$ (Lockie et al., 2018). Suppose the agency will hire only applicants with scores in the top 10% on each portion of the test. What is the lowest score an applicant can earn on the mountain-climbing portion of the test and still be eligible to be hired by the agency?

FIGURE 7.10 Physical Training Mornings

Answer:

A test score in the top 10% is any score above the 90th percentile. To find the score that represents the 90th percentile, first find the z-score that corresponds to a cumulative area of 0.9. In the standard normal table, the area closest to 0.9 is 0.8997. Therefore, the z-score that corresponds to an area of 0.9 is $z = 1.28$. To find the x-value, note that $\mu = 58.67$ and $\sigma = 8.49$, and use the formula

$$\begin{aligned} x &= \mu + z\sigma \\ &= 58.67 + (1.28)(8.49) \\ &= 69.5372. \end{aligned}$$

Therefore, the lowest score an applicant (regardless of gender) can earn on the mountain-climbing portion of the PT500 and still be eligible to be hired by the agency is approximately 70.

7.3.3 Exercises

Understanding Concepts

1. What does it mean to transform a random variable?

2. How does one transform a z-score to an x-value?

3. Tensile strength is known to have a normal distribution. An engineer computed the z-scores for several specimens. Do the z-scores have a measurement unit? If so, what is it?

4. If you know the z-score, is any additional information needed to determine the x-values?

5. If you are given a probability or a percentage, is it possible to determine the corresponding x-value?

6. What do the numbers in the body of a standard normal table represent?

True or false? In Exercises 7–12, determine whether the statement is true or false. If it is false, rewrite it as a true statement.

7. The area under the normal curve can be found by transforming a normal random variable to a standard normal value.

8. The purpose of transforming is to change the data to a more suitable form for a statistical test or method.

9. A z-score of 1 indicates 1 standard deviation above the mean.

10. A normal distribution can be used to find specific data values for given percentages.

11. Algebra can be used to transform a z-score to an x-value that has a normal distribution.

12. The body of the standard normal table contains probabilities, proportions, and percentiles.

Skill Building

13. Find the z-score for the following random variables that are normally distributed with a mean of 10 and a standard deviation of 3.

    a. $x = 4$
    b. $x = 10$
    c. $x = 0$
    d. $x = -8$

14. Find the x value for the following z-scores, given that X is a normally distributed random variable with mean 50 and standard deviation 5.

    a. $z = 0$
    b. $z = 2$
    c. $z = -1$
    d. $z = 4$

15. What does the z-score tell you about the data?

16. A study found that the amount of time a person spends listening to music in a week follows a normal distribution with a mean of 18 hours and a standard deviation of 2 hours. Find the z-score for a person who listens to music on average of 10 hours per week.

17. Was the z-score you found in Exercise 16 negative? Explain why that does or does not makes sense.

18. Which z-score corresponds to the following percentiles for a standard normal distribution?

    a. 80th percentile
    b. 50th percentile
    c. 20th percentile

FIGURE 7.11 Classical Antiques

19. Suppose two students are taking the same statistics class from different professors. Melissa scores a 40 on her exam. The range of values for her class's exam is from 0 to 50. The distribution of scores in her class follows a normal distribution with a mean of 50 and a standard deviation of 3. Linda scores an 80 on her exam. The range of values for her class's exam is 0 to 100. The scores follow a normal distribution with parameters (40, 5). Did Melissa or Linda score in the higher percentile on the exam? Explain.

20. Using the information in Exercise 19, what score must a student receive in Linda's class to score in the 80th percentile? What about in Melissa's class?

Extending Concepts

21. Find the value of a standard normal random variable X such that the probability of obtaining numbers greater *than that value* is 10%.

22. Find the value of a normal variable for which there is a 50% probability of having higher value.

23. What is the mean value of the distribution of a normal random variable that has been standardized?

24. What is standard deviation of a normal random variable that has been standardized?

25. Give three reasons why standardization of normal random variables is useful in practical applications.

26. The z-score for a value of a normal random variable X with a mean of 1 and standard deviation of 2 is $z = 0.4$. What is the X value?

7.4 Central Limit Theorem

In previous sections, each random variable represented a single value. We now allow random variables to represent a statistic. In particular, the random variable in the current section will represent the sample mean. As before, we will determine the distribution of the random variable.

7.4.1 Sampling Distributions

Every sample statistic has a sampling distribution. A sampling distribution is the probability distribution of a sample statistic that is formed when samples of size n are taken repeatedly from a population. If the sample statistic is the sample mean, $\bar{x}$, then the distribution is called the sampling distribution of the sample means.

Example:

Consider a population of values {1, 3, 7}. Determine the population mean, population variance, and standard deviation. List all possible samples of size $n = 2$ and calculate the mean of each sample. Finally, determine the mean and standard deviation of the sample means. Compare the results to the population mean and standard deviation.

Answer:

The population mean, variance, and standard deviation are

$$\mu = \frac{\Sigma x}{N} \approx 3.6667,\ \sigma^2 = \frac{\sum(\bar{x} - \mu)^2}{N} \approx 9.333, \text{ and } \sigma = \sqrt{\sigma^2} \approx 3.055.$$

Using the multiplication rule, there are a total of 3*3 = 9 samples of size 2 from the population. A list of the $m = 9$ samples and their means are in the table below:

SAMPLE	SAMPLE MEAN, $\overline{x}$
1, 3	2
1, 7	4
3, 7	5
3, 1	2
7, 1	4
7, 3	5
1, 1	1
3, 3	3
7, 7	7

Focusing solely on the $m = 9$ sample means, their mean is referred to as the *grand mean*:

$$\overline{\overline{x}} = \frac{\sum \overline{x}}{m} \approx 3.6667.$$

Notice that the notation for the grand mean has two bars above x while the sample mean has one. Their standard deviation is referred to as the standard error of the mean, $\sigma_{\overline{x}} \approx 1.8708$. The standard error of the mean is the standard deviation of the sample means. Square the standard deviation to determine the variance, $\sigma_{\overline{x}}^2 \approx 3.5$. Notice that the mean of the sample means equals the population mean. However, the variance of the sample means is smaller than the variance of the population.

7.4.2 Central Limit Theorem

The idea that the distribution of sample means has the same mean as the population, but its standard deviation is less than the standard deviation of the population is formally stated in the central limit theorem. The central limit theorem is one of the most important theorems in the field of statistics because it provides the foundation for the inferential branch of statistics. This theorem describes the relationship between the sampling distribution of the sample means and the population from which the samples originated.

Central Limit Theorem

1. If samples of size n, where $n > 30$, are drawn from *any* population with a mean μ and standard deviation σ, then the sampling distribution of the sample means has an approximately normal distribution. The larger the sample size, the better the approximation.

2. If the population itself is normally distributed, then the sampling distribution of the sample means is normally distributed for *any* sample of size n.

In either case, the sampling distribution of the sample means has a mean equal to the population mean

$$\mu_{\bar{x}} = \mu .$$

The sampling distribution of sample means has a variance equal to $\frac{1}{n}$ times the variance of the population and a standard deviation equal to the population standard deviation, divided by the square root of n.

$$\sigma_{\bar{x}}^{2} = \frac{\sigma^2}{n}$$

$$\sigma_{\bar{x}} = \frac{\sigma}{\sqrt{n}}.$$

7.4.3 Central Limit Theorem Applications

The central limit theorem has many real-life applications. For example, a database contains sensitive information about individuals. Researchers have quantified "privacy loss" and defined it as a random variable (Sommer et al., 2019). As with most random variables, the average privacy loss can be determined.

The central limit theorem states that the distribution of the sample averages is normal with the same mean as the population. Its variance is the same as the variance of the population divided by the sample size. Therefore, the expected privacy loss has a normal distribution with the same mean as the population. Its variance is the same as the variance of the population divided by the sample size.

The following real-life application is regarding average extreme temperatures.

Example:

Assam is a state in northeast India. The Indian Meteorological Department has 41 stations, and five are located in Assam (Dutta et al., 2018). Researchers theorize that once the values of the natural maximum temperature and the natural minimum temperature in locations in Assam are known, it would then be possible to know if the temperatures of locations in Assam have been influenced by unnatural factors. To accomplish this, they analyze past and present scenarios with respect to temperatures of the locations. The mean of the annual natural maximum and mean of the natural minimum temperature in Assam both have a normal distribution. Let the random variable $\bar{x}$ represent the mean of the annual natural maximum temperature

FIGURE 7.12 Women in Assam, India

in Assam. Assume that the population mean, and standard deviation are 24.6°C and 14.9°C, respectively. The average annual maximum temperature in degrees Celsius for each station in Assam is given in the table below (Chakrabarty & Gohain, 2015).

STATION NAME	$\overline{x}$ - VALUE (°C)
Dhubri	36.3875
Dibrugarh	36.7026
Guwahati	37.1857
Silchar	37.2000
Tezpur	36.8775

Suppose 10 years of temperatures from Dhubri are randomly chosen. What is the probability that the mean of the annual natural maximum temperature in Dhubri exceeds 36.3875°C?

Answer:

The random variable $\overline{x}$ represents the mean of the annual natural maximum temperature in Assam. Because the population is normally distributed, the central limit theorem can be used to conclude that the distribution of sample means is normally distributed, with a mean and a standard deviation of

$$\mu_{\overline{x}} = \mu$$
$$= 24.6,$$

and

$$\sigma_{\overline{x}} = \frac{\sigma}{\sqrt{n}}$$
$$= \frac{14.9}{\sqrt{10}}$$
$$\approx 4.7118.$$

The z-score that corresponds to 36.3875 is

$$z = \frac{\overline{x} - \mu}{\frac{\sigma}{\sqrt{n}}}$$
$$= \frac{36.3875 - 24.6}{\frac{14.9}{\sqrt{10}}}$$
$$\approx 2.50.$$

So, the probability that the mean of the annual natural maximum temperature in Dhubri exceeds 36.3875°C is

$$\begin{aligned} P(\bar{x} > 36.3875) &= P(z > 2.50) \\ &= 1 - P(z \leq 2.5) \\ &= 1 - .9938 \\ &= .0062. \end{aligned}$$

Therefore, there is a .62% chance that the mean of the annual natural maximum temperature in Dhubri exceeds 36.3875°C.

7.4.5 Exercises

Understanding Concepts

1. What is a sampling distribution?

2. What is the sampling distribution of the sample means referring to?

3. One can determine the probability distribution of the sample means using which theorem?

4. What is the standard error of the mean referring to?

True or false? In Exercises 5–9, determine whether the statement is true or false. If it is false, rewrite it as a true statement.

5. The notation for the sample mean has two bars, while the grand mean only has one bar.

6. For the central limit theorem to be applicable, the population from which the samples are drawn must be normal.

7. For the central limit theorem, the smaller the sample size, the better the approximation.

8. According to the central limit theorem, if the population itself is normally distributed, then the sampling distribution of the sample means is normally distributed for any sample of size, *n*.

9. According to the central limit theorem, the distribution of the sample means is normal, with the sample mean equal to the population mean. The variance of the sample means is the same as the variance of the population, but divided by the sample size.

Skill Building

10. Explain in your own words the central limit theorem.

11. Are sample means more or less variable than individual observations? How much smaller or larger?

12. Assume we have data that have a normal distribution with mean 50 and variance 10. What is the distribution of the sample mean?

13. Suppose individual grade point averages at a local university follow a normal distribution with mean 3 and standard deviation 0.5. If there are 26 people in your statistics class, what is the distribution of the sample mean of the grade point averages?

14. Using the information in Exercise 13, what is the probability that the sample mean is above 3.0?

15. True or false? The central limit theorem applies only to continuous distributions.

16. Consider the distribution below of individual data that follow a normal distribution with mean 100 and standard deviation 25. Draw the distribution of the sample mean for samples of size 100 over the distribution shown below.

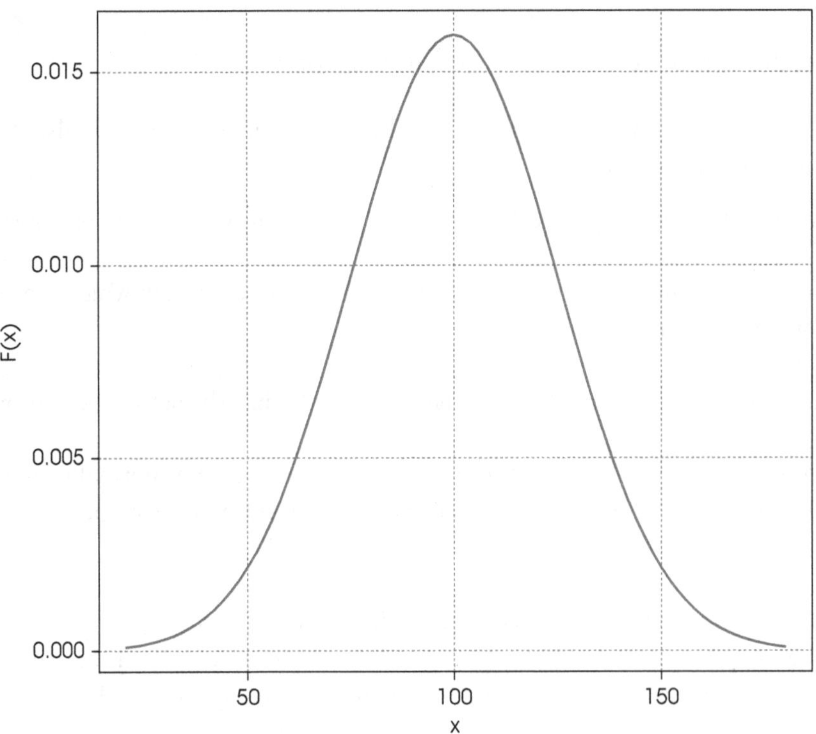

FIGURE 7.13 Distribution of Individual Data

17. Since 1998, Atlanta Hartsfield-Jackson International Airport has been recognized as the world's busiest airport. The time it takes for an individual to pass through security screening follows a normal distribution with a mean of 40 minutes and a standard deviation of 20 minutes. Suppose 16 people are selected multiple times to form a simple random sample (SRS). What is the distribution of the sample means for 16 people in the SRS to be screened to pass through security?

18. What is the probability that it takes less than 1 hour to pass through security screening for passengers in the simple random sample described in Exercise 17?

19. Explain why the central limit theorem is so important in statistics.

20. In 2020, the average time spent on Twitter was 3.39 minutes per session (Twitter, 2021). Students at a certain university spent more time on Twitter than average because their classes were online during the COVID-19 pandemic. They felt more free to use their Twitter accounts during lecture because they were not in a traditional classroom. Suppose the standard deviation of the average time spent on Twitter is 1.2 minutes. Determine the probability that the students at this university spent more than 5 minutes per session on Twitter. Assume that that average time spent on Twitter has a normal distribution.

Extending Concepts

21. Explain why the distribution of SAT scores of students is likely to be described by a normal curve.

22. Suppose random samples of size $n \geq 30$ are drawn from any population. Explain why the greater the sample size, the better the approximation of the distribution of sample means.

23. Why is the standard deviation of the distribution of sample means typically smaller than the population standard deviation?

24. If the standard error of the mean is 12 and the sample size is 6, what is the population variance?

25. What is the relationship between the expected value of the distribution of sample means and the population mean?

7.5 R and RStudio

7.5.1 Programming Assignments

Exercise 7.1

Assuming that the distribution of the height of adult men in the world is normal with an average of 69 inches and a standard deviation of 3 inches, estimate the proportion of adult men who are 7 feet tall or taller, referred to as *seven footers*.

Exercise 7.2

Use the answer to the previous exercise to estimate the number of men who are 7 feet tall or taller if there are about one billion men between ages 18 and 40 in the world.

Exercise 7.3

The mean test score on a college entrance exam is 72, and the standard deviation is 15.2. Assuming a normal distribution, what is the percentage of students scoring between 80 and 90 on this exam?

Exercise 7.4

The mean test score on a college entrance exam is 72, and the standard deviation is 15.2. Assuming a normal distribution, what should be the passing grade if we know that only the top 20% of applicants are admitted?

Exercise 7.5

Run the following code, and explain what it has to do with the 68–95–99.7 rule:

```
pnorm(1:3) - pnorm(-(1:3))

## [1] 0.6826895 0.9544997 0.9973002
```

Exercise 7.6

Although the binomial distribution is discrete and the normal distribution is continuous, the shapes of their densities are very similar. Because we know (Section 6.3) that the mean of a binomial distribution is np and the standard deviation is $\sqrt{npq}$, we can plot and compare on the same graph the shapes of the two distributions:

```
n=8
p=0.5
q=1-p
x=seq(0, n, length.out = 40)
barplot(dbinom(0:n, n, p), names=0:n, space=0, border="white",
ylim=c(0,0.3))
lines(x+1/2, dnorm(x, n*p, sqrt(n*p*q)), lwd=3, col="orange")
```

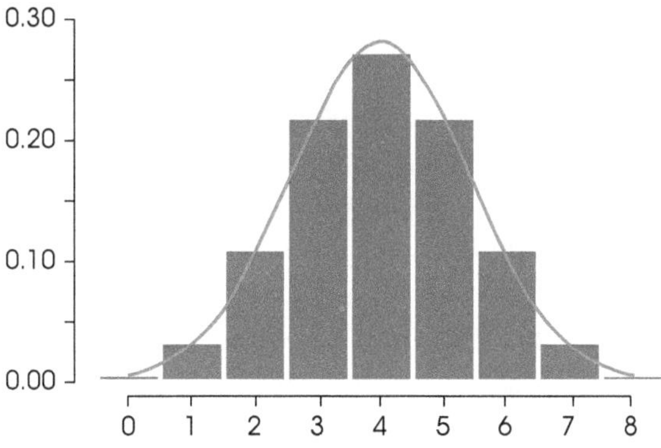

FIGURE 7.14 `Barplot()` of a Binomial Distribution and Corresponding Normal Distribution

This code shows the `barplot()` of a binomial distribution and also the corresponding normal distribution. In order to compare these two, we need to make a few observations:

- The binomial distribution is restricted to an enumerable set of categories, while the normal distribution has values even for $x < 0$ or $x > 8$.
- The default implementation of `barplot()` in R inserts spaces between bars because the horizontal coordinates are not important. All we need to represent are a finite number of categories that might have or not have numerical values. This is why we have to specify the option `space=0` in `barplot()` and add 1/2 to all x coordinates for the solid line.
- The agreement between the binomial and normal distributions is not only qualitative, but also quantitative. It is actually a mathematical fact that the binomial distribution approaches the normal distribution in the limit $n \to \infty$ and $n \to 0$ in such a way that np is finite.

Repeat the calculation for an asymmetric case, for example, with $n = 20$ and $p = 0.8$. Do you observe an improvement in the quality of the agreement? What other observations can you make? Can you explain these observations in terms of the central limit theorem?

Exercise 7.7

Write an R function to calculate the z-scores for a vector of numbers. What arguments do you need? Apply this function to the following list of numbers: 9 8 5 7 9 7 9 8 4 10, knowing that their mean is 8 and standard deviation is 2.2.

Exercise 7.8

Use the function `qnorm()` to find the lowest possible score of an IQ test a person can have and still be in the top 1% of all IQ scores. The IQ tests are typically standardized so that they have a mean of 100 and a standard deviation of 15.

Exercise 7.9

The goal of Exercises 7.9 and 7.10 is to investigate numerically the central limit theorem. Imagine the following experiment: Obtain 12 normal random variables, and report their sum. Repeat the experiment a large number of times, say 40 or 100, and look at the distribution of the sums. The central limit theorem says that no matter what kind of distribution those 12 numbers have, the distribution of their sum is approximately normal.

Let us test this idea with numbers uniformly distributed between 0 and 1. The sum of 12 such numbers can be anywhere between 0 and 12. We use the function `runif()` to get enough numbers for our experiment. Here N is the number of dozens we need.

```
N = 40
X = runif(N*12)
mean(X)
```

```
## [1] 0.4874283
```

```
sd(X)
```

```
## [1] 0.2857796
```

```
hist(X)
```

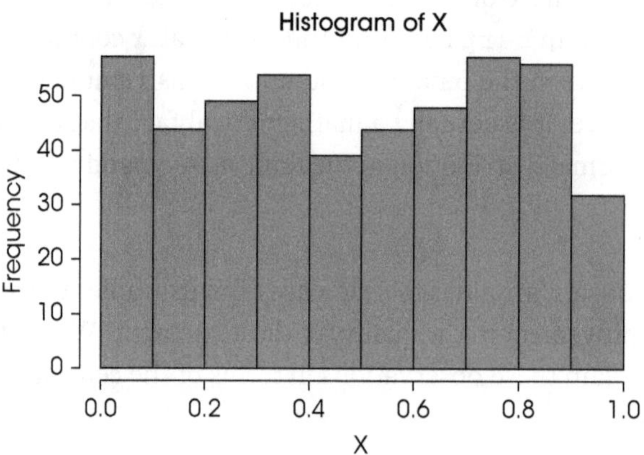

FIGURE 7.15 Histogram of X

Indeed, these numbers have the qualities we are looking for. Their mean is close to 1/2, and standard deviation is close to $1/\sqrt{12}$. The histogram shows that all numbers are between 0 and 1 in a distribution that is more or less flat.

In our experiment, we want to make groups of 12 and sum them up. In R we do this by first making a matrix with N rows, using the function `matrix()` and then obtaining the sum of each row in a vector of length N of sums named S:

```
M = matrix(X, nrow = N)
S = rowSums(M)
```

Take a look at the distribution of numbers in the *S* vector. Does its distribution look like a normal distribution? What is the mean and standard deviation? Does this correspond with what you expected?

Repeat the calculation with a larger number of dozens, say $n = 200$. Are your conclusions clearer now?

Exercise 7.10

Write an R program to investigate an experiment similar to the previous exercise, but this time toss a coin 12 times, and report the number of times the head comes up. This is equivalent to the random variable $\sum_{i=1}^{12} X_i$, where X_i is the random variable with a result of 1 for a head and 0 for a tail, when tossing one coin.

Use the function `rbinom(n, 12, 0.5)` to obtain directly the sum of number of successes (heads) in 12 tossings. Make a histogram and show the distribution with increasing *N*.

7.5.2 Group Experiments

Basketball Players' Weights

In this activity we will investigate the distribution of weight among professional basketball players. Each student will be identified with a sequential number and will write down a list of 10 to 20 basketball players and their weights on a piece of paper. Each student will also mark their paper with their number in the top right corner. To avoid repetition, agree on a system of collecting data. For example, each student will choose a different team. Students will enter the data as a vector in R and then pass the paper with their list to the student with the next number and receive the list from the student with the previous number. At the end, each student will have the lists from all the other students recorded in a data frame with the weights of 100 to 200 NBA players.

Use R functions `mean()`, `sd()`, `summary()`, and `hist()` to analyze this data.

FIGURE 7.16 NBA Game

Question 1:
What sampling strategy did you use to collect data? What advantages and disadvantages has this strategy compared with other possible sampling strategies?

Question 2:
What is the mean weight of the players?

Question 3:
What is the standard deviation of your sample? What information does it tell you?

Question 4:
Analyze the median, quartiles, and outliers for your sample.

Question 5:
What function do you use to represent the data to obtain a box-and-whisker plot for this data?

Question 6:
Explain why the shape of the distribution of weights is that of a normal distribution.

Question 7:
Explain and argue why the shape of the distribution of weights is NOT exactly one of a normal distribution?

Question 8:
Histograms were introduced in Section 1.3. Draw over the histogram a curve representing the density of a normal distribution with the mean and standard distribution of your sample.

Question 9:
Explain the agreement between the histogram and the curve for the density of the normal distribution.

Question 10:
What conclusions, if any, would change if you collected twice as many basketball players in your sample?

7.5.3 Case Scenarios

CASE SCENARIO

Bowling Night

FIGURE 7.17 Bowling

In the United States and Canada, the sport of bowling involves rolling a ball toward a target of 10 "bowling pins." The aim is to knock down a total of as many pins as possible after 10 frames. Points are scored based on the number of pins knocked down. Christine and Casey both enjoy bowling and are often very competitive at the sport. Christine's bowling scores follow a normal distribution with a mean of 150 and a standard deviation of 52. Casey's bowling scores follow a normal distribution with a mean of 185 and a standard deviation of 10.

1. During a Thursday night bowling event, Christine scores a 115, and Casey scores a 210. How many standard deviations is each score from its mean?
2. Assuming that Christine's bowling scores are independent of Casey's, what is the distribution of their combined bowling scores?
3. At the next game of bowling, what is the probability that Christine will score higher than Casey?
4. What do you notice about the distribution of Christine's and Casey's bowling scores? For example, is it likely that Casey will always win because his mean is higher than Christine's? Explain.

CASE SCENARIO

Genetic Counseling and Testing

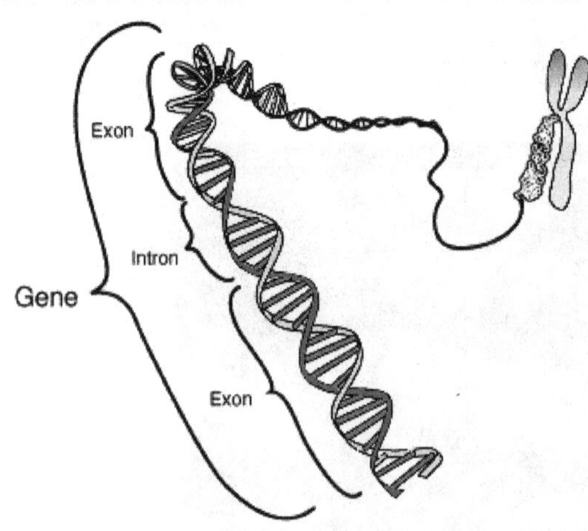

FIGURE 7.18 Genetics

According to a recent paper (De Mendoza et al., 2016),

> genetic counseling and testing (GCT) for hereditary breast and ovarian cancers (HBOC) can inform treatment decisions in survivors. Between 5 to 10% of all breast cancer cases are hereditary. Mutations in BRCA1 and BRCA2 genes are the most commonly identified mutations for hereditary breast and ovarian cancer cases. Unfortunately, not all ethnic groups have benefited equally from GCT. Despite having the highest breast cancer morbidity and mortality rates of all racial groups and also the highest breast cancer incidence rates in women under 40, fewer at-risk African-American women use GCT compared to White women. The underuse of beneficial technologies such as GCT may contribute to enhanced disparate outcomes.
>
> Breast cancer genetics knowledge is one modifiable factor that has been associated with genetic counseling/testing used in diverse populations and studied by researchers.

Researchers assessed breast cancer genetics knowledge with 13 items in which participants had to evaluate whether statements about breast cancer genetics were true or false. The numbers of correct responses were added to create a score ranging from 0–13. Higher scores mean higher breast cancer genetics knowledge. The individual knowledge scores are approximately normally distributed with a mean of 7.78 and standard deviation of 1.61.

1. If 20 women were sampled from the individual scores, what is the sampling distribution of the sample means for those 20 women?
2. What knowledge score must an individual woman receive to be in the 80th percentile?

3. What is the probability that the mean knowledge score is greater than 10?
4. In research, it is often difficult to obtain data on the entire population about which we want to make inferences. Why are we able to study a sample of data from a population that is normally distributed and use the sample statistics to make inferences on the entire population of interest?
5. Suppose you sampled data from a population that was not normally distributed. Would your answer to question 4 change? Explain.

Use these questions as a self-assessment checklist for this chapter:

1. Do you know how to interpret graphs of normal probability distributions?
2. Do you know how to use the standard normal table?
3. Do you know how to find areas under a standard normal curve?
4. Do you know how to find a z-score given the area under the standard normal curve?
5. Can you transform a z-score to an x-value?
6. Can you simulate normal random variables and determine normal probabilities using R?

References

Chakrabarty, D., & Gohain, M. (2015). Application of normal probability distribution in estimating annual maximum and minimum temperature in the context of Assam. *International Research Journal of Mathematics, Engineering and IT, 2*(3), 9–22. http://www.aarf.asia/

Dutta, U. P., Gogoi, P. P., Sengupta, P. P., & Phukon, P. (2018). Time series analysis of temperature and rainfall over Brahmaputra Basin, *Assam. Urban India, 38*(II), 72–84. https://www.niua.org/urban-india

Lockie, R. G., Dawes, J. J., Balfany, K., Gonzales, C. E., Beitzel, M. M., Dulla, J. M. M., & Orr, R. (2018). Physical fitness characteristics that relate to work sample test battery performance in law enforcement recruits. *International Journal of Environmental Research and Public Health, 15*(11), 2477–2489. https://doi.org/ 10.3390/ijerph15112477.

Papadopoulos, A. (2018). Geochemistry and REE content of beach sands along the Atticocycladic coastal zone, Greece. *Geosciences Journal, 22*, 955–973. https://doi.org/10.1007/s12303-018-0004-5

Sommer, D. M., Meiser, S., & Mohammadi, E. (2019). Privacy loss classes: The central limit theorem in differential privacy. *Proceedings on Privacy Enhancing Technologies, 2*, 245–269. https://doi.org/10.2478/popets-2019-0029

Surtado-de-Mendoza, A., Jackson, M., Anderson, L., & Sheppard, V. B. (2016). The role of knowledge on genetic counseling and testing in black cancer survivors at increased risk of carrying a BRCA1/2 mutation. *Journal of Genetic Counseling*, 1–9. https://doi.org/10.1007/s10897-016-9986-1

Twitter (2020). Q4 and Fiscal Year 2020 Letter to Shareholders. https://s22.q4cdn.com/826641620/files/doc_financials/2020/q4/FINAL-Q4'20-TWTR-Shareholder-Letter.pdf

Zhang, C., Hu, X., Sercombe, T., Li, Q., Wu, Z., & Lu, P. (2018). Prediction of ceramic fracture with normal distribution pertinent to grain size. *Acta Materialia, 145*(15), 41–48. https://doi.org/10.1016/j.actamat.2017.11.041

Zhao, S., Hu, F., Ding, X., Zhao, M., Li, C., & Pei, S. (2017). Dataset of tensile strength development of concrete with manufactured sand. *Data in Brief, 11*, 469–472. https://doi.org/10.1016/j.dib.2017.02.043

Figure Credits

Fig. 7.1: Copyright © 2019 by Melpomeni Kalliri. Reprinted with permission.
Fig. 7.3: Copyright © Unsplash/Juliet Furst.
Fig. 7.6: Copyright © 2012 Depositphotos/miflippo.
Fig. 7.8: Copyright © Unsplash/Marvin Meyer.

Fig. 7.9: Copyright © Unsplash/Scott Webb.
Fig. 7.10: Copyright © Unsplash/Luis Quintero.
Fig. 7.11: Copyright © Unsplash/Sudhith Xavier.
Fig. 7.12: Copyright © Unsplash/Trevor Cole.
Fig. 7.16: Copyright © Unsplash/NeONBRAND.
Fig. 7.17: Copyright © Unsplash/Persnickety Prints.
Fig. 7.18: Source: https://commons.wikimedia.org/wiki/File:Gene.png.

PART IV

Statistical Inference

CHAPTER

8

Confidence Intervals

CHAPTER OUTLINE

CHAPTER OBJECTIVES

After you have completed this chapter, you will know how to perform the following operations:

1. Construct confidence intervals for the mean given a large sample.
2. Construct confidence intervals for the mean given a small sample.
3. Construct confidence intervals for the population variance and standard deviation.
4. Construct confidence intervals for the population proportion.
5. Employ R and RStudio to construct various confidence intervals.

Edible flowers such as tulips (*Tulipa fosteriana*), roses (*Rosa*), lavenders (*Lavendula*), and sunflowers (*Helianthus*) are used to make salads, desserts, condiments, and beverages. In addition to their nutritional value, trace levels of toxic elements such as arsenic and cadmium may also be present in these delicacies. Countries such as Brazil do not have maximum allowable limits of such toxic elements in these edible flowers. Brazilian scientists use analytic techniques and confidence intervals to estimate the levels of nutrients as well as toxic elements in these edible flowers (dos Santos, et al., 2018).

FIGURE 8.1 La Vie en Rose

Chapter Vocabulary

- An interval estimate is a range of values used to estimate a population parameter.
- The level of confidence c is the fraction of the time that the constructed confidence interval will contain the true population parameter under repeated sampling.
- The margin of error is the greatest possible distance between the point estimate and the value of the parameter it is estimating.
- A critical value is a value from the random variable's distribution that helps to determine the upper and lower bounds of a parameter's confidence interval.
- If the distribution of a random variable X is approximately normally distributed and $n > 1$, then the random variable $\chi^2 = \frac{(n-1)S^2}{\sigma^2}$ has a χ^2-distribution with n–1 degrees of freedom.
- If the distribution of a random variable X is approximately normal, then the random variable $t = \frac{\overline{x} - \mu}{\frac{s}{\sqrt{n}}}$ has a t-distribution.
- The degrees of freedom are the number of free choices left after a sample statistic has been calculated.
- Meta-analysis combines several studies that address the same research questions.
- A point estimate is a single value estimate of a population parameter.

8.1 Confidence Intervals for the Population Mean: Large Samples

Estimating population parameters is fundamental to the inferential branch of statistics. Previous chapters discussed point estimators such as the sample mean $\overline{x}$, which estimates the population mean μ. However, as illustrated with continuous distributions, the probability that a parameter such as the population mean is exactly equal to an $\overline{x}$ value is zero. This is because the area under a vertical line is theoretically zero. On the other hand, assuming that $\overline{x}$ is close to μ is a reasonable assumption because the sample mean is an unbiased estimator of the population mean.

In this chapter, we focus on the interval of values that are "close" to μ. Such an interval of values is called an interval estimate. An interval estimate is a range of values used to estimate a population parameter.

8.1.1 Estimating Parameters and Margin of Error

To form an interval estimate, start by using the point estimate as the center of the interval on a real line, and then add and subtract a pair of percentages surrounding the estimate. This pair of percentages is called the margin of error. To determine the margin of error, we first need to decide how confident we want to be that the interval estimate contains the population parameter μ. That is, we decide on the level of confidence c.

The level of confidence c is the fraction of the time that the constructed confidence interval will contain the true population parameter under repeated sampling. Keep in mind that the interval may or may not contain the true value of the parameter being estimated.

In one case of the mean, the level of confidence c is the area under the standard normal curve between two critical values $-z_c$ and z_c. The critical values separate statistics that are probable from those that are improbable.

Example:

Assume the level of confidence is c = 95% when estimating the population mean. Determine the critical values.

Answer:

Because the level of confidence is c = 95%, the percentage of the area that lies between $-z_c$ and z_c is 95%. Since the total area under the curve is 100%, and the curve is symmetric, a total of 5% is remaining in the tails. The area to the left of $-z_c$ is 2.5%, and the area to the right of z_c is 2.5%. Look in the body of the standard normal table (Tables 7A and 7B in Appendix A) for .025. The corresponding critical value is $-z_c = -1.96$. The other critical value is $z_c = 1.96$.

The critical value is one of the values used to determine the margin of error. The margin of error is the greatest possible distance between the point estimate and the value of the parameter it is estimating. When estimating a population mean μ if σ is known, the margin of error is

$$E = z_c \sigma_{\bar{x}} = z_c \frac{\sigma}{\sqrt{n}}.$$

However, this equation is valid only under the assumption that the sample is a random sample. Additionally, the population must be normally distributed or the sample size $n \geq 30$ or both.

8.1.2 Confidence Intervals for Population Mean

A margin of error and a point estimate can be used to construct an interval estimate of a population parameter such as μ. This interval estimate is referred to as a confidence interval. A confidence interval for a population mean μ is

$$\bar{x} - E < \mu < \bar{x} + E.$$

Confidence intervals may be constructed both by hand and with software. Both will be illustrated in this chapter. The benefit of calculating it by hand is that it may help you to gain insight into the interpretation of confidence intervals. To construct a confidence interval for μ by hand when σ is known, follow the step-by-step process:

Step 1. Verify that σ is known, the sample is random, and either the population is normally distributed or $n \geq 30$.

Step 2. Determine n and $\overline{x}$.

Step 3. Use the standard normal table (Tables 7A and 7B in Appendix A) to find the critical value z_c that corresponds to the desired level of confidence.

Step 4. Determine the margin of error E.

Step 5. Determine the lower and upper bounds to determine the confidence interval.

$$(\overline{x} - E,\ \overline{x} + E).$$

Example:

In mechanical engineering, tensile strength is a measure of the force required to pull something, such as a rope, wire or structural beam, apart until it breaks. Tensile strength is measured in units of force per unit area such as pounds per square inch (psi) or megapascals, $f_{st,t}$(MPa). Researchers perform an experimental study on tensile strength development of concrete with manufactured sand.

Researchers note that the mean tensile strength of concrete historically has been $\mu = 3.5$ with standard deviation $\sigma = 1.1603$. Tensile strength is also known to have a normal distribution. Five experimenters are working on this research project. Construct a 95% confidence interval for the tensile strength of concrete. A random sample of tensile strength from five specimens are presented in the table below (Zhao et al., 2017). Construct a 95% confidence interval for the mean tensile strength of concrete.

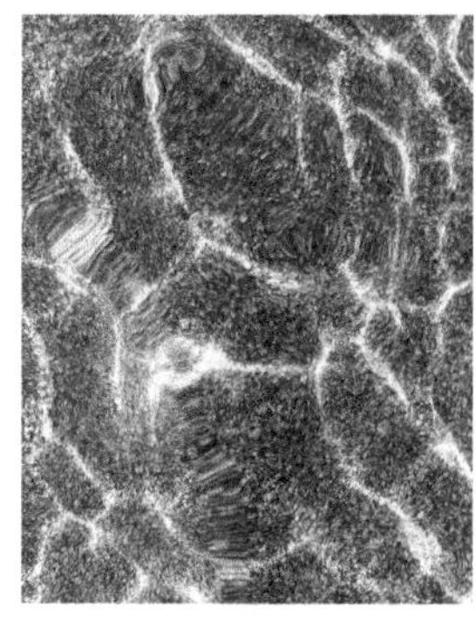

FIGURE 8.2 Magical Waters, Mykonos, Greece

SPECIMEN	*z*-SCORES	TENSILE STRENGTH (MPa)
Specimen 1	−1.0256	2.31
Specimen 2	−0.4740	2.95
Specimen 3	1.6461	5.41
Specimen 4	−0.3964	3.04
Specimen 5	1.2755	4.98

Answer:

The population standard deviation $\sigma = 1.1603$ is known, the sample is random, and the population is normally distributed. The sample size is n = 5, and the sample standard deviation is $\overline{x} = 3.738$. The critical value z_c that corresponds to a 95% confidence interval is 1.96. The margin of error is

$$\begin{aligned} E &= z_c \sigma_{\overline{x}} \\ &= z_c \frac{\sigma}{\sqrt{n}} \\ &= (1.96)\left(\frac{1.1603}{\sqrt{5}}\right) \\ &\approx 1.0170. \end{aligned}$$

The lower bound is

$$\begin{aligned} \overline{x} - E &= 3.783 - 1.0170 \\ &= 2.766, \end{aligned}$$

and the upper bound is

$$\begin{aligned} \overline{x} + E &= 3.783 + 1.0170 \\ &= 4.800. \end{aligned}$$

Therefore, a 95% confidence interval for the mean tensile strength of concrete is (2.766, 4.800). The correct interpretation of this confidence interval is that we are 95% confident that the population mean tensile strength of concrete is between 2.766 and 4.800. That is, after constructing confidence intervals from repeated samples, 95% of the intervals will contain the population mean and 5% will not. Does the interval (2.766, 4.800) contain the true mean tensile strength of concrete? Who knows? We can only say that we are 95% confident that it does.

Note that an incorrect interpretation of the confidence interval is that there is a 95% probability that the mean tensile strength of concrete is in the interval (2.766, 4.800). The probability that the population mean lies in the interval is either zero or one because the population mean either does or does not lie in the interval.

8.1.3 Minimum Sample Size to Estimate Mean

There is a trade-off between the level of confidence and the precision with which a parameter is being estimated. The higher the level of confidence, the less precise and the wider the confidence interval. Ideally, we would want to be 100% confident, but this provides no precision.

One way to improve the precision of an estimate without decreasing the level of confidence is to increase the sample size. This brings us to the question of how large a sample should be in order to guarantee a certain level of confidence. Using algebra, the margin of error formula

$$E = z_c \frac{\sigma}{\sqrt{n}}$$

can be transformed to find the minimum sample size, n.

Given a c-confidence level and a margin of error E, the minimum sample size n needed to estimate the population mean is

$$n = \left(\frac{z_c \sigma}{E}\right)^2.$$

If the population standard deviation σ is unknown, then the sample standard deviation s is an unbiased estimator for σ, provided the preliminary sample is greater than or equal to 30 elements.

Example:

Consider the tensile strength example. How many specimens must be included in the sample to be 90% confident that the sample mean is within 0.02 MPa of the population mean?

Answer:

First, use the standard normal table, Tables 7A and 7B in Appendix A, to determine $z_c = 1.645$. Using $c = 0.90$, $E = 0.25$, and $\sigma = 1.1603$ from the previous example, the minimum sample size is

$$\begin{aligned} n &= \left(\frac{z_c \sigma}{E}\right)^2 \\ &= \left(\frac{1.645 \cdot 1.1603}{0.25}\right)^2 \\ &\approx 58.2898. \end{aligned}$$

Always round up to the next convenient number. Therefore, a minimum of $n = 59$ specimens is needed. Note that $n = 59$ is a minimum. However, the larger the sample, the better the estimate.

8.1.4 Exercises

Understanding Concepts

1. Name two types of estimators for a parameter.

2. What is a range of values used to estimate a population parameter?

3. In a continuous distribution, what is the probability that the sample mean is exactly equal to the population mean? Explain your answer.

4. What is the level of confidence of a confidence interval?

True or false? In Exercises 5–8, determine whether the statement is true or false. If it is false, rewrite it as a true statement.

5. An interval estimator and a point estimator serve the same purpose.

6. It is helpful to construct a confidence interval for the sample mean, $\overline{x}$.

7. When calculating the minimum sample size to estimate the population mean, you should always round up.

8. A 95% confidence interval for the population mean μ indicates that the probability that the interval contains the population mean is .95.

Skill Building

9. We have a simple random sample of the systolic blood pressure (measured in mm Hg) of 20 individuals. The recorded readings are 120, 165, 133, 118, 110, 133, 125, 147, 89, 102, 111, 128, 140, 155, 156, 170, 131, 101, 112, and 104. What is the sample mean? What is the standard error of the mean?

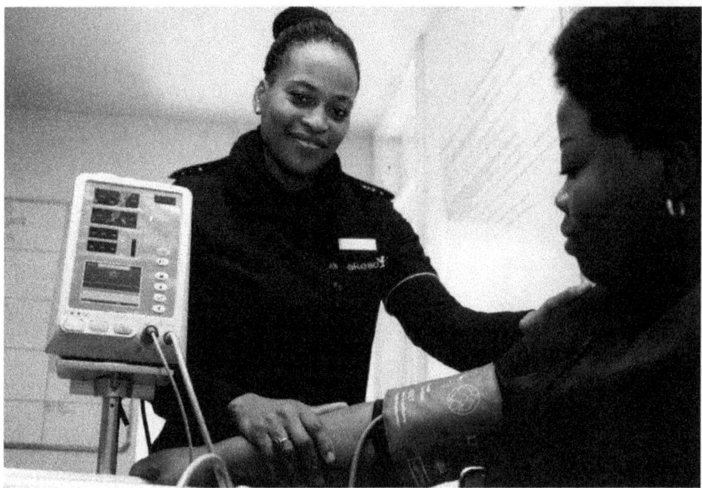

FIGURE 8.3 Measuring Blood Pressure

10. The standard deviation for the amount of time college students spend online per day is 5.5 hours. This number is based on a simple random sample of 36 college students. What is the standard error of the mean?

11. Find the critical values for the following levels of confidence:

    a. 95%

    b. 80%

    c. 65%

12. Would a 95% confidence interval produce a smaller or larger confidence interval than a 65%? Explain your answer.

Use the following to answer questions 13–20:

> The amount of time (in minutes) it takes a simple random sample of 25 students in a basic statistics class to finish the final exam are: 25, 60, 120, 130, 40, 45, 60, 66, 101, 90, 88, 31, 60, 62, 26, 20, 100, 85, 90, and 23.

13. What is the sample mean?

14. What is the standard deviation?

15. What is the standard error of the mean?

16. What is the margin of error?

17. Provide an 80% confidence interval for the mean.

18. Provide a 99% confidence interval for the mean. Was this interval larger or smaller than the interval you calculated in Exercise 17? Why does that make sense?

19. Provide ways to reduce the margin of error in Exercise 16.

20. What sample size would you need to have a margin of error less than 5 based on an 80% confidence interval?

Extending Concepts

21. A physics student takes repeated measurements of mass on a scale for which the standard deviation is known to be 1.0 g. How many measurements are needed to get a result within a 0.1 g margin of error for a 95% level of confidence?

22. Use Table 7.A and 7.B from Appendix A to find the confidence level when a critical z is chosen to be $z_c = 1.5$.

23. Which R command can you use to obtain the critical value z_c corresponding to the confidence level c?

24. Use R to calculate the critical value z_c corresponding to a confidence level of 92%.

25. What is a point estimate?

8.2 Confidence Intervals for the Population Mean: Small Samples

In the previous section, the population standard deviation was known. Since in many real-life situations the population standard deviation σ is unknown, it is replaced by the sample standard deviation s. If the sample size is large enough, then $s \approx \sigma$, and the central limit theorem implies that the distribution of

$$\frac{\overline{x} - \mu}{\frac{s}{\sqrt{n}}}$$

is approximately standard normal. However, if the sample size is small, less than 30, then the above formulation is a random variable that has a *t*-distribution.

8.2.1 The *t*-Distribution

The *t*-distribution was developed by W. S. Gosset in 1908. Gosset was an employee of the Guinness brewery. Because the company would not allow him to publish his important work in his own name, he used the pseudonym "Student" (Box, 1981). This is why the *t*-distribution is also known as the Student's *t*-distribution. It is defined as follows. If the distribution of a random variable X is approximately normally distributed, then the random variable

$$t = \frac{\overline{x} - \mu}{\frac{s}{\sqrt{n}}}$$

has a *t*-distribution. It satisfies the following properties:

- The mean, median, and mode of the *t*-distribution are equal.
- The *t*-distribution is bell-shaped and symmetric about the mean.
- The total area under the curve of a *t*-distribution is 1.
- The tails of a *t*-distribution are "heavier" than that of a standard normal distribution, which means the vertical distance between the distribution and the horizontal axis is greater in the *t*-distribution.
- The standard deviation of the *t*-distribution varies with the sample size.
- The *t*-distribution is a family of curves, each uniquely defined by a parameter called the degrees of freedom.
- The degrees of freedom are the number of free choices left after a sample statistic has been calculated.
- When the *t*-distribution is used to estimate a population mean, the degrees of freedom are determined by subtracting 1 from the sample size, $df = n - 1$.
- As the degrees of freedom increase the *t*-distribution looks more and more like a standard normal distribution. That is, the *t*-distribution approaches a normal distribution.
- After 30 degrees of freedom, the *t*-distribution is close to the standard normal distribution.

We use t_c to denote critical values of the *t*-distribution.

8.2.2 Determining Critical Values of the *t*-Distribution

Recall that in the standard normal table, Tables 7A and 7B in Appendix A, the critical values were a combination of the first column and first row. In the *t*-distribution table (Table 8 in

Appendix A), the critical values are in the body of the table. The first column represents the degrees of freedom. The first three rows in the header represent the levels of confidence and the areas in the tail of the distribution, respectively.

Example:

Recall the tensile strength example in Section 7.3.1 where researchers perform an experimental study on the tensile strength of concrete. The mean tensile strength of concrete has historically been $\mu = 3.5$. Consider a modified tensile strength example in which the population standard deviation σ is unknown. Find the critical value t_c for a 95% confidence level when the sample size is five.

FIGURE 8.4 It's a Trap

Answer:

Because $n = 5$, the degrees of freedom are

$$df = n - 1 = 5 - 1 = 4.$$

According to the table for the *t*-distribution (Table 8 in Appendix A), the critical value $t_c = 2.776$.

Interpretation:
For a *t*-distribution with a curve with 4 degrees of freedom, 95% of the area under the curve lives between $t = \pm 2.776$.

In the previous example, the degrees of freedom were found in the table. If the degrees of freedom were some value not in the table, choose the closest value that is less than the value needed. This choice leads to a wider confidence interval and a greater level of confidence.

8.2.3 Constructing a Confidence Interval Using the *t*-Distribution

To construct a small sample confidence interval for μ by hand when σ is unknown, follow the step-by-step process:

Step 1. Verify that $n < 30$ and the population is normally distributed.

Step 2. Determine the values s and $\overline{x}$ from the sample.

Step 3. Calculate the degrees of freedom $n - 1$.

Step 4. Use the *t*-distribution table (Table 8 in Appendix A) to find the critical value t_c that corresponds to the desired level of confidence.

Step 5. Determine the margin of error $E = t_c \dfrac{s}{\sqrt{n}}$.

Step 6. Determine the lower and upper bounds to determine the confidence interval

$$(\overline{x} - E,\ \overline{x} + E).$$

Example:

Consider the modified tensile strength example in which the population standard deviation is unknown, and construct a 95% confidence interval for the population mean μ.

SPECIMEN	TENSILE STRENGTH (MPa)
Specimen 1	2.31
Specimen 2	2.95
Specimen 3	5.41
Specimen 4	3.04
Specimen 5	4.98

Answer:

Because σ is unknown, the sample is random, and the population is normally distributed, the t-distribution is the appropriate distribution. The margin of error for the 95% confidence interval is

$$\begin{aligned} E &= t_c \frac{s}{\sqrt{n}} \\ &= (2.776)\left(\frac{1.3680}{\sqrt{5}}\right) \\ &\approx 1.6983. \end{aligned}$$

The lower bound is

$$\begin{aligned} \bar{x} - E &= 3.783 - 1.6983 \\ &= 2.0847, \end{aligned}$$

and the upper bound is

$$\begin{aligned} \bar{x} + E &= 3.783 + 1.6983 \\ &= 5.4813. \end{aligned}$$

A 95% confidence interval for the mean tensile strength of concrete is (2.0847, 5.4813).

Interpretation:
We are 95% confident that the population mean tensile strength of concrete is between 2.0847 and 5.4813. Comparing this interval to the interval created using the standard normal distribution, the latter is more precise for a given level of confidence.

FIGURE 8.5 Flowers All Around

When should we use the standard normal distribution and when should we use the *t*-distribution? The answer to this question falls in one of these mutually exclusive six cases:

Case 1:

When the population is normal with σ known, then the standard normal distribution can be used to construct the confidence interval irrespective of the sample size.

Case 2:

When the population is not normal with σ known and $n > 30$, then the standard normal distribution can be used to construct the confidence interval.

Case 3:

If σ is unknown and $n \geq 30$, the standard normal distribution can be used to construct the confidence interval irrespective of the distribution of the population.

Case 4:

If σ is unknown, $n < 30$, and the population is normal, then the *t*-distribution can be used to construct the confidence interval for the mean.

Case 5:

If σ is unknown, $n < 30$, and the population is not normal, then neither the standard normal distribution nor the *t*-distribution is appropriate. An appropriate choice would be to use a distribution-free method. These methods are referred to as *nonparametric* methods, which are found in Chapter 12 of this textbook.

Case 6:

If σ is known, $n < 30$, and the population is not normal, then neither the standard normal distribution nor the *t*-distribution is appropriate. An appropriate choice would be to use a distribution-free method. These methods are referred to as nonparametric methods which are found in the last chapter of this textbook.

8.2.4 Exercises

Understanding Concepts

1. What is the difference between the *t*-distribution and a student's *t*-distribution?

2. How do the tails of a *t*-distribution compare to that of a normal distribution?

3. Which parameter(s) define a *t*-distribution?

4. Do the same parameters define both a *t*-distribution and a normal distribution?

5. If the population standard deviation is unknown, the sample size is less than 30, and the population is normally distributed, then which distribution can be used to construct a confidence interval for the population mean, the normal or t-distribution? Explain your answer.

6. To determine the margin of error when constructing a confidence interval for the population mean when using a t-distribution, which values are multiplied?

True or false? In Exercises 7–12, determine whether the statement is true or false. If it is false, rewrite it as a true statement.

7. A t-distribution is a continuous distribution.

8. There is one difference between a t-distribution and a student's t-distribution.

9. When referring to a t-distribution, a sample is considered small when it contains less than 20 elements.

10. A t-distribution is a distribution that can be represented by a graph.

11. When constructing a confidence interval for the mean, if the population standard deviation is unknown, the sample is random, and the population is normally distributed, then the t-distribution is the correct distribution to use when computing the margin of error.

12. If neither the t-distribution nor the normal distribution is applicable, one can use nonparametric statistics to construct a confidence interval.

Skill Building

13. If you want to construct a confidence interval for the population mean from a simple random sample with measurements on five individuals, how many degrees of freedom are there for the critical value of the t-distribution?

14. For small samples sizes, is the t-distribution skewed or symmetric? Provide a graph of such a t-distribution for this situation.

15. Is the t-distribution a continuous or discrete distribution?

16. Provide the critical values for the t-distribution based on the following information:

    a. 95% confidence level and a sample size of 9

    b. 99.8% confidence level and sample size of 12

    c. 80% confidence level and a sample size of 15

17. When the sample size is large, a t-distribution is approximately what distribution?

18. The average number of movies that an SRS of 16 people watch per month is 10. Find an 80% confidence interval based on a sample standard deviation of 2.

19. Assume you have an SRS of 100 individuals in which the distribution of their height (in inches) is approximately normal. Would you base a confidence interval of the mean on the *t*-distribution or normal distribution? Explain your answer.

20. Are confidence intervals for the mean used to provide a range of values for the sample mean or the population mean? Why?

Extending Concepts

21. A physics student makes repeated measurements of mass on a scale with an unknown standard deviation. Assuming that measurements are normally distributed, are 10 measurements enough to obtain a margin of error of at most 0.08 g? Assume that the sample standard deviation for the sample is 0.1 g, and that the confidence level is 95%.

22. Use Table 8 to find the critical value of a *t*-distribution corresponding to an 85% confidence level for an experiment repeated eight times. Assume the population has a normal distribution.

23. Which R command can you use to obtain the critical value(s) of a *t*-distribution that corresponds to the confidence level, *c*, in an experiment that is repeated a small number of times, *n*? Assume that the population has a normal distribution.

24. Use R to calculate the critical values for a *t*-distribution that corresponds to a confidence level of 92% in an experiment with 10 degrees of freedom.

25. How big is the sample size for which the critical value(s) of a *t*-distribution is identical to that of the standard normal distribution to three significant digits, and at the 95% level of confidence? Use Table 8 and Tables 7A and 7B to find the answer.

8.3 Confidence Intervals for the Population Variance and Standard Deviation

We now consider the normal distribution of random variable X with mean μ and variance σ^2. Assume that both μ and σ^2 are unknown. Then

$$\chi^2 = \frac{\Sigma(x - \bar{x})^2}{\sigma^2} = \frac{(n-1)S^2}{\sigma^2}$$

has a χ^2-distribution with $(n - 1)$ degrees of freedom. The Greek letter χ is pronounced “kaai,” as in “kite.”

8.3.1 The Chi-Square Distribution

The chi-square distribution is a skewed-right distribution that is used to form confidence intervals for the population variance and standard deviation. If the distribution of a random variable X is approximately normally distributed and $n > 1$, then the random variable

$$\chi^2 = \frac{(n-1)S^2}{\sigma^2}$$

has a χ^2-distribution. It satisfies the following properties:

- All values of χ^2 are greater than or equal to 0.
- The χ^2-distribution is a family of curves, and each is uniquely determined by the degrees of freedom.
- A confidence interval for σ^2 is formed using the χ^2-distribution with degrees of freedom equal to one less than the sample size, $df = n - 1$.
- The total area under the χ^2-distribution curve equals 1.
- The χ^2-distribution is skewed right.
- As the degrees of freedom increase, the χ^2-distribution approaches a normal distribution.

In statistics, the variance and standard deviation of a random variable are just as important as the mean. There are many real-life applications that involve estimating variability. For example, in a meta-analysis study, researchers wanted to estimate the between-study variability (Veroniki et al., 2016). Meta-analysis combines several studies that address the same research questions. Therefore, variability is present in such studies due to the differences in how each study was conducted.

FIGURE 8.6 The Magic of Learning

For example, when products such as ventilators are manufactured, it is important to keep the variation of the diameters of the parts as small as possible so that they will fit together properly. In pharmaceutical companies, the variance and standard deviation of the ingredients of the medication need to be small so that dosage is correct.

Because IQ tests are normally distributed, we can construct a confidence interval for the population standard deviation and variance. This procedure starts with determining the critical value that corresponds to a given level of confidence.

8.3.2 Determining Critical Values and the Chi-Square Distribution

Confidence intervals for the mean are constructed with one critical value. Because the χ^2-distribution is not symmetric, confidence intervals for variances and standard deviations consist of two critical values. There is a left-tail critical value χ^2_L and a right-tail critical value χ^2_R.

The critical values from the chi-square distribution can be found using software or a X^2-distribution table. The first column of Table 9 contains the degrees of freedom, and the first row contains the area to the left of the the chi-square random variable X. In Table 9 of Appendix A, $\propto = 1 - c$ and qchisq($\propto$, df) is the chi-square random variable χ with degrees of freedom (df) that has area $\propto$ to its left.

Example:

Determine the critical values X_L^2 and X_R^2 for a 99% confidence interval when the sample size is 30.

Answer:

Because the sample size is 30, $df = n - 1 = 30 - 1 = 29$. Because it is a 99% confidence interval, $c = .99$. The area to the left of X_L^2 is determined by $\frac{1+c}{2} = \frac{1+0.99}{2} = .995$, and the area to the right of X_R^2 is determined by $\frac{1-c}{2} = \frac{1-0.99}{2} = 0.005$. From the X^2-distribution table, the critical values are $X_L^2 = 13.121$ and $X_R^2 = 52.336$.

8.3.3 Confidence Intervals for Variance and Standard Deviation

Constructing confidence intervals for variances and standard deviations is a slightly different procedure from those for the population mean. Recall that confidence intervals for the mean consist of a point estimate, critical value, and a standard error. The point estimate for the population variance σ^2 is the sample variance s^2. The procedure for constructing confidence intervals by hand for the variance and standard deviation of a normal population is as follows:

Step 1. Verify that the population has a normal distribution.

Step 2. Determine the sample size n and the degrees of freedom $df = n - 1$.

Step 3. Determine the sample variance s^2.

Step 4. Use the X^2-distribution table (Table 9 in Appendix A) to determine the critical values X_L^2 and X_R^2 that correspond to the given level of confidence c and the degrees of freedom.

Step 5. The confidence interval for the population variance σ^2 is

$$\left(\frac{(n-1)s^2}{X_R^2}, \frac{(n-1)s^2}{X_L^2} \right).$$

Step 6. The confidence interval for the population standard deviation σ is

$$\left(\sqrt{\frac{(n-1)s^2}{X_R^2}}, \sqrt{\frac{(n-1)s^2}{X_L^2}} \right).$$

8.3.4 Exercises

Understanding Concepts

1. Which distribution would you use to form confidence intervals for the population variance and standard deviation?

2. How would you describe the shape of a χ^2-distribution with $n - 1$ degrees of freedom?

3. Which parameter(s) uniquely define a χ^2-distribution?

4. What are the possible values of a random variable that has a χ^2-distribution?

5. When using a χ^2-distribution to construct a confidence interval for the standard deviation or variance, how many critical values will you need to compute?

True or false? In Exercises 6–10, determine whether the statement is true or false. If it is false, rewrite it as a true statement.

6. There is no difference in the procedures for constructing a confidence interval for population variances and for population means.

7. When constructing a confidence interval for a population standard deviation using a χ^2-distribution, you should verify that the population is normally distributed.

8. The χ^2-distribution table can be used to determine the critical values corresponding to confidence intervals for the population standard deviation.

9. To construct a confidence interval for the population variance, first determine the positive square roots of both the lower bound and upper bound of the confidence interval.

10. The degrees of freedom of a χ^2-distribution are functions of the sample size.

Skill Building

11. How many parameters are needed to draw a chi-square distribution? Decide on a value for these parameters and draw a chi-square distribution of your choice.

12. Determine the critical values for a chi-square distribution based on a confidence level of 99% with the following factors:

    a. Degrees of freedom of 10

    b. Degrees of freedom of 1

    c. A sample size of 50

13. Compute the critical values for a chi-square distribution for the lower bound and upper bounds of a confidence interval for the variance and standard deviation based on the following levels of confidence with a sample size of 20:

    a. 90%

    b. 65%

    c. 80%

14. The sample standard deviation for the amount of time a random sample of 18 students sleeps per night is 6 hours. Provide a confidence interval for the population variance and standard deviation.

15. Is the confidence interval you computed in the previous exercise symmetric around the estimate? Explain why or why not.

16. The 95% confidence interval for the population variance of the amount of money students spend each week in U.S. dollars is (20.38, 80.87). What is the 95% confidence interval for the population standard deviation?

FIGURE 8.7 Student Life

Use the following information to answer questions 17–20:

> Data are provided on the time it takes for 17 random students to travel from their home to campus (in minutes): 3, 45, 10, 5, 6, 7, 25, 30, 20, 21, 43, 25, 20, 18, 30, 35, 45.

17. Provide some sample statistics.

18. What distribution would be used to compute a confidence interval for the standard deviation? Provide the distribution along with its appropriate parameters.

19. What is the 95% confidence interval for the standard deviation?

20. What is the 80% confidence interval for the variance?

Extending Concepts

21. Why do we need the two critical values, left and right, to find the margin of error for estimates of some distributions? Explain your answer.

22. What is the probability for obtaining $P(-1 < x < -0.95)$ when x is sampled from a chi-squared distribution with 4 degrees of freedom?

23. Use Table 9 to find the right-tail critical value, given that the left-tail critical value approximately equals 6.6 for a 90% level of confidence.

24. Can the chi-square distribution be used to estimate the margin of error for the variance of a distribution that is not normal?

25. A sample containing 25 elements is selected from a normal distribution. A 95% confidence interval for the population variance is (1.2, 5.6). What is the confidence interval for the corresponding population standard deviations?

8.4 Confidence Intervals for the Population Proportion

Many statistical studies involve finding a proportion of the population that has a certain characteristic. We introduced proportions in Chapter 6 as a parameter p that defines Bernoulli and binomial distributions. We will now return our focus to the parameter p.

8.4.1 Point Estimate for Population Proportion

If a random variable X represents the number of successes in n trials, then an unbiased estimator of the population proportion p *is* $\hat{p} = \frac{x}{n}$.

Example:

Consider the Gullah Geechee example in Section 6.2. A total of 109 peer-reviewed publications about Gullah were identified using the Web of Science database. Approximately 40% of the peer-reviewed publications focused on health science, while the remaining 60% centered on the social sciences. If a random sample of 80 publications are selected, and 55 focus on the social sciences, determine a point estimate for the population proportion of publications that focus on Gullah in the social sciences.

Answer:

Using $n = 80$ and $x = 55$,

$$\begin{aligned}\hat{p} &= \frac{x}{n} \\ &= \frac{55}{80} \\ &= .6875.\end{aligned}$$

Therefore, a point estimate for the population proportion of publications in the database that focus on Gullah in the social sciences is 68.75%.

8.4.2 Confidence Intervals for Population Proportion

The procedure for constructing a confidence interval for a population proportion p is similar to constructing a confidence interval for a population mean. Analogous to a confidence interval for the population mean, the sample size n needs to be large enough so that the sampling distribution of the statistic $\hat{p}$ is approximately normal. This information is needed in order to determine the critical value. There are several research-based rules to help determine a sufficient sample size. For simplicity, we will use a commonly used rule that states both np and $n(1 - p)$ must be greater than 5. The procedure for constructing confidence intervals by hand for a population proportion is as follows:

Step 1. Determine the values x and n, where x is the number of successes and n is the sample size.

Step 2. Determine the point estimate $\hat{p} = \frac{x}{n}$.

Step 3. Verify that the sampling distribution of $\hat{p}$ can be approximated by a normal distribution by verifying that both $n\hat{p} \geq 5$ and $n(1 - \hat{p}) = n\hat{p} \geq 5$.

Step 4. Determine the margin of error $E = z_c\sqrt{\frac{\hat{p}\hat{q}}{n}}$.

Step 5. The confidence interval for the population proportion is $(\hat{p} - E, \hat{p} + E)$.

Example:

Consider the Gullah Geechee example from Section 6.2. A total of 109 peer-reviewed publications about Gullah were identified using the Web of Science database. Approximately 40% of the peer-reviewed publications focused on health science, while the remaining 60% centered on the social sciences. If a random sample of 80 publications are selected, and 55 focus on the social sciences, construct a 95% confidence interval for the population proportion of publications that focus on Gullah in the social sciences.

Answer:

From the previous example, $\hat{p} = \frac{x}{n} = \frac{55}{80} = 0.6875$. So, the point estimate for the proportion of publications that do not focus on Gullah in the social sciences is $\hat{q} = 1 - \hat{p} = 1 - 0.6875 = 0.3125$.

Using $n = 80$, verify that $n\hat{p} = (80)(0.6875) = 55 \geq 5$ and $n\hat{q} = (80)(0.3125) = 25 \geq 5$. From the standard normal table (Tables 7A and 7B in Appendix A), $z_c = 1.96$. The margin of error is

$$\begin{aligned} E &= z_c\sqrt{\frac{\hat{p}\hat{q}}{n}} \\ &= 1.96\sqrt{\frac{(0.6875)(0.3125)}{80}} \\ &\approx .1016. \end{aligned}$$

Using the lower and upper bound formulas $(\hat{p} - E, \hat{p} + E)$, the 95% confidence interval is $(0.6875 - 0.1016, 0.6875 + 0.1016)$, which is (0.5859, 0.7891).

Interpretation:
With 95% confidence, we can say that the population proportion of publications that focus on Gullah in the social sciences is between 0.5859 and 0.7891.

8.4.3 Minimum Sample Size to Estimate Proportion

As with the case of the population mean, one way to increase the precision of a confidence interval for the population proportion without decreasing the level of confidence is to increase the sample size. To determine a minimum sample size to estimate the population proportion p, use the formula that is derived from the margin of error, E. That is, use algebra to solve $E = z_c\sqrt{\frac{\hat{p}\hat{q}}{n}}$ for n, the minimum sample size to estimate p given a c-confidence level and a margin of error E,

$$n = \hat{p}\hat{q}\left(\frac{z_c}{E}\right)^2.$$

Note that this formula assumes that there are preliminary estimates of $\hat{p}$ and $\hat{q}$. Otherwise, assume both equal 0.05.

Example:

Consider the Gullah Geechee example from Section 6.2. Suppose we want to construct a 90% confidence interval for the proportion of publications that focus on Gullah in the social sciences. Determine the minimum sample size needed to be accurate within 15% of the population proportion.

Answer:

The preliminary estimates, $\hat{p} = \frac{X}{n} = \frac{55}{80} = 0.6875$ and $\hat{q} = 1 - \hat{p} = 0.3125$ were calculated previously. From the standard normal table, $z_c = 1.645$. Therefore,

$$n = \hat{p}\hat{q}\left(\frac{z_c}{E}\right)^2$$

$$= (0.6875)(0.3125)\left(\frac{1.645}{.15}\right)^2$$

$$\approx 25.8388.$$

Always round up to the nearest convenient number, 26.

Interpretation:
We would need a sample of at least 26 to be accurate with 15% when forming a 95% confidence interval.

8.4.4 Exercises

Understanding Concepts

1. What is standard notation for the population proportion?

2. When constructing a confidence interval for a population proportion, p, the sample size, n, needs to be large enough so that the sampling distribution of what statistic can be approximated by which distribution?

3. When constructing a confidence interval for a population proportion, p, which two formulas are commonly used to determine the necessary sample size?

4. What is one way to increase the precision of a confidence interval for the population proportion without decreasing the level of confidence?

5. If a random variable X represents the number of successes in n Bernoulli trials, then what is an unbiased estimator of the population proportion, p?

6. What is the equation for the proportion of failures?

True or false? In Exercises 7–13, determine whether the statement is true or false. If it is false, rewrite it as a true statement.

7. The confidence interval for a population proportion has a minimum sample size requirement to ensure that the statistic $\hat{p}$ has an approximately normal distribution.

8. The sampling distribution of the statistic $\hat{p}$, the sample proportion, is approximately normal.

9. The procedure for constructing a confidence interval for the population proportion is analogous to constructing a confidence interval for the population mean.

10. You will never need to construct a confidence interval for the sample proportion, $\hat{p}$.

11. After constructing a 95% confidence interval for a population proportion, you can say that you are 95% confident that your confidence interval contains the population proportion.

12. After constructing a 95% confidence interval for a population proportion, you can say that there is a .95 probability that your confidence interval contains the population proportion.

13. A confidence interval is a type of statistical estimator.

Skill Building

14. A random sample of 150 students finds that 10 are math majors. What is the sample estimate of the overall proportion that are math majors?

FIGURE 8.8 The World of Mathematics

15. What is the standard error of the sample proportion in Exercise 14?

16. Provide a 90% confidence interval for the true proportion of students who are math majors based on the information provided in Exercises 14 and 15.

17. Suppose we need a minimal margin of error of .002 to estimate the true population proportion of people who will vote in the next Spanish general election. Using a 90% level of confidence, how many people in Spain would we need to sample, assuming we do not know the sample proportion?

18. If you estimate that the sample proportion of people that vote in the next Spanish general election is 0.7, would your answer to Exercise 17 change? If so, how?

FIGURE 8.9 The Power of Vote

19. Suppose a sample proportion of American students who attend a university outside of their home state is 0.3 (based on a sample size of 90). Compute a 90% confidence interval for the true proportion of students who attend a university outside of their home state.

20. Would the confidence interval you computed in Exercise 19 be larger, smaller, or remain the same, if you changed the level of confidence to 95%?

FIGURE 8.10 McGill University, Montreal, Canada

Extending Concepts

21. A die that is supposed to be fair is rolled 200 times and the 6 face appears 33 times. Find a confidence interval for the probability of getting a 6 at the 95% confidence level.

22. How many times do you need to flip a supposedly fair coin to obtain approximately equal probabilities for heads and tails such that the margin of error for the probability for getting heads is at most 0.01 for a 95% confidence interval?

23. Which sample size would reduce an estimated margin of error by one-half for the same level of confidence?

24. Is a more narrow confidence interval for estimating a population proportion obtained by increasing or decreasing the confidence level? Is it obtained by increasing or decreasing the sample size? Explain your answer.

25. A 99% confidence interval for the population proportion of obtaining heads when flipping a coin 200 times is (0.54, 0.72). Calculate the point estimate for the population proportion.

8.5 R and RStudio

8.5.1 Programming Assignments

Exercise 8.1

Sometimes measuring a whole population is practically impossible, although in principle such measurement makes sense. Many times, the population is simply too large, so we have to rely on a random sample data in order to estimate some population parameters of interest. Because we do not have access to every element of the population, we cannot know exactly the mean or the standard deviation of the population. Instead, we obtain more or less precise estimates based on the available samples.

The package `MASS` contains functions and data sets to support Venables and Ripley's (2002) book *Modern Applied Statistics with S* (Springer-Verlag). The data frame `survey` in the MASS package has the outcome of a survey of students at the University of Adelaide.

Load the survey data set, and write a few paragraphs describing the data. How many records are there? What data were recorded for each student? Evaluate the quality of the data just by glancing over it. Do you believe that these data are representative for the whole university student population, Australian student population, or global higher education student population?

The `MASS` package comes installed with your R version, but it needs to be pre-loaded into workspace before use.

```
library(MASS)
head(survey)
help(survey)
```

Exercise 8.2

This exercise refers to the data set loaded for Exercise 8.1. It is impossible for us to know the mean university students' height. However, we get an idea about it because this was one of the questions in the survey. The sample mean that we get by using the function `mean()` serves as a good point estimate.

Find the sample mean height, and be careful that some records are missing a value for the height. You will need to filter out the missing values by using the `na.rm` option. What exactly does this option do for the `mean()` function?

Exercise 8.3

This exercise refers to the data set loaded for Exercise 8.1. How accurate is the point estimate of the mean height you obtained in Exercise 8.2? We can estimate a confidence interval because we make some assumptions regarding the data.

```
options(digits=4)
```

First, we believe that the mean we calculated has a normal distribution, and if we bother to collect more samples from the population, the corresponding means will be part of this distribution. The central limit theorem supports this assumption. Next, we want to find the interval that contains a certain large amount of our result, let's say 95%. We begin by looking at the standard normal distribution and find *zc1*, the value of the random variable for which we have $\alpha = 2.5\%$ of the population to the left of it, and *zc2*, the value for which 2.5% of the population is at its right. This means that 95% of the population is in the interval $zc1 \leq z \leq zc2$. The function *qnorm()* is exactly what we need because it gives us the 2.5th and 97.5th percentiles of the standard normal distribution.

```
c = 95
a = (1-c/100)/2
zc1 = qnorm(a)
zc2 = qnorm(1-a)
```

The second assumption that we can make is to use some value for the standard deviation σ for our population. This might be either well known or given to us. According to the central limit theorem, the standard deviation for the sample means is $\sigma / \sqrt{n}$. This means that we can write $\overline{x} = \mu + z\sigma / \sqrt{n}$, expressing the fact that the distribution of the sample means is a translated and scaled version of the standard normal distribution. Therefore, with 95% confidence, or whatever other level of confidence c we want, the population mean μ is estimated to be in the interval calculated in this R program:

```
height.response = na.omit(survey$Height)
n = length(height.response)
xbar = mean(height.response)
sigma = 9.48  # this is an assumption
xbar + sigma/sqrt(n)*c(zc1, zc2)
```

```
## [1] 171.1 173.7
```

Could you have obtained this result directly by calculating `qnorm(0.025, mean = xbar, sd = ...)`, for example? Verify that you get the same result. Explain.

The bottom line is that the mean height that our sample provides is 172.4, and we are about 95% sure that the true mean height of the population is somewhere between 171.1 and 173.7. In what situation would we be 100% sure?

Exercise 8.4

The package `TeachingDemos` contains a number of useful functions that help understanding of various concepts. In this library, the function `z.test()` will test a hypothesis about the mean of some data, assuming that the standard deviation is known.

Install, load, and learn how to use the `z.test()` function. Execute this function on the height data set you use in the previous exercises, and verify that the results are consistent. Change the confidence level to 99%, and report how the results change.

Exercise 8.5

Our knowledge of the parameters of the population under study will improve if we are able to increase the size of our sample, to the limit that we will have perfect knowledge about the population if we can measure ALL individuals, which might be impossible, of course. However, if our target is to achieve a reasonable margin of error at a given confidence level, what is the minimum sample size that is required to achieve this goal?

Assuming a known standard deviation σ of the student height survey (see Exercises 8.1, 8.2, and 8.3), find the minimum size of the sample needed to achieve a 1.2 centimeters margin of error at a 95% confidence level. Use the equation: $\Delta x = z_{\alpha/2}\sigma / \sqrt{n}$ to get n. Use the function `qnorm()` to find the corresponding z for the given confidence level. Package this calculation in a function that has three arguments: the standard deviation, the target margin of error, and the confidence level, and returns the requested sample size (it should be an integer, so you have to round it up).

Exercise 8.6

The distribution of the sample means is normal because the sample mean can be interpreted as a weighted sum of identical normal random variables, and we know that the sum of normal random variables is in turn normal. The variance, though, is the sum of squares of normal random variables and does not have a normal distribution. A simple reason for that is that the variance, unlike a normal random variable, cannot have negative values. The sum of m squared of independent standard normal random variables is called a chi-square distribution with m degrees of freedom. The goal of the next two exercises is to explore this continuous distribution. Mathematically we write that:

$$V = X_1^2 + X_2^2 + \cdots X_m^2 \sim \chi^2_{(m)}.$$

The symbol $\sim$ means "the density of this random variable is .... ." As usual in R, all functions that have to do with this distribution are written as `*chisq()`, where `*` stands for any of `d`, `p`, `q`, or `r`, to work with the density, the cumulative function, quantiles or random variates, respectively.

Let's see a graph of the chi-square distribution.

```
x = seq(0,20, length.out = 100)
plot(x, dchisq(x, 7), 'l', main="Chi-Square distribution")
grid()
```

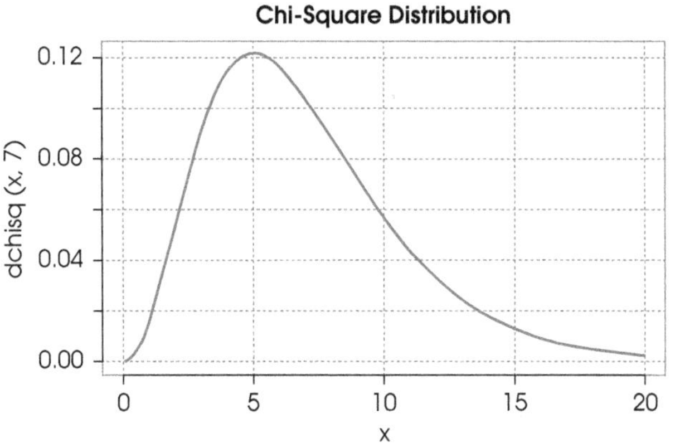

FIGURE 8.11 Chi-Square Distribution Graph

This distribution starts from the origin, has a maximum value, and then decreases slowly.

Represent on the same plot the graphs for two more distributions, say for 10 and 15 degrees of freedom, and demonstrate what happens with the maximum, the mean, and the standard deviation for this distribution when the number of degrees of freedom increases.

Exercise 8.7

Draw the plot of the chi-square distribution with 7 degrees of freedom. Like a normal distribution, it seems that the most values in this distribution appear around a value in which the distribution has a maximum, but unlike a normal distribution the chi-square does not have equal numbers of populations to the right and to the left of the maximum. The chi-square distribution is not symmetrical.

If we are interested to define a level of confidence and find an interval where most values are concentrated, we need to distinguish between left and right critical values, because chi-square lacks symmetry.

Use the function `qchisq( ..., df = 7)` to calculate the value of x_L, such that 5% of the population is smaller, and of $x_{R,}$ for which 5% of the population has values greater that x_R. Therefore, we show that 90% of the population is concentrated in the interval $2.17 < x < 14.1$.

Exercise 8.8

The idea of confidence intervals stems from the fact that the random variable

$$Z = \frac{\frac{1}{n}\sum_{i}^{n} X_i - \mu}{\sigma / \sqrt{n}}$$

is a standard normal variable as long as the sample size n is large enough In practice, this means $n > 30$. Random variables X_i are identical and can have any distribution. The standard deviation of Z is given and fixed. This is a reasonable assumption for a large n, but not so for a smaller n. Instead, the standard deviation is the square root of the variance, which, as a sum of squared identical normal random variables, has a chi-square distribution. This seemingly complicated situation is summarized by the following definition.

The ratio of a standard normal random variable Z and the square root of a $\chi^2_{(m)}$ random variable V with m degrees of freedom

$$t = \frac{Z}{\sqrt{V/m}} \sim t_{(m)}$$

is a Student's t-distribution with m degrees of freedom. To use this in R, you need the usual four functions: `dt()`, `pt()`, `qt()`, or `rt()`, for which the degrees of freedom parameter *df* needs to be specified.

Make a graph of the density of probability for a t-distribution with 5 degrees of freedom. Compare and discuss the features of the graph in reference with the standard normal distribution.

Explain why the Student's t-distribution is symmetrical and how this helps in defining the interval of confidence.

Use the function `qt()` to calculate the 2.5th and 97.5th percentiles of the t-distribution with 5 degrees of freedom and to show that 95% of its population is concentrated in the interval $-2.5706 < x < 2.5706$.

Exercise 8.9

Use functions `rnorm()` and `rchisq()` to generate 10,000 standard normal numbers and 10,000 chi-square numbers with 5 degree of freedom. If those numbers are recorded in vectors `sn` and `cs`, respectively, calculate the vector `td = sn/sqrt(cs/5)`. Draw a histogram of the numbers in the vector `td`, and plot on the same graph the density distribution for the Student's t with 5 degrees of freedom by using the function `dt(x, df = 5)`.

Discuss and draw conclusions.

Exercise 8.10

The number of successes in a repetition of n Bernoulli trials is modeled as a binomial distribution with one parameter, p, the success rate in one trial. The ratio of number of successes in one trial and the number of repetitions provides an estimate for p. This procedure is known as a point estimate for population proportion. We are also interested to know the probable interval in which is the unknown true value of p, according to a given confidence level.

The survey of students used in Exercise 8.1 also has a gender category. We want to know the proportion of the university population that is female.

```
gender.response = na.omit(survey$Sex)
n = length(gender.response)              # total number of students
k = sum(gender.response == "Female")     # total number of females
pbar = k/n   # point estimate for population proportion
```

We have seen (see Exercise 7.6) that for reasonable parameters, the binomial distribution is well approximated by a normal distribution with mean pn and standard deviation $\sqrt{np(1-p)}$. Therefore we can use the critical values for the standard normal distribution corresponding to a given confidence level c to establish a confidence interval for p. This is obtained with the formula

```
zcr = qnorm(1 - (1 - c/100)/2).
```

For a large number of repetition n, the ratio of the number of successes and n has a normal distribution with the mean value p, and standard deviation $\sqrt{p(1-p)/n}$. Therefore, the margin of error for the point estimate for population proportion is $z_{cr}\sqrt{p(1-p)/n}$.

Compute the margin of error, and estimate the confidence interval for the female students' proportion in `survey` at a 95% confidence level.

8.5.2 Group Experiments

Place of Birth

The goal of this activity is to find the proportion of students in this school that were born in this state.

FIGURE 8.12 States

Make a list on which students mark with a "yes" or "no" if they were born in this state. Count the number of yes and no responses. Calculate the point estimate for the population proportion of students born in this state. Define in words the random variable that describes your experiment.

Question 1:
What discrete distribution is most useful to model your experiment?

Question 2:
Can this distribution be approximated with a normal distribution? What is the justification? What can you do if it is not justifiable?

Question 3:
Define the parameters of the approximate normal distribution in terms of the unknown proportion.

Question 4:
Find the margins of error and the confidence intervals for the following levels of confidence: 70%, 80%, 90%, 95%, and 99%.

Question 5:
Draw a graph of the density of normal distribution approximation for the random variable in your problem.

Question 6:
Print the graph, and mark with different colors the following points: the point estimate of the population proportion, and the bounds of the confidence intervals for several confidence levels.

Question 7:
Plot on the same graph three probability distributions: one corresponding to the point estimate of the population proportion and the two extreme values at the end of the interval corresponding to the 90% confidence level. Estimate the area of overlap between the graph, and interpret it in terms of probabilities.

Question 11:
State pro and con arguments about why you think the proportion might be different at other universities. Design a possible experiment that might validate or invalidate your ideas.

8.5.3 Case Scenarios

CASE SCENARIO **Campus Crime**

FIGURE 8.13A Escape Crime

FIGURE 8.13B Escape Crime

There are over 4,000 colleges and universities in the United States. Campus crime rates are generally lower than the national average. However, thousands of crimes take place on college campuses daily. In one unpublished study, student researchers examined the crime rates on 144 randomly selected campuses throughout the United States. All institutions selected were four-year, non-profit, private, or public schools. The crime rate associated with each institution was the number of criminal offenses that had occurred on campus per 1,000 students. The data are in the file titled "Campus crime."

1. What is the population of interest for this study?
2. Do a preliminary analysis of the data, and report your findings.
3. Is the sample size large enough to have a margin of error less than 0.01 at an 80% confidence level? Explain.
4. Provide a 95% confidence interval for the true mean rate of campus crimes. Explain the test that you used and why that test is appropriate.
5. Based on your analysis, what would the data tell you about how safe college campuses are around the world?

QR Code Sidebar 8.1

https://DataAnalysisUsingR.com/datasets/campus_crime.dat

QR Code Sidebar 8.2

https://DataAnalysisUsingR.com/datasets/software.dat

CASE SCENARIO

Statistical Software

FIGURE 8.14 Computational Statistics

Statistical software plays an important role in modern statistical applications. For a long time, statistical analysis was considered difficult, not due to its theoretical background but because of the intensive computational needs. It also takes years of training in mathematics and statistics to fully understand the computational details of those statistical methods before a person can program statistical analysis algorithms in open-source computer languages. For decades, these difficulties have made many useful statistical tools inaccessible to users from applied fields. Nowadays, there is an extensive collection of statistical software readily available to users at all levels and from all fields. These user-friendly software packages make complex statistical analysis accessible to users with only minimal statistics and computer training.

The significance of statistical software in data analysis is partially the reason that many universities require students to take statistics classes that require the use of software. Students' statistics education would be incomplete without appropriate training in statistical software, such as R.

Researchers explored factors that may affect students' learning outcomes in statistics courses that require the use of software. They wanted to understand the challenges students face when they learn software. They conducted a small nationwide survey among universities where statistics is taught.

The researchers invited students who were enrolled in statistics classes via a random sample of 100 universities where statistical software packages were taught. These students then participated in a short online survey about their software learning experience. The researchers collected 114 complete student responses. The data are located in the file "Software."

The variables in the data file include (values coded as 1= yes, 0 = no):

Prior_lang_cat—Student knew at least one statistical software before taking a statistics course.

Aids_books—Student found books useful in learning a statistical software.

Aids_classes—Student found the statistics course useful in learning statistical software.

Aids_websites—Student found websites useful in learning statistical software.

Aids_programs—Student found other programs useful in learning statistical software.

The bar graph below displays the survey results.

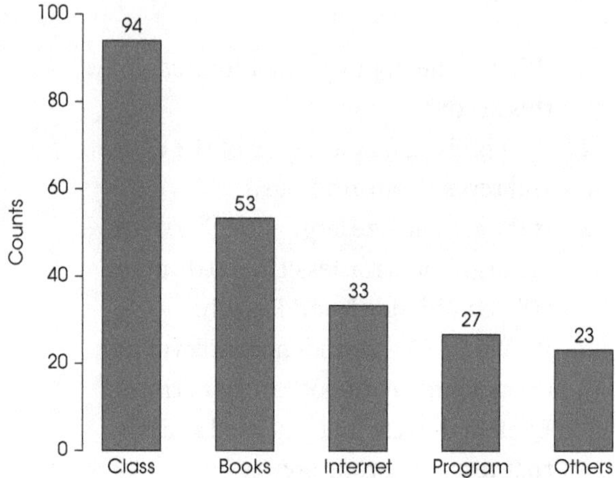

FIGURE 8.15 Bar Graph: Software Learning Experience

One of the survey questions asked, "How proficient are you with statistical software?" The results are shown in the figure below:

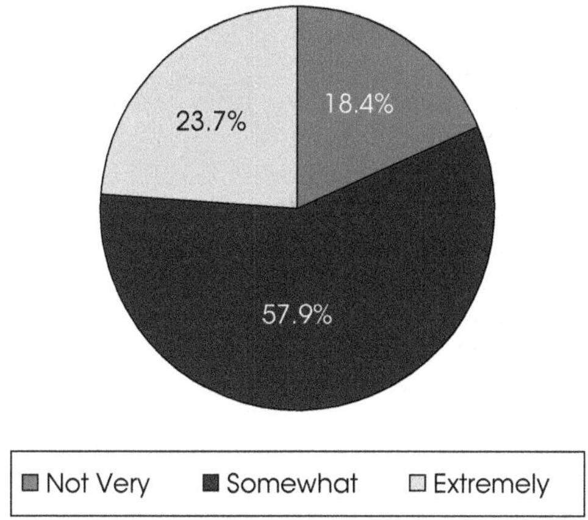

FIGURE 8.16 Pie Chart: How Proficient Are You With Statistical Software?

1. How many students responded that they were not very proficient? How many responded that they were extremely proficient? Show your work.
2. Which learning aid was most helpful?
3. Provide confidence intervals for the true population proportion for each learning aid.
4. Interpret in your own words the meaning of the confidence intervals computed in question 3.
5. Currently, you are learning the statistical software package R for this course. Discuss the pros and cons of learning R. What did you find most useful in learning R? What was least useful?

Use these questions as a self-assessment checklist for this chapter:

1. Do you know what qualifies as a large sample or a small sample in statistics?
2. Do you know the correct interpretation of a confidence interval?
3. Do you know how to construct confidence intervals for the population mean when you have a large sample?
4. Do you know how to construct confidence intervals for the population mean when you have a small sample?
5. Do you know how to construct confidence intervals for the population variance and standard deviation?
6. Do you know how to construct confidence intervals for the population proportion?
7. Do you know how to use R to construct confidence intervals and output the confidence both with and without additional information?

References

Box, Joan Fisher (1981). Gosset, Fisher, and the *t* distribution. *The American Statistician, 35*(2), 61-66, DOI: 10.1080/00031305.1981.10479309

Jackson, M. C., Lu, J., Gray, M., & Solana, H. (2011). The effects of integrating a certificate program into the classroom teaching environment. *International Mathematical Forum,* 6(50), 2481–2487. http://www.m-hikari.com/imf-2011/49-52-2011/jacksonIMF49-52-2011.pdf

Santos, A. C., Silva, E. F., Santos, W. N., Silva, E., Santos, L. O., Santos, B., Sauthier, M. C., & Santos, W. (2018). Evaluation of minerals, toxic elements and bioactive compounds in rose petals (*Rosa* spp.) using chemometric tools and artificial neural networks. *Microchemical Journal, 138,* 98-108.

Veroniki, A. A., Jackson, D., Viechtbauer, W., Bender, R., Bowden, J., Knapp, G., Kuss, O., Higgins, J. P. T., Langan, D., & Salanti, G. (2016). Methods to estimate the between-study variance and its uncertainty in meta-analysis. *Research Synthesis Methods, 7,* 55–79. https://doi.org/10.1002/jrsm.1164

Zhao, S., Hu, F., Ding, X., Zhao, M., Li, C., & Pei, S. (2017). Dataset of tensile strength development of concrete with manufactured sand. *Data in Brief, 11,* 469–472. https://doi.org/10.1016/j.dib.2017.02.043

Figure Credits

Fig. 8.1: Copyright © 2020 by Melpomeni Kalliri. Reprinted with permission.
Fig. 8.2: Copyright © 2020 by Melpomeni Kalliri. Reprinted with permission.
Fig. 8.3: Copyright © Unsplash/Hush Naidoo.
Fig. 8.4: Copyright © Unsplash/Aaron Burden.
Fig. 8.5: Copyright © 2020 by Melpomeni Kalliri. Reprinted with permission.
Fig. 8.6: Copyright © Unsplash/Aaron Burden.
Fig. 8.7: Copyright © Depositphotos/Rawpixel.
Fig. 8.8: Copyright © Unsplash/Roman Mager.
Fig. 8.9: Copyright © Unsplash/Arnaud Jaegers.
Fig. 8.10: Copyright © 2020 by Melpomeni Kalliri. Reprinted with permission.
Fig. 8.12: Copyright © Unsplash/Nathan Anderson.
Fig. 8.13a: Copyright © Unsplash/Bill Oxford.
Fig. 8.13b: Copyright © Unsplash/Pattern.
Fig. 8.14: Copyright © Unsplash/Markus Spiske.

CHAPTER

9

Hypothesis Testing

CHAPTER OUTLINE

CHAPTER OBJECTIVES

After completing this chapter, you will know how to do the following:

1. Determine whether two samples are independent or dependent.
2. Determine which hypothesis test is appropriate for a given research hypothesis.
3. Perform hypothesis tests for a population mean and a population proportion.
4. Use R and RStudio to perform hypothesis testing.

Westmount is an affluent suburb of Montreal, Quebec, in Canada. Libraries in Westmount, Montreal, and Quebec City hosted citizen workshops to address the high prevalence of medication overuse among people over 65 years old. Workshop participants received an evaluation questionnaire from organizers. Data such as knowledge gained were also collected from participants. Hypothesis testing results showed that participants reported significant knowledge gain with a sample mean difference of 2.1 (Massougbodji et al., 2020). As illustrated in the Westmount research study, in this chapter you will learn how to use sample data to make inferences about the population mean using hypothesis testing.

FIGURE 9.1 Westmount, Canada

Chapter Vocabulary

- A **Type I error** is to reject H_0 when the H_0 is true. For example, convicting a defendant who is innocent is a Typė I error.
- A **Type II error** is to fail to reject the H_0 when it is false, for example, failing to convict a defendant who is guilty.
- The **level of significance**, α (the Greek letter alpha), is a value set by the researcher prior to conducting a hypothesis test, equivalent to the maximum allowable probability of making a Type I error.
- The **power of a statistical test** represents the probability of rejecting the null hypothesis when it is false.
- Two samples are **independent** when the sample selected from one population is not related to the sample selected from the other population; otherwise, the samples are **dependent**.

9.1 Hypothesis Testing for the Population Mean

The inferential branch of statistics relies on two main types of methodologies to make inferences about the population from which a sample was obtained. We have discussed one type, estimation, for which we determined point estimators and interval estimators. Hypothesis testing is another way to make statistical inferences. A statistical hypothesis is a statement concerning the distribution of a random variable, a population parameter, or the relationship between variables. Therefore, a statistical hypothesis is an educated guess. The following example illustrates the concept of hypothesis testing.

An important problem in concrete engineering is the tensile strength of concrete, as illustrated in the tensile strength example in Section 7.3.1. Suppose an engineer invents an additive to increase the tensile strength of concrete. The mean tensile strength of the concrete without the additive is at most 3.5 Mpa. She randomly tests $n = 50$ specimens of concrete and then makes a decision about the population on the basis of the sample information. Such decisions are called statistical decisions. In attempting to reach decisions, it is useful to make an initial conjecture, or hypothesis, about the population involved. Sometimes the results from the sample may be markedly different from those expected under the hypothesis. In this case, the observed differences are statistically significant and would not happen by chance. Thus, the engineer would be inclined to reject the initial hypothesis. The procedure that enables the engineer to decide whether to reject the hypothesis or to determine whether the observed samples differ significantly for expected results is called *hypothesis testing.* This chapter will illustrate two step-by-step approaches for hypothesis testing regardless of the parameter. One approach for hypothesis testing is the p-value approach. The other is the rejection region approach. We start by describing these approaches for conducting a hypothesis test for the population mean. The following sub-section describes how to perform a hypothesis test for a population mean μ assuming the standard deviation σ is known.

9.1.1 Large Sample, One Sample Tests

We will establish the foundation for all hypothesis testing using an illustration from the large sample, one sample case. As stated earlier, a hypothesis is an educated guess. In hypothesis testing, these "guesses" are referred to as the *null* hypothesis H_0 and the alternative hypothesis H_a. The null H_0 is read "*H* naught" or "*H* sub-zero," with sub indicating a subscript. The alternative H_a is read "*H* sub-a." The null hypothesis is the status quo, and the alternative hypothesis is an alternative to the status quo.

Below are some possible pairs of null and alternative hypotheses for the mean $\mu = k$, where k is a real number.

- **Case 1:** Lower-tailed test (the probability α is the area in the lower tail of the curve)
  - $H_0 : \mu \geq k$
  - $H_a : \mu < k$
- **Case 2:** Upper-tailed test (the probability α is the area in the upper tail of the curve)
  - $H_0 : \mu \leq k$
  - $H_a : \mu > k$
- **Case 3:** Two-tailed test (the probability α is the area that is evenly divided into both the upper and lower tail of the curve)
  - $H_0 : \mu = k$
  - $H_a : \mu \neq k$

We can either reject the null hypothesis or fail to reject the null hypothesis. However, we should never accept the null hypothesis. Accepting the null hypothesis is equivalent to saying that an individual who is charged with a crime then found not guilty is innocent of the crime. Actually, one can only say that the jury found the individual not guilty. That is, there was not enough evidence to prove that they were guilty. This is further illustrated below.

Hypothesis testing can be compared to the legal system used in the United States.

FIGURE 9.2 Legal System in the United States

	TRUTH ABOUT DEFENDANT	
VERDICT	**INNOCENT**	**GUILTY**
NOT GUILTY	Justice	Type II error
GUILTY	Type I error	Justice

For example, suppose the prosecution wants to establish that a certain person is guilty. The null hypothesis is that the person is innocent because one is assumed to be innocent until proven guilty.

H_0: Defendant is innocent.

H_a: Defendant is guilty.

If it is not a hung jury, the jury can either reject the null hypothesis, which means that they feel that they have enough evidence to conclude that the defendant is not innocent (in that case, the defendant is found guilty), or they can fail to reject the null hypothesis. If the jury fails to reject the null hypothesis, it does not mean that the defendant is innocent. It merely means that the jury did not find enough evidence to support that the defendant is guilty.

As with any guess, there is a chance of making an error. In statistical hypothesis testing, these errors are called Type I and Type II errors. A Type I error is to reject the H_0 when the H_0 is true. For example, convicting a defendant who is innocent is a Type I error. A Type II error is to fail to reject the H_0 when it is false. In other words, letting the criminal go free is a Type II error. These errors are summarized in the table below:

	TRUTH OF H_0	
DECISION	H_0 **TRUE**	H_0 **FALSE**
DO NOT REJECT H_0	Correct decision	Type II error
REJECT H_0	Type I error	Correct decision

In hypothesis testing, the level of significance α (the Greek letter alpha) is a value set by the researcher prior to conducting a hypothesis test and it is the maximum allowable probability of making a Type I error. We set the level of significance at a small value if we want the probability of rejecting a true null hypothesis to be small. There are three commonly used levels of significance: $\alpha = 0.10$, $\alpha = 0.05$, and $\alpha = 0.01$. For instance, $\alpha = 0.01$ implies a 1% chance of rejecting H_0 when it is true.

The probability of a Type II error is denoted by the Greek letter β. Note that when you decrease α, you increase β. The value 1− β is called the power of a statistical test. It represents the probability of rejecting the null hypothesis when it is false. We will not compute the power as it is beyond the scope of this book.

FIGURE 9.3 Acropolis of Athens, Greece

Now back to the large sample, one sample case. When σ is known, one can use a z-test for hypothesis testing for the population mean. This involves determining the standardized value z for the test statistic $\overline{x}$. The standardized test statistic is

$$z = \frac{\overline{x} - \mu}{\frac{\sigma}{\sqrt{n}}}$$

if the following two conditions are met:

- The sample is random.
- Either the population is normally distributed, $n \geq 30$, or both are true.

As mentioned earlier, there are two approaches for making a decision in a hypothesis test, the p-value approach and the rejection region approach. We will first describe the p-value approach. Next, we will provide the steps for both the p-value approach and the rejection region approach.

Under the assumption that H_0 is true, the p-value or probability value of a hypothesis test is the probability of obtaining a sample statistic with a value as extreme or more extreme than the one determined from the sample data. For example, suppose your home was in the same town as a state prison and you heard that there was an escapee on the loose. Railroad tracks happen to be on the other side of your large backyard. One spring evening you look through your kitchen window and see someone wearing an orange jumpsuit walking along the railroad tracks. Do you automatically assume the person is the escapee? Possibly not. Now suppose you can make out some sort of writing on the back of the jumpsuit. Next, you hear chains jingling. At this point, you will ask yourself, under the assumption that the person has not been convicted of a crime, what is the chance that so much evidence would point to the probability that this person were *not* the escapee? In other words, what is the probability that you would find someone like that walking along the railroad tracks or something even more extreme (perhaps hound dogs running behind the person) if that were not the escapee. That probability would be extremely small. This is the idea behind why we would reject the null hypothesis if the p-value is small. Specifically, in the p-value approach, the null hypothesis should be rejected if p-value $\leq \propto$. Here are the steps for both the rejection region and p-value approaches for constructing a hypothesis test for the population mean μ when σ is known. Both approaches use Step 1 through Step 5. Step 6 is specific to the rejection region approach. Step 7 through Step 9 are specific to the p-value approach. Both approaches use Step 9:

- Step 1. Verify that σ is known, the sample is random, and either the population has a normal distribution or $n \geq 30$.
- Step 2. Mathematically write the null and alternative hypotheses.
- Step 3. Determine which case to use. See Case 1 (lower-tailed), Case 2 (upper-tailed), and Case 3 (two-tailed).
- Step 4. Specify the level of significance $\propto$.
- Step 5. Determine the standardized test statistic $z = \frac{\overline{x} - \mu}{\frac{\sigma}{\sqrt{n}}}$.

- Step 6. Sketch a standard normal curve, determine the critical value (z_α *or* $z_{\alpha/2}$), and shade the rejection region (rejection region approach)
  - Case 1 (lower-tailed)
    - $P(Z < z_\alpha)$
  - Case 2 (upper-tailed)
    - $P(Z > z_\alpha)$
  - Case 3 (two tailed)
    - $P(Z < -z_{\alpha/2})$ and $P(Z > z_{\alpha/2})$
- Step 7. Place the test statistic and critical value on the standard normal curve. If the test statistic lies in the rejection region, reject the null hypothesis at the $\propto$ level of significance. Otherwise, fail to reject the null hypothesis. (rejection region approach).
- Step 8. Use the standard normal table, Tables 7A and 7B in Appendix A, to determine the *p*-value based on the case (*p*-value approach)
  - Case 1 (lower-tailed)
    - *p*-value = $P(Z < z)$
  - Case 2 (upper-tailed)
    - *p*-value = $P(Z > z)$
  - Case 3 (two-tailed)
    - If $z < 0$, then *p*-value = $2*P(Z < z)$.
    - If $z > 0$, then *p*-value = $2*P(Z > z)$.
- Step 9. Compare the *p*-value to the level of significance $\propto$ (*p*-value approach).
  - If *p*-value $\leq \propto$, then reject $H_{0.}$
  - If *p*-value $> \propto$, then fail to reject $H_{0.}$
- Step 10. Interpret the decision in the context of the problem.

Example:

Recall the tensile strength example of Section 7.3.1. Suppose an engineer invents an additive to increase the tensile strength of concrete. The mean tensile strength of the concrete without the additive is at most 3.5 Mpa with a standard deviation of $\sigma = 1.1603$. She randomly tests $n = 50$ specimens of concrete and records their average $\overline{x} = 3.9$ Mpa tensile strength. At the $\alpha = 0.05$ level of significance, test her claim that her additive is increasing the tensile strength. Use the *p*-value approach.

FIGURE 9.4 Engineering Inventions

Answer:

This is an example of

Case 2: Upper-tailed test (the probability α is the area in the upper tail of the curve)

- $H_0 : \mu \leq k$
- $H_a : \mu > k$

Therefore,

$$H_0: \mu \leq 3.5$$
$$H_a: \mu > 3.5$$

The test statistic is $z = \frac{\bar{x}-\mu}{\frac{\sigma}{\sqrt{n}}}$.

So,

$$z = \frac{3.9 - 3.5}{\frac{1.1603}{\sqrt{50}}} \approx 2.44$$

$$p\text{-value} = P(Z > 2.44) = 1 - P(Z < 2.44) = 1 - 0.9927 = 0.0073.$$

Because $0.0073 < 0.05$, reject the null hypothesis at the $\alpha = 0.05$ level of significance. Conclude that the concrete engineer's additive indeed increases the tensile strength of concrete.

Example:

Consider the tensile strength example. Now use the rejection region approach to make a decision.

FIGURE 9.5 Strength

Answer:

Recall that the level of significance is $\alpha = 0.05$, and the test statistic is $z = \frac{3.9 - 3.5}{\frac{1.1603}{\sqrt{50}}} \approx 2.44$. Because $H_a: \mu > 3.5$, this is an upper-tailed test. According to the standard normal table (Tables 7A and 7B in Appendix A), the critical value is $z_\alpha = z_{0.05} = 1.645$. Since this is an upper-tailed test, shade to the right of the critical value. The shaded region is called the critical region. Note that the test statistic falls in the rejection region. Reject the null hypothesis at the $\alpha = 0.05$ level of significance. Conclude that the concrete engineer's additive indeed increases the tensile strength of concrete.

Also, note that the p-value approach agrees with the rejection region approach. The two approaches always reach the same conclusion. When doing hypothesis testing by hand, the rejection region approach is typically used. When using software, the p-value approach is typically used.

9.1.2 Small Sample, One Sample Tests

If the population standard deviation σ is not known when conducting a hypothesis test for the population mean μ, the t-distribution with degrees of freedom $df = n - 1$ can be used if

- The sample is a random sample.
- The population has a normal distribution.
- The sample size $n < 30$.

The standardized test statistic is

$$t = \frac{\overline{x} - \mu}{\frac{s}{\sqrt{n}}}.$$

Example:

Consider the tensile strength example. Suppose that the population standard deviation σ is not known. Also suppose that only $n = 25$ specimens were sampled, and their average tensile strength was $\overline{x} = 4.1$ Mpa with a sample standard deviation of $s = 1.12$. Use the rejection region approach to test the concrete engineer's claim at the $\alpha = 0.05$ level of significance.

Answer:

Recall that the level of significance is $\alpha = 0.05$. The test statistic is $t = \frac{4.1 - 3.5}{\frac{1.12}{\sqrt{25}}} \approx 2.6786$. Because $H_a : \mu > 3.5$, this is an upper-tailed test. From the t-table (Table 8 in Appendix A), for $n - 1 = 25 - 1 = 24$ df, the critical value is $t_{n-1, 0.05} = t_{24, 0.05} = 1.711$. Since this is an upper-tailed test, shade to the right of the critical value. The shaded region is called the critical region. Note that the test statistic falls in the rejection region. Therefore, reject the null hypothesis at the $\alpha = 0.05$ level of significance. Conclude that the concrete engineer's additive indeed increases the tensile strength of concrete.

The p-value approach using the t-test can also be done by hand. However, because the p-value is typically not one of the limited values provided in the t-table (Table 8 in Appendix A), we would have to interpolate the p-values. Therefore, the p-value approach is typically performed with software instead of using the t-table (Table 8 in Appendix A).

9.1.3 Exercises

Understanding Concepts

1. Name two approaches for hypothesis testing.

2. Convicting a defendant who is innocent is an example of what type of error in hypothesis testing? Explain your answer.

3. Which hypothesis is the status quo? Explain your answer.

4. Failing to convict a defendant who is guilty is an example of what type of error in hypothesis testing? Explain your answer.

True or false? In Exercises 5–9, determine whether the statement is true or false. If it is false, rewrite it as a true statement.

5. The p-value approach in hypothesis testing always results in the same conclusions as the rejection region approach in hypothesis testing.

6. The power of a statistical test represents the probability of rejecting the null hypothesis when it is false.

7. The lower the power of a statistical test, the better.

8. The p-value approach in hypothesis testing can either be done by hand or with software.

9. The level of significance is a value set by the researcher after conducting a hypothesis test, and it is the maximum allowable probability of making a Type I error.

Skill Building

Use the following to answer questions 10–12:

> Suppose we have $n = 8$ observations with a sample mean of 12. You plan to conduct a one-sample t-test to evaluate
>
> $$H_0: \mu = 10 \text{ vs. } H_a: \mu \neq 10.$$

10. State the degrees of freedom for this test statistic.

11. Is the one-sample t-test a one-sided or two-sided test?

12. State the value of the test statistic.

Use the following to answer questions 13–15:

> The website www.salary.com reports that the average salary of a mathematician in 2020 was $82,063 U.S. dollars. We sampled 40 mathematicians and asked them their salary. We found that the sample mean was $75,000, and the standard deviation was $8,750.

13. State the null and alternative hypotheses you would use to test that the mean salary of a mathematician was different from the reported mean by www.salary.com.

14. Compute the p-value based on the hypothesis test in Exercise 13.

15. What are your conclusions based on a significance level of 0.5?

Use the data below to answer questions 16–19:

6	12	3	20	3	7	8	12	9	11
7	5	13	8	6	8	7	9	4	3

16. What assumptions are required to conduct a one-sample t-test?

17. Does the data meet that assumption?

18. Compute the sample statistics needed to conduct a one-sample t-test (e.g., mean, standard deviation, and standardized test statistic).

19. What is the distribution (with parameters) that is used to conduct a one-sample t-test to test whether the mean of the sample data is greater than 6?

20. Perform a one-sample t-test to determine if the mean is greater than 6. State the p-value and results, assuming a significance level of .01.

Extending Concepts

21. Explain why in statistical hypothesis testing we cannot bring evidence to accept the null hypothesis.

22. Are the null and the alternative hypotheses mutually exclusive? Explain your answer.

23. Why is there more than one approach for hypothesis testing?

24. Is it possible to obtain different results for testing when using the p-value approach and rejection region approach?

25. Provide an example of when a one-tailed z-test could be used for hypothesis testing.

9.2 Hypothesis Testing for the Difference Between Means

The focus of the previous section was hypothesis testing involving one sample. We now expand the scope of hypothesis testing to include two samples. When considering two samples, the samples may either be independent or dependent. We first consider the independent case.

9.2.1 Large Sample, Independent Sample Tests

Recall that two random variables are independent if the probability of the occurrence of one random variable has no bearing of the probability of the occurrence of another random variable. Likewise, two samples are independent when the sample selected from one population is not related to the sample selected from the other population.

Below are some possible pairs of null and alternative hypotheses for the two population parameters μ_1 and μ_2.

- **Case 1:** Lower-tailed test (the probability α is the area in the lower tail of the curve)
  - $H_0 : \mu_1 \geq \mu_2$
  - $H_a : \mu_1 < \mu_2$
- **Case 2:** Upper-tailed test (the probability α is the area in the upper tail of the curve)
  - $H_0 : \mu_1 \leq \mu_2$
  - $H_a : \mu_1 > \mu_2$
- **Case 3:** Two-tailed test (the probability α is the area that is evenly divided into both the upper and lower tail of the curve)
  - $H_0 : \mu_1 = \mu_2$
  - $H_a : \mu_1 \neq \mu_2$

A hypothesis test for the difference between two population means μ_1 and μ_2 has the test statistic $\overline{x}_1 - \overline{x}_2$ and the standardized test statistic

$$z = \frac{(\overline{x}_1 - \overline{x}_2) - (\mu_1 - \mu_2)}{\sqrt{\frac{\sigma_1^2}{n_1} + \frac{\sigma_2^2}{n_2}}}.$$

The standardized test statistic has a standard normal distribution provided the following conditions are met:

- The population standard deviations σ_1 and σ_2 are both known.
- The samples are random.
- The samples are independent.
- The populations are normally distributed or both sample sizes $n_1 \geq 30$ and $n_2 \geq 30$.

Example:

Consider all factors such as teaching, research, and service as being equal. A salary equity study of faculty members at a certain university—sample salaries of 32 male associate professors and 30 female associate professors—yield the follow statistics:

	SALARY MEAN	SALARY STANDARD DEVIATION
MALE PROFESSOR	$75,820	$8,345
FEMALE PROFESSOR	$70,820	$7,620

Use the rejection region approach to test the hypothesis that the mean salary of male professors is more than the mean salary of female professors at the university. Use a level of significance $\alpha = 0.05$.

Answer:

Let μ_1 represent the population mean salaries for male professors, and μ_2 represent the population mean salaries for female professors. This example falls under

Case 2: Upper-tailed test (the probability α is the area in the upper tail of the curve)

- $H_0: \mu_1 = \mu_2$
- $H_a: \mu_1 > \mu_2$

Therefore,

$$H_o: \mu_1 = \mu_2$$

$$H_a: \mu_1 > \mu_2$$

The test statistic is

$$z = \frac{(\overline{x}_1 - \overline{x}_2) - (\mu_1 - \mu_2)}{\sqrt{\frac{\sigma_1^2}{n_1} + \frac{\sigma_2^2}{n_2}}}$$

$$z = \frac{(75{,}820 - 70{,}820) - 0}{\sqrt{\frac{(8345)^2}{32} + \frac{(7620)^2}{30}}}$$

$$z \approx 2.47.$$

Because $\alpha = 0.05, z_\alpha = z_{0.05} = 1.645$. Since the test statistic falls in the rejection region, reject the null hypothesis at the $\alpha = 0.05$ level of significance. Conclude that the salaries for male professors are greater than that of female professors even in the case for which all factors such as teaching, research, and service are equal.

9.2.2 Small Sample, Independent Sample Tests

The previous section presented a hypothesis test for the difference between two population means when both population standard deviations are known. However, in many real-life situations, both population standard deviations are typically unknown. This section uses a *t*-test for testing the difference between two population means μ_1 and μ_2 using independent samples from each population when the population standard deviations σ_1 and σ_2 are unknown. The standardized test statistic is

$$t = \frac{(\bar{x}_1 - \bar{x}_2) - (\mu_1 - \mu_2)}{\sqrt{\frac{s_1^2}{n_1} + \frac{s_2^2}{n_2}}}.$$

When should we use the standard normal distribution and when should we use the *t*-distribution? The answer to this question falls in one of these mutually exclusive six cases:

Case 1:

When the population is normally distributed with σ_1 and σ_2 known, the standardized test statistic has a standard normal distribution irrespective of the sample size.

Case 2:

When the populations are not normally distributed, the standard deviations σ_1 and σ_2 are both known, and both $n_1 > 30$ and $n_2 > 30$, the standardized test statistic has a standard normal distribution.

Case 3:

When both σ_1 and σ_2 are unknown and both populations are normally distributed, irrespective of the sample size, one of the two sub-cases applies:

Case 3a: If we can reasonably assume from the two sample standard deviations that the population standard deviations are $\sigma_1 = \sigma_2$, $\hat{\sigma}$ is an estimate of the population standard deviation, then the standardized test statistics has a *t*-distribution with the standard deviation of the difference between two means

$s_{\bar{x}_1 - \bar{x}_2} = \hat{\sigma}\sqrt{\frac{1}{n_1} + \frac{1}{n_2}}$ and $df = n_1 + n_2 - 2$.

Case 3b: If we can reasonably assume from the two sample standard deviations that the population standard deviations are $\sigma_1 \neq \sigma_2$, $\hat{\sigma}$ is an estimate of the population standard deviation, then the standardized test statistics has a *t*-distribution with the standard deviation of the difference between two means

$s_{\bar{x}_1 - \bar{x}_2} = \sqrt{\frac{1}{n_1} + \frac{1}{n_2}}$ and degrees of freedom the smaller of $df = n_1 - 1$ and $df = n_2 - 1$.

Case 4:

When both σ_1 and σ_2 are unknown, neither population is normally distributed, and both $n_1 \geq 30$ and $n_2 \geq 30$, one of the two sub-cases applies:

Case 4a: If we can reasonably assume from the sample standard deviations that the population standard deviations are $\sigma_1 = \sigma_2$, $\hat{\sigma}$ is an estimate of the population standard deviation, then the standardized test statistics has a *t*-distribution with the standard deviation of the difference between two means $s_{\bar{x}_1 - \bar{x}_2} = \hat{\sigma}\sqrt{\frac{1}{n_1} + \frac{1}{n_2}}$ and $df = n_1 + n_2 - 2$.

Case 4b: If we can reasonably assume from the sample standard deviations that the population standard deviations are $\sigma_1 \neq \sigma_2$, then the standardized test statistics has a *t*-distribution with the standard deviation of the difference between two means $s_{\bar{x}_1 - \bar{x}_2} = \sqrt{\frac{1}{n_1} + \frac{1}{n_2}}$ and degrees of freedom the smaller of $df = n_1 - 1$ and $df = n_2 - 1$.

Case 5:

When both σ_1 and σ_2 are unknown, neither population is normal, either $n_1 < 30$ or $n_2 < 30$, then an appropriate choice would be to use a distribution-free method. These methods are referred to as nonparametric methods, which are found in the last chapter of this textbook.

Case 6:

When both σ_1 and σ_2 are known, neither population is normal, either $n_1 < 30$ or $n_2 < 30$, then an appropriate choice would be to use a distribution-free method. These methods are referred to as nonparametric methods, which are found in the last chapter of this textbook.

Example:

A dietician wants to evaluate a new low-fat weight-loss diet she has developed to compare it to a regular established diet. Sixty obese people were randomly selected. Of the 60 people, 30 participants were randomly allocated to the new low-fat diet and the remaining 30 were placed on the regular diet. At the end of three weeks, the weight loss (in pounds) of each of the 60 people was measured. Using the rejection region approach, conduct a hypothesis test to determine if the diets are equally effective. The resulting data are given in the table below (White et al., 2019). Assume both populations have a normal distribution. Assume neither population variance is known, but they are assumed to be unequal. Use the $\alpha = 0.10$ level of significance.

	DIET	*N*	$\bar{x}$	*S*
Weight loss (pounds)	Low-fat	25	9.007	4.034
	Regular	20	5.863	3.811

FIGURE 9.6 Low-Fat Smoothies

Answer:

Let μ_1 represent the population mean weight loss under the low-fat diet, and μ_2 represent the population mean weight loss under the regular diet. The null and alternative hypotheses are

$$H_0 : \mu_1 = \mu_2$$
$$H_a : \mu_1 \neq \mu_2$$

This is a two-sided hypothesis that falls under Case 3b with standardized test statistic

$$t = \frac{(\overline{x}_1 - \overline{x}_2) - (\mu_1 - \mu_2)}{\sqrt{\frac{s_1^2}{n_1} + \frac{s_2^2}{n_2}}},$$

and degrees of freedom the smaller of $df = n_1 - 1$ and $df = n_2 - 1$

$$t = \frac{(9.007 - 5.863) - (0)}{\sqrt{\frac{16.2731}{25} + \frac{14.5238}{20}}}$$
$$\approx 2.679.$$

The smaller of $df = 25 - 1 = 24$ and $df = 20 - 1 = 19$ is the latter.

The critical value is $t_{\frac{\alpha}{2}, df} = t_{.05,19} = 1.725$. Because the test statistic falls in the rejection region, reject the null hypothesis at the $\alpha = 0.10$ level of significance. Conclude that the diets are not equally effective.

9.2.3 Small Sample, Dependent Sample Tests

The two earlier sub-sections detailed tests for the difference between two means. This section is about the mean of the differences of paired data entries for dependent samples. The assumptions of this test are:

- The samples are random.
- The sample sizes are equal, $n_1 = n_2$.
- The samples are paired, hence dependent.
- The populations are normally distributed or $n \geq 30$; n represents the number of pairs of data.

The test statistic for this test is $\overline{d} = \frac{\sum d}{n}$, where d is the difference between the data entry in the first sample and the corresponding data entry in the second sample, and s_d is the standard deviation of differences between the data entry in the first sample and the corresponding data value in the second sample. The standardized test statistics is

$$t = \frac{\overline{d} - \mu_d}{\frac{s_d}{\sqrt{n}}}$$

with degrees of freedom $df = n - 1$.

Example:

Body mass index (BMI) is a number that reflects a person's body weight adjusted for height. BMI is universally expressed in kg/m^2. Researchers study the relationship between BMI and breast cancer (Premenopausal Breast Cancer Collaborative Group, 2018). Because maintaining a healthy weight through lifestyle change is important, researchers put six subjects on a healthy weight regimen that consists of good eating habits and exercise, and they measure the BMIs at the beginning and end of the 30-day regimen.

At $\alpha = 0.10$, is there enough evidence that BMI has decreased after 30 days? The before and after BMIs of the six participants are in the table below. Assume the samples are random and dependent, and the population is normally distributed.

SUBJECT	1	2	3	4	5	6
BMI (before)	30.2	28.7	29.9	37.3	27.9	25.1
BMI (after)	28.7	28.4	28.1	36.5	26.8	26.2

Answer:

Because the samples are random and dependent, and the populations are normally distributed, a *t*-test can be used. First, calculate each difference

d = (BMI before health-weight regimen) – (BMI after health-weight regimen).

SUBJECT	1	2	3	4	5	6
BMI (before)	30.2	28.7	29.9	37.3	27.9	25.1
BMI (after)	28.7	28.4	28.1	36.5	26.8	26.2
d	1.5	0.3	1.8	0.8	1.1	−1.1

Let μ_d represent the hypothesized mean of the differences of the paired data (BMI before and BMI after) in the population.

The null and alternative hypotheses are

$$H_o : \mu_d = 0$$

$$H_a : \mu_d > 0.$$

The standardized test statistic is

$$t = \frac{\bar{d} - \mu_d}{\frac{s_d}{\sqrt{n}}},$$

with $df = n - 1$.

$$t = \frac{\bar{d} - \mu_d}{\frac{s_d}{\sqrt{n}}}$$

$$= \frac{0.7333 - 0}{\frac{1.0405}{\sqrt{6}}}$$

$$\approx 1.73.$$

$n - 1 = 6 - 1 = 5$, and the critical value is $t_{0.10,5} = 1.476$. Because the standardized test statistic lies in the rejection region, reject the null hypothesis at the $\alpha = .10$ level of significance.

9.2.4 Exercises

Understanding Concepts

1. When testing the mean of the differences of paired data entries in dependent samples, what does notation n represent?

2. What does it mean for two samples to be dependent?

3. When testing the mean of the differences of paired data entries in dependent samples, what conditions must be met?

4. When testing the mean of the differences of paired data entries in dependent samples, how many samples are there?

True or false? In Exercises 5–9, determine whether the statement is true or false. If it is false, rewrite it as a true statement.

5. A hypothesis test for the difference between the means is different from a hypothesis test for the mean of the differences.

6. When conducting a hypothesis test for the mean of the differences, it is assumed that the samples are independent.

7. The test statistic for a hypothesis test for the mean of the differences has an approximate normal distribution.

8. You can use either the p-value approach or the rejection region approach when conducting a hypothesis test for the mean of the differences. However, the conclusions will sometimes differ because of the approach.

9. One way to use R to perform a hypothesis test for the difference between means is to enter the data in two vectors and use a third vector in which you store the calculated difference for each pair.

Skill Building

10. For the following scenarios, state whether you would use an independent sample test or a dependent sample test.

    a. Volunteers were selected to determine which restaurant had the best burgers. Forty volunteers each tasted the burgers from two different restaurants and ranked them on a scale from 1–10.

    b. A study investigates whether a new medication provided relief from allergy symptoms. Forty volunteers with seasonal allergies were selected for the study. Twenty were given a placebo, and 20 were given the new medication. The results from the two groups were compared.

    c. Are Android cell phones better than Apple cell phones? Twelve volunteers were given an Android phone to use for a week and asked to rate the quality of the phone at the end of the week. The second week, the same volunteers were given an Apple phone to use and rated the phone. The results were compared to determine which phone ranked the best.

    d. Who is happier in a marriage? A set of 20 married couples were asked to rank the level of happiness in their marriage on a scale of 1–12. Each husband and wife provided a separate rating of their marriage. Researchers analyzed the data to determine whether the husbands or wives reported being happier.

FIGURE 9.7 Who Is Happier in a Marriage?

Use the summary statistics below to answer questions 11–14:

	STANDARD DEVIATION	MEAN	SAMPLE SIZE
Sample 1	20	55	25
Sample 2	39	76	26

11. What are the degrees of freedom for the test statistic that would be used to conduct an independent sample test?

12. What is the test statistic that would be used to conduct an independent sample test?

13. For

$$H_0: \mu_1 = \mu_2$$
$$H_a: \mu_1 \neq \mu_2$$

calculate the p-value.

14. Assuming a significance level of 0.05, do the data provide evidence against the null hypothesis that the means are equal? Explain?

Use the following to answer questions 15–20:

Researchers measured the effectiveness of two popular weight loss methods. During the first month, participants purchased prepared frozen meals and ate only from the planned menu of frozen foods. During the second month, the same participants prepared their own foods with calorie restrictions. The participants recorded their weight loss at the end of each month on each diet. The data are shown below:

FIGURE 9.8 Weight-Loss Diet

	WEIGHT LOSS FOR PARTICIPANT									
MONTH	1	2	3	4	5	6	7	8	9	10
1	8	8	4.5	6	11	8	8	16	18	5
2	6	4	3	8	5	6	6	8	2	0

15. Would you use an independent or dependent sample test to determine if there was a difference in the mean weight loss of the two diets?

16. What are the assumptions for the hypothesis test you would use to test the difference in the means? Have those assumptions been reasonably met? Explain.

17. State the null and alternative hypotheses for the hypothesis testing of the difference of the means.

18. Provide the test statistic that would be used to test the difference in the means.

19. What are the degrees of freedom for the distribution of the test statistic that would be used to test the difference of the means?

20. Compute the p-value, and state the conclusions, assuming a significance level of .05.

Extending Concepts

21. What kind of hypothesis test can you use for two samples that have sizes greater than 30 and are both known to be normal?

22. Which hypothesis test can you use to test the difference between population means when the first sample size is 10, the standard deviation is known, and the population is normal; the second sample size is 50, the standard deviation is not known, and the population is not normal?

23. Can you use a dependent sample hypothesis test when testing the difference between means if the sample sizes are not equal?

24. The means of two samples from independent populations are equal, and the null hypothesis is that their population means are equal. The p-values is greater than the level of significance. What conclusions can your draw from the hypothesis test?

25. Why is the sample size important in any hypothesis test?

9.3 Hypothesis Testing for the Population Proportion

Now suppose we want to test the difference between two population proportions, p_1 and p_2. A z-test can be used for this.

9.3.1 *z*-Test for Population Proportions

These conditions are necessary to use a z-test to test the difference between two population proportions.

- The samples are normally distributed.
- The samples are independent.

- The values $q_1 = 1 - p_1$ and $q_2 = 1 - p_2$; also, the samples are large enough to use a normal sampling distributional assumptions. Specifically
  - $n_1p_1 > 5$
  - $n_1q_1 > 5$
  - $n_2p_2 > 5$
  - $n_2q_2 > 5$

The test statistic is $\hat{p}_1 - \hat{p}_2$, and the standardized test statistic is

$$z = \frac{(\hat{p}_1 - \hat{p}_2) - (p_1 - p_2)}{\sqrt{\overline{p}\,\overline{q}\left(\frac{1}{n_1} + \frac{1}{n_2}\right)}},$$

where $\overline{p} = \frac{x_1 + x_2}{n_1 + n_2}$ and $\overline{q} = 1 - \overline{p}$. To use this formulation, we must also determine $x_1 = n_1\hat{p}_1$ and $x_2 = n_2\hat{p}_2$. However, there is an alternative formula.

9.3.2 Alternative Formula for *z*-Test

Depending on the information provided, an equivalent alternative formula can also be used for this z-test.

Example:

Domestic content restrictions in the United States are provisions that require items purchased using specific funds appropriated by the U.S. Congress to be produced or manufactured in the United States. Researchers claim that for every $100 U.S. dollars spent on exports from China, the proportion spent on domestic content p_1 is greater than the proportion spent on foreign content p_2. Suppose a random sample of $n_1 = n_2 = 36$ exports from China to the United States show that the proportion spent on domestic content to be $\hat{p}_1 = 0.5917$, and the proportion spent on foreign content is $p_2 = 0.4083$ (Ma et al., 2015). Assume that the populations are normally distributed and the samples are independent. At the $\alpha = 0.01$, test the researchers' claim.

FIGURE 9.9 U.S. Congress

Answer:

The null and alternative hypotheses are

$$H_0: p_1 = p_2$$
$$H_a: p_1 > p_2$$

The standardized test statistic is

$$z = \frac{(\hat{p}_1 - \hat{p}_2) - (p_1 - p_2)}{\sqrt{\frac{\hat{p}_1\hat{q}_1}{n_1} + \frac{\hat{p}_2\hat{q}_2}{n_2}}}$$

$$z = \frac{(0.5917 - 0.4083) - (0)}{\sqrt{\frac{(0.5917)(0.4083)}{36} + \frac{(0.4083)(0.5917)}{36}}}$$

$$\approx 2.24.$$

For $\alpha = 0.01$, the critical value $z_{0.01} = 2.325$. Because the standardized test statistic does not fall in the rejection region, fail to reject the null hypothesis at the $\alpha = 0.01$ level of significance. We conclude that proportion spent on domestic content equals that of the proportion spent on foreign content for every $100 U.S. dollars spent.

9.3.3 Exercises

Understanding Concepts

1. When conducting a hypothesis test to the difference between two population proportions, p_1 and p_2, what must you always assume that p_1 equals?
2. When conducting a hypothesis test of the difference between two population proportions, p_1 and p_2, what do p_1 and p_2 represent?
3. What is the difference between the notation p and $\hat{p}$?
4. When the conditions necessary to use a z-test to test the difference between two population proportions are met, what is the sampling distribution of the statistic for the difference between the two sample proportions?
5. When the conditions necessary to use a z-test to test the difference between two population proportions are met, what is the mean of the sampling distribution of the statistic for the difference between the two sample proportions?

6. How is the mean of the sampling distribution for the difference between the two sample proportions calculated when the population proportion is unknown?

True or false? In Exercises 7–12, determine whether the statement is true or false. If it is false, rewrite it as a true statement.

7. When the sampling distribution of the statistic for the difference between two sample proportions is normally distributed, you can use a z-test to test the difference between two population proportions.

8. When conducting a two-sample z-test for the difference between population proportions, you first need to verify that the samples are random and independent.

9. When conducting a two-sample z-test for the difference between population proportions, you need to specify the level of significance after determining the standardized test statistic so that you can reject the null hypothesis if desired.

10. A hypothesis test for the difference between population proportions can always be conducted using the p-value approach.

11. If the p-value is less than or equal to the level of significance, do not reject the null hypothesis.

12. The "p" in p-value stands for proportion.

13. The purpose of a two-sample z-test for the difference between two population proportions is to determine whether a difference in sample proportions indicate an actual difference in the population proportions or whether the sample proportion differences are merely due to sampling error.

Skill Building

Use the following to answer questions 14–18:

> The recommended daily allowance (RDA) of vitamin D is 600 international units (IUs) for adults between the ages of 19–50. We sampled 45 college students and found that only 30% met the recommended daily allowance.

14. How many students met the recommended allowance of vitamin D consumption per day?

15. Using the information provided above, suppose the national average for the percentage of those who consume the RDA of vitamin D is 40%. What is the test statistic for the hypothesis to test that the population proportion is equal to 40%?

FIGURE 9.10 Vitamin D

16. What distribution is the test statistic based on in Exercise 15?

17. What assumptions are necessary to test the hypothesis that the true mean is equal to 40%? Were the assumptions met?

18. What is the *p*-value to test $H_0: p = 0.4$ and $H_a: p \neq 0.4$, using the information in the previous exercises?

Use the following to answer questions 19–21:

> Professor Dunson teaches statistics at a U.S. university. She has been teaching for many years, and 90% of students pass her class. This semester she has 19 students taking her statistical software class, and 17 are passing.

FIGURE 9.11 Statistics Class

19. What proportion of students are passing Dr. Dunson's class?

20. Compute the test statistic to test $H_0: p = 0.9$ and $H_a: p \neq 0.9$.

21. Based on the results from Exercise 20, what is the p-value? State your conclusions assuming a significance level of 0.05.

Extending Concepts

22. Which statistical test can be used to compare the heads or tails proportions when tossing two fair coins from two independent populations?

23. What is an appropriate sample size for conducting a hypothesis test for the proportion of heads when tossing two fair coins from two independent populations?

24. A researcher wants to know how two colleges differ in the percentage of students who smoke e-cigarettes. A survey reveals that in College 1, there are 47 e-cigarette smokers among the 125 students who were randomly sampled, while in College 2, there are 53 e-cigarette smokers among the 153 students who were randomly sampled. Calculate the p-value under the null hypothesis that the percentages of students who smoke e-cigarettes in the two colleges are equal.

25. What do you expect to happen to the z-score in testing population proportions when the sample size increases?

26. Is a population proportion a test for categorical or numerical data?

9.4 R and RStudio

9.4.1 Programming Assignments

Exercise 9.1

A company claims that a lithium ion battery for laptops will function correctly for at least 300 charge-recharge cycles. We tested 30 batteries and found that, on average, they lasted 290 cycles. Assuming that the standard deviation for the numbers of cycles for the battery population is 20, can we reject the claim at a 0.05 significance level?

The question is: Does our sample mean seem to be lower because of some random fluctuation or because the population mean is actually lower than what is stated? In terms of the z-score, we are looking to see if the sample z is to the left of the critical z_c as deduced from the significance level, or in other words, we need to perform a lower tail z-test of the population mean.

Because there is no pre-installed *z-test* procedure in *R*, write a *R* function that takes the following arguments:

- m = the sample mean
- M = the hypothesized population mean
- n = the sample size
- sd = the standard deviation for the population, known by other means, or given to us
- a = the desired significance level

and returns *TRUE* or *FALSE* if the hypothesis that $m > M$ is rejected or not.

This function should calculate the z score for sample as $z = (m - M)/(sd/\sqrt{n})$ and compare it with the critical z_c obtained by using the `qnorm()` function.

Exercise 9.2

For the same situation as in Exercise 9.1, write the function that obtains the same result by calculating the p-value. For a given z, this represents the probability of obtaining results that are extreme, or even more extreme, which, in this case, is the area under the standard normal density distribution to the left of that z. In R, we calculate this with function `pnorm()`. The function then compares the p-value with the desired significance level to infer a decision.

Exercise 9.3

The reason R has no standard function for the z-test is that it is not very often used in practice, but it is very useful for beginner students who have not yet learned about the t-test. A function `z.test()` exists in the supplementary package `TeachingDemos`. Install, activate, and execute this function to solve Exercise 9.1. You will discover that this function has an extra argument called `alternative` than can be specified to be either `two.sided`, `less`, or `greater`, depending on what kind of z-test is required. For Exercise 9.1, you should use `alternative = "less"`.

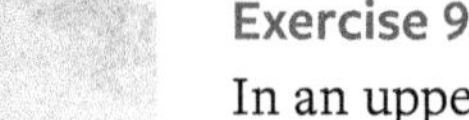

FIGURE 9.12 Milk and Sugar

Exercise 9.4

In an upper-tail test of the population mean we are looking at a situation in which the sample mean does not deviate too much toward larger values, so we are looking at the upper tail. In other words, we don't care if the sample mean is too small. Solve the following problem by using the `z.test()` function from the `TeachingDemos` package, with the option `alternative = "greater"`.

A company claims that a can of condensed milk has no more than 20 grams of sugar. We sample 35 cans and discovered that, on average, the cans have 21 grams of sugar. Assuming that the amount of sugar in each can has a standard deviation of 2.5 grams, can we reject the claim at a 0.05 significance level?

Exercise 9.5

FIGURE 9.13 Dogs and Mean Weight

Suppose that the mean weight of a breed of dogs is 12.4 kg with a population standard deviation of 2.2 kg. Our sample of 35 dogs is 11.3 kg. At a 0.05 significance level, can we reject the null hypothesis that the population mean should apply to our sample?

In this case we need to use a two-tailed test of the population mean because the deviations from what we expect could be in both directions. Therefore, we take the significance level, cut it in half, and assign it to both the upper and lower tails of the standard normal distribution. The critical zc is calculated as,

```
alpha = 0.05
zc = qnorm(1 - alpha/2)  #critical z at the upper tail
result = !((z < zc) && (z > -zc))  # z is NOT in (-zc, zc) interval
```

and we reject the hypothesis (`result` is `TRUE`) if the z score is not in the confidence interval for the given significance level.

Check the result by using the `z.test()` function from the `TeachingDemos` package, with the option `alternative = "two.sided"`

Exercise 9.6

In general, the t-test is more powerful than a simple z-test because we don't have to know the population standard deviation, and it works even for small sample sizes. The `t.test()` function in R performs one and two sample t-tests on vectors of data and can be applied for all tail cases.

Use the `t.test()` function to solve Exercise 9.1, in which the tested 24 batteries had the results: 264, 298, 292, 275, 284, 277, 290, 267, 291, 309, 272, 284, 296, 322, 294, 288, 291, 302, 274, 317, 316, 294, 291, and 277. Interpret the results.

Exercise 9.7

A company claims that a can of condensed milk has no more than 20 grams of sugar. We sample 15 cans and measure the following quantities of sugar in grams: 17, 18, 23, 24, 16, 22, 22, 22, 15, 13, 19, 23, 20, 22, and 24. Can we reject the claim at 0.05 level of significance?

Compare the results obtained by using function `t.test()` with the following code, where x is the vector of values, $M = 20$ is the hypothetical population mean, and $a = 0.05$ is the desired significance level.

```
pt((mean(x) - M)/(sd(x)/sqrt(length(x))), df=length(x), lower.tail=
FALSE) < a
```

Can you explain this code?

Exercise 9.8

Data on weights for 20 men and 20 women are contained in the data set `genderweight` in the package `datarium`. Install this package, and import the data set by using the command `data("genderweight", package = "datarium")`. Separate the data for men and for women,

```
women_weight=genderweight$weight[genderweight$group == "F"]
men_weight=genderweight$weight[genderweight$group == "M"]
```

and run a two sample t-test.

```
t.test(women_weight, men_weight)
```

Interpret the results.

Exercise 9.9

When the two samples we want to compare are NOT independent, for example, coming from repeated observations of the same subject but under different circumstances, we need to use a paired t-test.

Get the data set `immer` from the preloaded package `MASS`, which records the barley yield in years 1931 and 1932 of the same field.

```
library(MASS)
head(immer)
```

```
##    Loc Var    Y1    Y2
## 1   UF   M  81.0  80.7
```

```
## 2   UF    S 105.4  82.3
## 3   UF    V 119.7  80.4
## 4   UF    T 109.7  87.2
## 5   UF    P  98.3  84.2
## 6    W    M 146.6 100.4
```

Assuming the data have a normal distribution, we want to find if the yields from the two years are significantly different, at 0.05 level. The H_0 hypothesis is, therefore, that the mean of the two populations is the same. The same function `t.test()` can be used, but with the option `paired=TRUE` because the populations are not independent.

```
t.test(immer$Y1, immer$Y2, paired = TRUE)
##
##  Paired t-test
##
## data:  immer$Y1 and immer$Y2
## t = 3.324, df = 29, p-value = 0.002413
## alternative hypothesis: true difference in means is not equal to
0
## 95 percent confidence interval:
##   6.121954 25.704713
## sample estimates:
## mean of the differences
##                15.91333
```

Interpret the result calculated by R, and draw a conclusion.

Exercise 9.10

Last year 12% of students required financial aid. This year 30 out of 214 surveyed students require financial aid. The null hypothesis is that the ratio of students that require financial aid this year is below 12%. Can we reject this hypothesis at 0.05 significance level?

Is this an upper-tail or a lower-tail test about population proportions? Use the function `prop.test()` with the correct alternative argument to answer the question. This function can be also used to make two-sample population proportions tests.

9.4.2 Group Experiments

It's All Business

In this exercise students collect 40 stock prices from stocks traded on the New York Stock Exchange (NYSE) and 32 NASDAQ stocks. They calculate a current three-day average and a three-day average from a week ago for each stock. We have the idea that an increase in stock prices is the same for NYSE and NASDAQ, so we look at the proportion of stocks that increased on average from 10 days ago as compared to today.

Organize the work as a group such that each student does a part of the work. Take a careful sample, record the decisions the group made during the sample. Write the stock numbers in a neatly organized table. Use R to create a data frame with the data, and save it as a file in a computer using the command `save()`. Formulate the hypotheses, and define the problem the group wants to solve as a category, for example, is it a lower-tail small one-sample test?

Question 1:
What sampling strategy did the group use?

Question 2:
What is the group's null hypothesis?

Question 3:
What is the group's alternative hypothesis?

Question 4:
What kind of test is required to solve this problem?

Question 5:
Define in words the random variable, and the probability spaces for this problem.

Question 6:
What is the test statistic to be used for this problem?

Question 7:
Calculate the test statistic using the group's data.

Question 8:
What is group's conclusion? Formulate the conclusion as clear as possible, and explain the steps taken to arrive at this conclusion.

Question 9:
Draw a graph, and label it appropriately. Shade the actual level of significance.

Question 10:
What is the p-value?

9.4.3 Case Scenarios

CASE SCENARIO **Face-to-Face vs. Online Classes**

FIGURE 9.14 Online Class

The global pandemic in 2020 caused by COVID-19 forced many universities around the world to suddenly shift the modality of the way courses were taught from the traditional face-to-face formats to online. Students and professors were concerned about the impact on student knowledge this shift might have caused. The file "grades" contains data on 25 students in a basic statistic class. The data are student grades from two exams that occurred the same semester as the modality shift resulting from the coronavirus pandemic. Both exams were scored on a scale of 1–100, the higher the score the better. Exam 1 was taken while the class was being taught in the face-to-face format. Exam 2 occurred after classes shifted to the online format. The same students took both exams.

FIGURE 9.15 Face-to-Face Class

1. Provide the summary statistics for both exams.
2. In previous years, the mean grade on exam 1 was 80, and the mean score on exam 2 was 75. Based on the class data, test the hypothesis that the mean score on exam 1 is 80. Also test the hypothesis that the mean score on exam 2 is 75. State the test you used, the null and alternative hypothesis, test statistic, and p-value.
3. State your conclusion for Exercise 2, using $\alpha = 0.05$.
4. What test would you use to determine if there was a difference between the means of exam 1 and exam 2 grades? Explain why you chose this test.
5. Are all assumptions reasonably met for the test you propose in Exercise 4?
6. State the null and alternative hypotheses for the test to determine if there was a difference between the exam 1 and exam 2 grade means.
7. Perform the test you stated in Exercise 2. Provide the appropriate test statistics and p-value.
8. Assuming that $\alpha = 0.05$, what are your conclusions? Did students perform any differently after classes moved online?

QR Code Sidebar 9.1

https://DataAnalysisUsingR.com/datasets/grades.dat

9. Students who received a total of at least 160 points on the combined score of exam 1 and exam 2 passed the class. What proportion of the students passed the class?
10. In previous semesters, 95% of the students passed the class. Test the hypothesis that the true proportion of students who passed the class is at least 95%. Provide the null and alternative hypotheses, test statistic, and p-value.
11. What are your conclusions based on a 0.05 significance level?
12. Based on your data analysis, what impact, if any, did the COVID-19 global pandemic have on student learning outcomes for this class?

Use these questions as a self-assessment checklist for this chapter:

1. Do you know the difference between independent and dependent samples?
2. Do you know how to choose an appropriate hypothesis test for your research question?
3. Do you know how to perform hypothesis tests for the population mean and population proportion?
4. Do you know how to use R to obtain various statistics for hypothesis tests such as the p-value?

References

Ma, H., Wang, Z., & Zhu, K. (2015). Domestic content in China's exports and its distribution by firm ownership. *Journal of Comparative Economics, 43*(1), 3–18. https://doi.org/10.1016/j.jce.2014.11.006

Massougbodji, J., Zomahoun, H. T. V., Adisso, E. L., Sawadogo, J., Borde, V., Cameron, C., Moisan, H., Paquette, J., Akbaraly, Z., Châteauneuf, L., David, G., & Légaré, F. (2020). Citizen workshops in public libraries to disseminate and discuss primary care research results: A scaling-up study. DOI: 10.21203/rs.3.rs-136811/v1 PPR: PPR260023

The Premenopausal Breast Cancer Collaborative Group. (2018). Association of body mass index and age with subsequent breast cancer risk in premenopausal women. *Journal of the American Medical Association Oncology*, 4(11), e181771. https://doi.org/10.1001/jamaoncol.2018.1771

White, P., Redford, P., & Macdonald, J. (2019). An example motivated discourse of the independent samples t-test and the Welch test. *Quantitative Research Methods Project,* UWE. https://uwe-repository.worktribe.com/output/3217554

Figure Credits

Fig. 9.1: Copyright © 2020 by Melpomeni Kalliri. Reprinted with permission.
Fig. 9.2: Copyright © Unsplash/Bill Oxford.
Fig. 9.3: Copyright © 2020 by Melpomeni Kalliri. Reprinted with permission.
Fig. 9.4: Copyright © Unsplash/ThisisEngineering RAEng.
Fig. 9.5: Copyright © Unsplash/Vicky Sim.
Fig. 9.6: Copyright © Unsplash/Brooke Lark.
Fig. 9.7: Copyright © Unsplash/Nathan Dumlao.
Fig. 9.8: Copyright © Unsplash/Brooke Lark.
Fig. 9.9: Copyright © Unsplash/Louis Velazquez.
Fig. 9.10: Copyright © 2020 by Melpomeni Kalliri. Reprinted with permission.
Fig. 9.11: Copyright © Unsplash/Fran Innocenti.
Fig. 9.12: Copyright © Unsplash/Irene Kredenets.
Fig. 9.13: Copyright © Unsplash/Alvan Nee.
Fig. 9.14: Copyright © Unsplash/Bruno Cervera.
Fig. 9.15: Copyright © Unsplash/NeONBRAND.

CHAPTER

10

Chi-Square Tests and *F*-Distribution

CHAPTER OUTLINE

CHAPTER OBJECTIVES

After completing this chapter, you will be able to perform the following:

1. Use the chi-square distribution to test goodness-of-fit and to test independence.
2. Use the *F*-distribution to compare two variances.
3. Use one-way and two-way analysis of variance to test hypotheses involving three or more means.
4. Perform Chi-square tests, *F*-tests, and ANOVA using R and RStudio.

Dandelions (*Taraxacum officinale*) are sometimes seen as a way to make wishes come true. However, many health food enthusiasts also view dandelions as the perfect health food. This perennial herb is highly nutritious and loaded with vitamins, minerals, and fiber. It is also very versatile. The leaves can be tossed with salads or sautéed. Its yellow flowers are used to make dandelion jelly. This herb can also be used to make beverages such as tea, coffee substitutes, beer, and wine. Dandelion honey has many health benefits as well. Researchers conducted a survey of consumer preferences on the bee product market. They used a χ^2 test of independence to determine whether age was independent on the frequency of dandelion honey consumption (Kobala, et al., 2019). In this chapter you will learn how to conduct such a χ^2 test of independence as well other hypothesis tests that use the χ^2 and the F-distributions.

FIGURE 10.1 Make a Wish

Chapter Vocabulary

- A multinomial experiment is a probability experiment consisting of a fixed number of independent trials in which there are more than two possible outcomes for each trial. The probability of each outcome remains the same from trial to trial, and each outcome is grouped into a category.
- The observed frequency O of a category is defined as the number of sample elements contained in a specific category.
- The expected frequency E of a category is defined as the calculated frequency for the category.
- A chi-square goodness-of-fit test is a statistical test used to determine whether a frequency distribution fits an expected distribution.
- The chi-square distribution is a probability distribution obtained from the values of $(n-1)s^2/\sigma^2$ when random samples are selected from a normally distributed population with a variance of σ^2.
- A chi-square independence test is a statistical test used to determine whether the occurrence of one variable affects the probability of the occurrence of another variable.
- A probability density function (pdf) is a statistical expression that defines the likelihood of an outcome for a continuous random variable.
- A cumulative distribution function (cdf) is a statistical expression that defines the probability that a continuous or discrete random variable X will take a value less than or equal to the realized value x.
- The F-distribution is continuous distribution. It is a family of distributions characterized by the ratio of the variances of two normally distributed populations; F stands for Fisher.
- The F-test is a statistical test in which the test statistic has an F-distribution under the assumption that the null hypothesis is true.
- ANOVA (analysis of variance) is a statistical test that separates the observed variation in a data set into two parts, between groups and within groups. ANOVA is used to compare differences of means among more than two groups.
- A main effect is the effect of one independent variable on the dependent variable.
- The interaction effect is the effect of both independent variables on the dependent variable.
- SSB—Sum of squares between groups
- SSW—Sum of squares within groups

10.1 Chi-Square Tests

Several statistical hypothesis tests rely on the chi-square distribution. This section covers two such tests—the chi-square goodness-of-fit test and the chi-square test of independence.

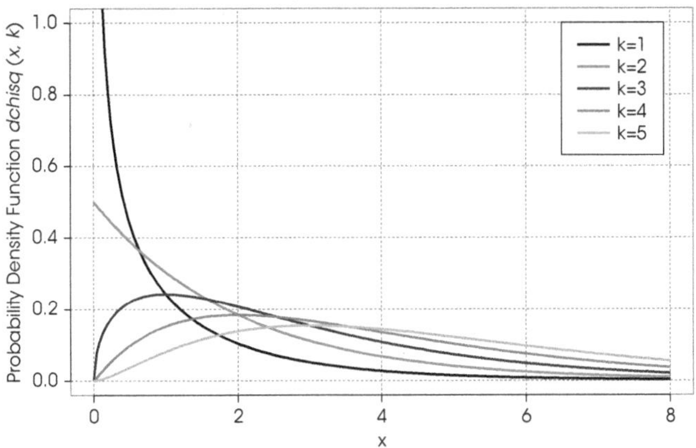

FIGURE 10.2 Chi-Square Probability Density Function (PDF)

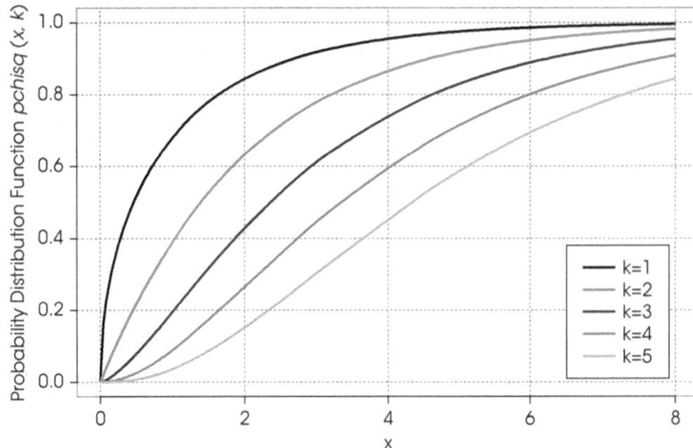

FIGURE 10.3 Chi-Square Cumulative Distribution Function (CDF)

A chi-square goodness-of-fit test is a test for goodness-of-fit in categorical data analysis. It determines whether a frequency distribution fits a specific pattern. The chi-square test of independence is a hypothesis test for determining whether the occurrence of one random variable affects the probability of the occurrence of another random variable.

10.1.1 Chi-Square Goodness-of-Fit Test

A nonprofit partner of the U. S. Small Business Association, SCORE (2016), wants to determine the proportions of top challenges for small business owners. To determine these proportions, the nonprofit can perform a multinomial experiment.

A multinomial experiment is an extension of a binomial experiment. Whereas as binomial experiment is a probability experiment consisting of a fixed number of independent trials in which there are only two possible outcomes for each trial, a multinomial experiment is a probability experiment consisting of a fixed number of independent trials in which there are more than two possible outcomes for each trial. The probability of each outcome remains constant from trial to trial, and each outcome is grouped into a category.

Because the nonprofit organization wants to test the claim concerning the expected distribution of proportions of top challenges for small business owners, it can compare the distribution of proportions obtained in the multinomial experiment to the expected distribution.

The nonprofit claims that the expected distribution of challenges for small business owners is as shown in the table (SCORE, 2016).

FIGURE 10.4 Thank-You Sign

DISTRIBUTION OF TOP SMALL BUSINESS CHALLENGES	
Cash flow	22%
Costs of running business	19%
Revenue/sales	13%
Credit availability	9%
Various other challenges	37%

To test this claim, the nonprofit can perform a chi-square goodness-of fit test using the null and alternative hypotheses:

H_0: The expected distribution of top small business challenges is 22% for cash flow, 19% for costs of running a business, 13% for revenue/sales, 9% for credit availability, and 37% for various other challenges.

H_a: The distribution of top small business challenges differs from the expected distribution.

The observed frequencies and expected frequencies are used to calculate the test statistic for the chi-square goodness-of-fit test. The **observed frequency O** of a category is the number of sample elements contained in a specific category. For example, if university students have a choice among class formats, then the formats fall in four specific categories:

1. Online synchronous
2. Online asynchronous
3. Traditional
4. Hybrid

The **expected frequency E** of a category is the calculated frequency for the category. The formula for the expected frequency of category i is

$$E_i = np_i,$$

where n is the number of trials (sample size) and p_i is the probability of the ith category. In the class formats example above, there are four categories in which the expected frequency E_i of category i can be calculated using the above formulation.

Two assumptions must be met to perform a chi-square goodness-of-fit test:

1. The observed frequencies must be obtained from a random sample.
2. Each expected frequency must be at least 5.

Example:

A business coach randomly selects 300 small businesses and asks owners to identify the top business challenges.

Survey results are shown in the table.

SURVEY RESULTS (N = 300)	
Cash flow	76
Costs of running business	67
Revenue/sales	39
Credit availability	27
Various other challenges	91

FIGURE 10.5 Local Toy Store

Determine the observed and expected frequencies for the top small business challenges.

Solution:

The observed frequency for each small business challenge is the number of small business owners in the survey identifying a challenge. The expected frequency for each challenge is the product of the number of small business owners in the survey who named that specific challenge and the probability that a business owner will name that specific challenge. The observed frequencies and expected frequencies are shown in the table.

TOP BUSINESS CHALLENGES	% OF OWNERS	OBSERVED FREQUENCY	EXPECTED FREQUENCY
Cash flow	22%	76	(300)(.22) = 66
Cost of running business	19%	67	(300)(.19) = 57
Revenue/sales	13%	39	(300)(.13) = 39
Credit availability	9%	27	(300)(.09) = 27
Various other challenges	37%	91	(300)(.37) = 111

There are several types of goodness-of-fit tests in statistics that rely on various distributions. A chi-square goodness-of-fit test is a statistical test used to determine whether a frequency distribution fits an expected distribution.

The sampling distribution of the chi-square goodness-of-fit test is a chi-square distribution with $k - 1$ degrees of freedom, where k is the number of categories. The test statistic is

$$\chi^2 = \Sigma(O - E)^2/E,$$

where O represents the observed frequency of each category, and E represents the expected frequency of each category.

Like the t-distribution, the chi-square distribution is a continuous distribution that is characterized by a family of curves parametrized by degrees of freedom. The symbol for chi-square is χ^2, which is the Greek letter chi, pronounced "ki."

Like the t-distribution, the chi-square distribution is related to the normal distribution. The chi-square distribution is a probability distribution obtained from the values of $(n - 1)s^2/\sigma^2$ when random samples are selected from a normally distributed population with a variance of σ^2.

Additional properties of a chi-square random variable include that it is positive and that its distribution is skewed to the right. The distribution becomes symmetric when the degrees of freedom approach 100. Appendix A, Table 9 provides percentiles for the chi-square distribution. Additionally, the *qth* percentile can be obtained from the R function `qchisq(alpha, df)`, where *alpha* represents the cumulative probability, and *df* represents degrees of freedom.

Example:

A nonprofit organization claims that the top challenges for small business owners are as shown in the table (SCORE, 2016).

DISTRIBUTION OF TOP SMALL BUSINESS CHALLENGES	
Cash flow	22%
Costs of running business	19%
Revenue/sales	13%
Credit availability	9%
Various other challenges	37%

A business coach randomly selects 300 small businesses and asks owners to identify the top challenges. Survey results are shown in the table.

SURVEY RESULTS (N = 300)	
Cash flow	76
Costs of running business	67
Revenue/sales	39
Credit availability	27
Various other challenges	91

At the $\alpha = 0.01$ level of significance, test the nonprofit's claim.

Solution:

The observed and expected frequencies were calculated in the first example. Because the observed frequencies were obtained using a random sample, and each expected frequency is a least 5, we can use the chi-square goodness-of-fit test to test the proposed distribution. The null and alternative hypotheses are below.

H_0: The expected distribution of top small business challenges is 22% for cash flow, 19% for costs of running a business, 13% for revenue/sales, 9% for credit availability, and 37% for various other challenges.

H_a: The distribution of top small business challenges differs from the expected distribution

Because there are five categories, the chi-square distribution has $df = k - 1 = 5 - 1 = 4$ degrees of freedom. Since $df = 4$ and $\alpha = 0.01$, the critical value is $\chi_0^{\,2} = 13.277$. This percentile can be obtained from the chi-square table found in Appendix A, Table 9 or from the R command:

```
> qchisq(.99,4).
```

The rejection region is $\chi^2 > 13.277$. The test statistic is

$$\begin{aligned}\chi^2 &= \Sigma\,(O - E)^2/E \\ &= (76 - 66)^2/66 \\ &\quad + (67 - 57)^2/57 \\ &\quad + (39 - 39)^2/39 \\ &\quad + (27 - 27)^2/27 \\ &\quad + (91 - 111)^2/111 \\ &= 310.87.\end{aligned}$$

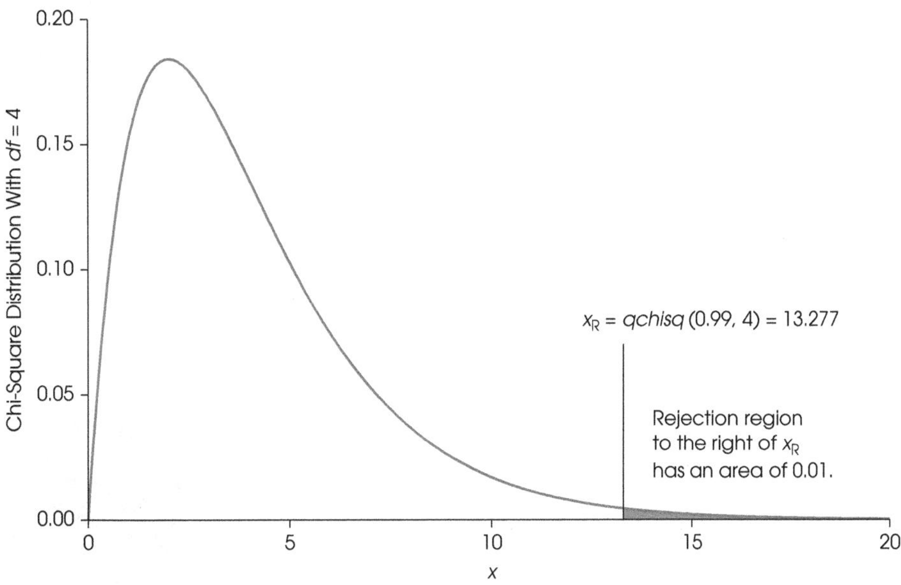

FIGURE 10.6 Rejection Region for Chi-Square Distribution

The figure shows the rejection region and the chi-square test statistic. Because the test statistic is in the rejection region, we reject the null hypothesis at the $\alpha = 0.01$ level of significance. We can conclude that there is enough evidence at the 1% level of significance to reject the claim that the actual distribution of small business challenges and the expected distribution are the same.

10.1.2 Chi-Square Test of Independence

Alcoholics Anonymous (AA) is one of the most well-known treatment approaches for recovering from alcohol abuse (See https://www.aa.org/). In AA, members are encouraged to follow a 12-step program and to attend daily meetings for the rest of their lives in order to help motivate and keep one another accountable for their alcohol use.

Addiction specialists have criticized AA for its low sobriety success rate of between 8% and 12% (American Addiction Centers, 2020). AA has also been criticized for encouraging some members to leave their marriages if the spouse is a nonalcoholic or not a member of AA. They have also been accused of destroying marriages one step at time (12 Step, 2015).

A psychologist wants to determine if AA membership is independent of encouraging a member to file for divorce. A chi-square independence test can be used to answer such a question.

A **chi-square independence test** is a statistical test used to determine whether the occurrence of one variable affects the probability of the occurrence of another variable. This test has two assumptions:

- Observed frequencies were obtained from a random sample.
- Each expected frequency is at least 5.

To perform the chi-square independence test, follow these steps:

Step 1. Obtain observed frequencies from a random sample.

Step 2. Determine each expected frequency. The computing formula for the expected frequency of each category for a contingency table cell is

$E_{r,c}$ = [(row r sum)(column c sum)]/(sample size).

Step 3. Compute the test statistic:

$\chi^2 = \Sigma\ (O - E)^2/E$, where O represents the observed frequency of each category and E represents the expected frequency of each category.

Example:

A psychologist surveyed a random sample of alcoholics who were married to nonalcoholics. The respondents were using a treatment approach for their alcoholism and had recently filed for divorce. They were asked if their treatment program was a major contributing factor in encouraging them to file for divorce.

At the $\alpha = 0.01$ level of significance, the psychologist would like to determine if AA membership is related to encouragement for filing for divorce.

FIGURE 10.7 Divorce Figures

Solution:

The contingency table shows the observed frequencies.

	TREATMENT PROGRAM ENCOURAGED DIVORCE	
AA member	Yes	No
Yes	64	34
No	40	51

The following table contains both the observed frequencies and the expected frequencies for the contingency table cells.

TREATMENT PROGRAM ENCOURAGED DIVORCE FILING			
AA member	Yes	No	Total
Yes	64 (53.93)	34 (44.07)	98
No	40 (50.07)	51 (40.93)	91
Total	104	85	189

Because each expected frequency is at least 5 and the respondents were randomly selected, we can use the chi-square independence test to test whether the variables AA Membership and Treatment Program Encouraged Divorce Filing are independent. The null and alternative hypotheses are:

H_0: The variables AA Membership and Treatment Programing Encouraged Divorce Filing are independent.

H_a: The variables AA Membership and Treatment Programing Encouraged Divorce Filing are dependent.

Because the contingency table has two rows and two columns, the chi-square distribution has (r - 1)(c - 1) = (2 - 1)(2 - 1) = 1 degree of freedom. Because $df = 1$ and $\alpha = 0.01$, the critical value is $X_o^2 = 6.635$. This percentile can be obtained from the chi-square table or from the

```
> qchisq(.99,1).
```

The rejection region is $\chi^2 > 6.635$. The test statistics is

$$\begin{aligned}\chi^2 &= \Sigma(O - E)^2/E \\ &= (64 - 53.93)^2/53.93 \\ &\quad + (34 - 44.07)^2/44.07 \\ &\quad + (40 - 50.07)^2/50.07 \\ &\quad + (51 - 40.93)^2/40.93 \\ &= 8.684.\end{aligned}$$

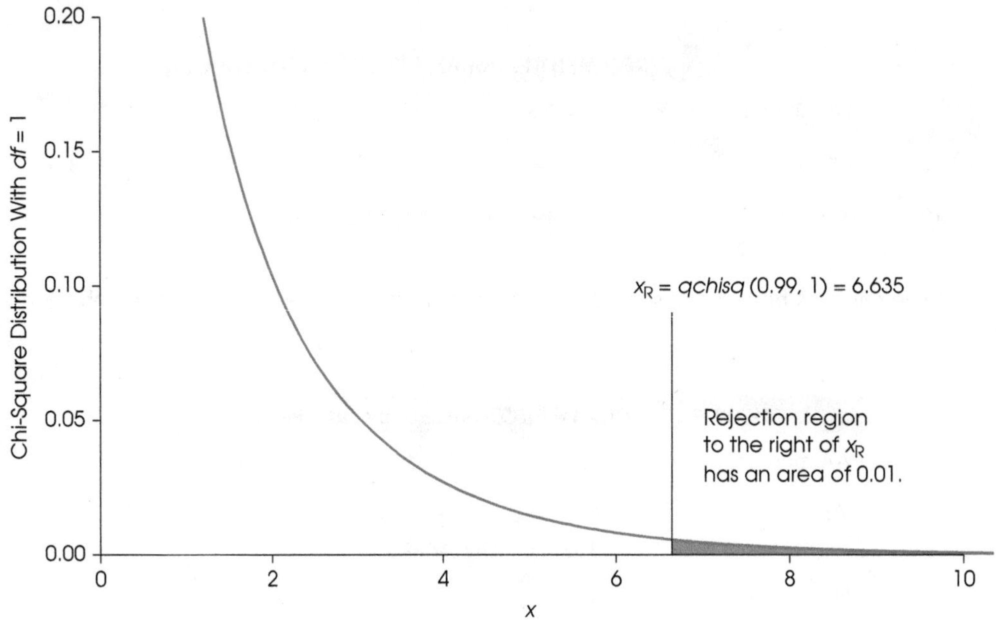

FIGURE 10.8 Critical Value for Chi-Square Statistic

The figure shows the location of the rejection region and the chi-square test statistic. Because the test statistic lies in the rejection region, we reject the null hypothesis at the $\alpha = 0.01$ level of significance.

Interpretation:
We can conclude that there is enough evidence at the 1% level of significance that AA membership is dependent on a treatment programing encouraging divorce.

In addition to the hypothesis tests mentioned in this textbook, there is a chi-square test that compares a single sample variance to a specific population variance. For the comparison of two variances or standard deviations, an *F*-test is used. The *F*-test is the topic of the next section.

10.1.3 Exercises

Understanding Concepts

1. Name two kinds of chi-square tests.

2. Which chi-square test determines whether a frequency distribution fits a specific pattern?

3. Which chi-square test is used to determine whether the occurrence of one variable affects the probability of the occurrence of another variable?

True or false? In Exercises 4–8, determine whether the statement is true or false. If it is false, rewrite it as a true statement.

4. Researchers in the Kobala et al. (2019) study used a chi-square goodness-of-fit test to determine whether age was independent of the frequency of dandelion honey consumption.

5. A chi-square goodness-of-fit test is a test for goodness of fit in qualitative data.

6. Like the *t*-distribution, the chi-square distribution is a discrete distribution that is characterized by a family of curves parametrized by degrees of freedom.

7. The chi-square goodness-of-fit test is one of several goodness-of-fit tests in the field of statistics.

8. Chi-square random variables are always positive.

Skill Building

9. Houston, Texas, USA, is located in Harris County. An article in the *Houston Chronicle* (Daniel, 2012) compared the demographics of Harris County juror pools to the demographics of Harris County citizens, according to the 2010 census The percentages and frequencies are provided in the table below.

	WHITE	AFRICAN AMERICAN	HISPANIC	ASIAN	OTHER	TOTAL
Jury Percentage	59	17	16	5	2.7	100
County Percentage	45	26	23	5.3	0.7	100
	-------	-----	----	----		-----
Jury Frequency	37,300	10,800	10,200	3,200	1707	63,207

a. What is(are) the variable(s)?

b. What is the measurement type of each variable?

c. What is the null hypothesis?

d. Calculate the goodness-of-fit test between the observed and expected values using the table above.

e. If the critical value for a chi-square ($df = 4$, $\alpha = .05$) = 9.44, what do you decide? How about if we use the $\alpha = .005$ level, with a critical value = 14.86?

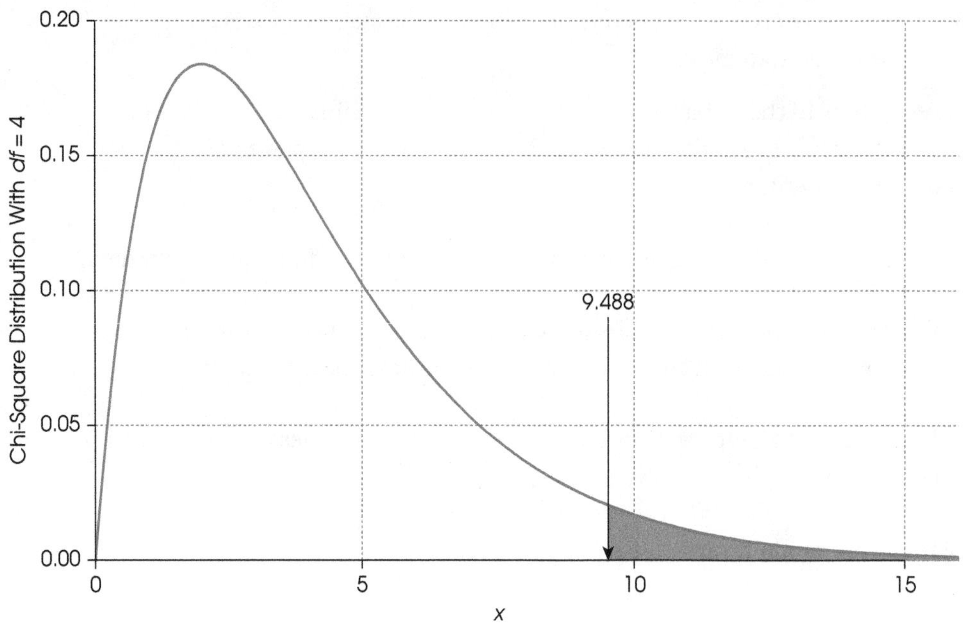

FIGURE 10.9 A Theoretical Distribution

10. At a speed-dating event, researchers compared males' and females' interest in a second date (yes/no).

SECOND DATE?	FEMALE—YES	FEMALE—NO	TOTAL
MALE—YES	63	83	146
MALE—NO	64	66	130
TOTAL	127	149	276

a. What are the variables?

b. What is the measurement type of each variable?

c. What is the null hypothesis?

d. Calculate the chi-square test of independence for male and female decisions on a second date.

11. Did the *Titanic*'s passengers' class (quality of room) predict survival? How would you test this question?

PASSENGERS	SURVIVED	DIED	TOTAL
First-class	203	122	325
Third-class	178	528	706
Total	381	650	1,031

Use a test of independence to see if similar percentages of passengers died in first- and third-class.

12. Pediatric optometrists asked the parents of young patients about the use of lights in the child's room at night. They wondered if darkness (no light) versus the use of a night light or room light during their child's first two years might be related to nearsightedness in the child. The data are below.

	DARK	NIGHT LIGHT	ROOM LIGHT
Nearsighted	18	78	41
Not Nearsighted	34	154	34
TOTAL	172	232	75

a. What is (are) the variable(s)?

b. What is the measurement type of each variable?

c. What is the null hypothesis?

d. Calculate the chi-square test of independence between nearsightedness and light during sleep using this information.

13. DEIP Flap: Postmastectomy Breast Implant Alternative

FIGURE 10.10 Sean Boutros, MD, FACS

Breast cancer is the most common type of cancer among women in the United States. In 2022, the American Cancer Society estimates that there will be 287,850 new cases of breast cancer (Siegel et al., 2022). Breast cancer treatments include radiation therapy, chemotherapy, and surgery. A *mastectomy* is a type of breast cancer surgery that removes the entire breast. Breast reconstruction can be done or started by plastic surgeons at the time of the mastectomy or after the incisions have healed. Dr. Sean Boutros, MD, FACS (Fellow of the American College of Surgeons) is a board-certified plastic surgeon who practices in Houston, Texas. He specializes in advanced plastic surgery procedures, such as cosmetic, reconstructive, and craniofacial procedures. Dr. Boutros pioneered the cosmetic deep inferior epigastric perforator (DIEP) flap, a natural breast augmentation surgery that does not require breast implants. It instead uses a woman's own body tissue that is transferred from the abdomen to microsurgically reshape and volumize the breast. Dr. Boutros conducted a study to determine if surgical procedures on the breast called "single vein" and "double vein" are independent of flap fat necrosis (Boutros, 2013). *Flap fat necrosis* is a noncancerous condition that commonly develops after an injury or any type of trauma to the breast tissue. Dr. Boutros performed a chi-square test of independence with a Yates correction that corrected for small sample sizes and obtained a p-value = 0.404.

a. State the null hypothesis.

b. State the alternative hypothesis.

c. At the 0.05 level of significance, use the p-value from the chi-square test of independence to determine if there is a statistically significant difference between type of surgery and fat necrosis.

d. Interpret your answer in the context of the problem.

Extending Concepts

14. In which way is the hypothesis test for a population proportion related to the chi-square goodness-of-fit test?

15. Which hypothesis test can be used to determine whether gender is independent of a person's favorite fruit? For this hypothetical test, 400 college students were randomly selected and their favorite fruit was recorded.

16. What happens to the mode of the chi-square distribution as the number of degrees of freedom increases?

17. By examining Figure 10.3, what is the right-tail critical value for the chi-square distribution with 4 degrees of freedom that corresponds to 20% of the values being greater than the critical value?

18. A spinning wheel with numbers from 0 to 9 is spun 100 times, and the results are recorded. If we want to use a chi-square test under the assumption that the spinner is fair, what is the expected count for spinning a 5? Which chi-square test should you use?

10.2 Comparing Two Variances

Related to the chi-square distribution is the F-distribution. An F random variable is the ratio of two chi-square random variables divided by their degrees of freedom.

There are numerous applications of the F-distribution. One such application is a hypothesis that is used to determine if two population variances are equal.

10.2.1 *F*-Distribution

The **F-distribution** was developed by British statistician and geneticist Sir Ronald Fisher (1890–1962). Fisher is known as the father of modern, or 20th century, statistics and known for creating such tests as the **F-test** and analysis of variance. The F stands for Fisher. Because Fisher is the father of 20th-century statistics, his contributions are well respected in the field. However, his views on race, ethnicity, and superiority were quite controversial even for his generation (Brattain, 2007).

Fisher developed the F-distribution to study the behavior of two variances from random samples that were taken from two independent normal populations. Knowing whether two population variances are equal is important in selecting the appropriate statistical method to study population means.

There are four distinguishing characteristics of the *F*-distribution:

- The *F*-distribution is a family of curves based on the degrees of freedom of the variance of the numerator and the degrees of freedom of the variance of the denominator.
- The test statistic for the *F*-test, *F*, is always non-negative.
- The distribution is positively skewed.
- The mean value of the test statistic *F* is approximately equal to 1. This is true for all *F*-distributions.

10.2.2 *F*-Test for Variances

The phrase visit-to-visit variability (VVV) is often used when referring to patients who have health conditions concerning hypertension or high cholesterol. High cholesterol is known in the medical field as hypercholesterolemia. For patients with hypercholesterolemia, a high VVV means that the cholesterol levels changed drastically each time the patient visited a doctor. Kim, et al. (2017) noted that a high VVV in cholesterol levels has been shown to be an "independent predictor of major adverse cardiovascular events in patients with coronary artery disease." Researchers are interested in comparing the variances of cholesterol of men to that of women. A statistical hypothesis test that can be used to make such a comparison is called the *F*-test.

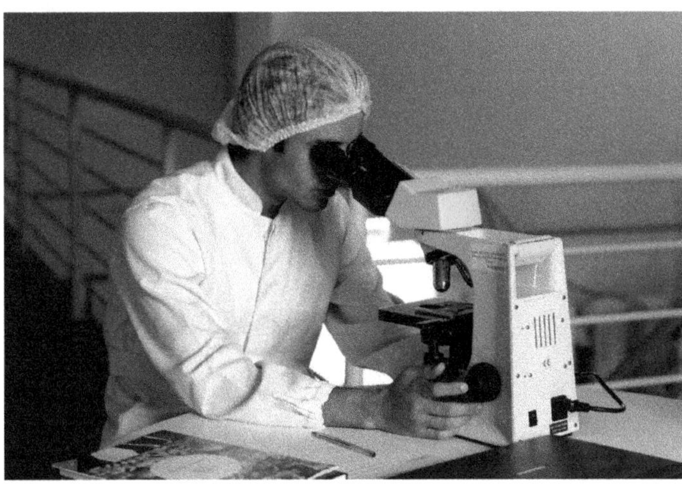

FIGURE 10.11 Scientist at Work

The *F*-test is used to compare two variances or two standard deviations. The test statistic for the *F*-test is

$$F = s_1^2 / s_2^2 ,$$

where the larger of the two variances is usually placed in the numerator regardless of the subscripts. The *F*-test has degrees of freedom for both the numerator $n_1 - 1$ and the denominator $n_2 - 1$. You can use Tables 10A–D in Appendix A to find the critical *F* values for various combinations of parameters.

Example:

A statistical study of serum cholesterol level by gender and race was performed. The researchers claim that the variance for women is greater than that for men (Tharu & Tsokos, 2017). They assume that two samples were selected from two normally distributed populations in which the population variances are equal. Because the assumptions of an *F*-test are met, they can proceed with a hypothesis test. They test at the α = 0.05 level of significance.

WOMEN	MEN
$n_1 = 2{,}262$	$n_2 = 9{,}602$
$s_1^2 = 2{,}736.34$	$s_2^2 = 2{,}345.47$

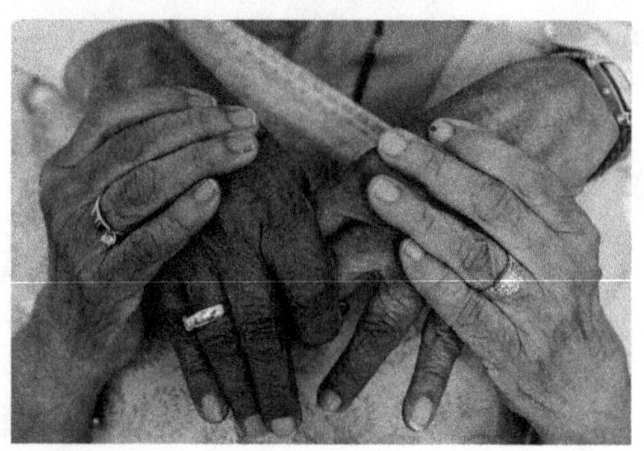

FIGURE 10.12 Love

Answer:

The null and alternative hypotheses are

$$H_0: \sigma_1^2 = \sigma_2^2$$
$$H_a: \sigma_1^2 > \sigma_2^2,$$

where σ_1^2 and σ_2^2 represent the variances of serum cholesterol levels for women and men, respectively.

The test statistic is

$$F = s_1^2 / s_2^2$$
$$F = 2{,}736.34/2{,}345.47$$
$$= 1.17.$$

The critical value is obtained from the R command:

```
> qf(.95,2261,9601)
```

which is $F_{crit} = 1.055332$. Therefore, the researchers reject the null hypothesis at the α = 0.05 level of significance and conclude that there is enough evidence to support the claim that the cholesterol variability of women is higher than that of men.

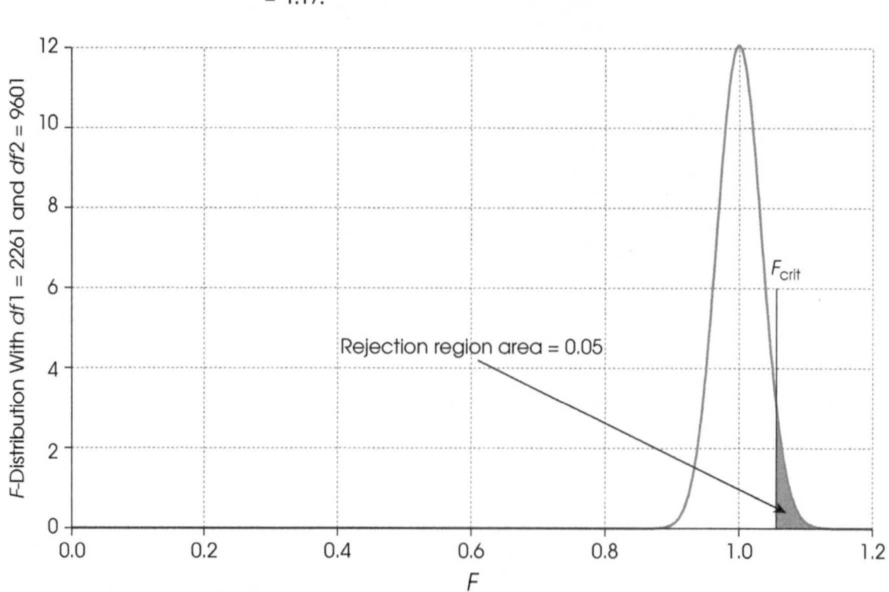

FIGURE 10.13 Critical Value for *F*-Statistic

10.2.3 Exercises

Understanding Concepts

1. The F random variable is the ratio of what?

2. The F-distribution is a family of curves based on the degrees of freedom of what?

3. Describe the shape of the F-distribution.

4. When determining the test statistic for the F-test, the larger of the two sample variances is usually placed in the numerator regardless of the subscripts. This means that the test statistic, F, is always greater than or equal to what number?

True or false? In Exercises 5–9, determine whether the statement is true or false. If it is false, rewrite it as a true statement.

5. The F-distribution is a family of curves, each of which is determined by two types of degrees of freedom.

6. Similar to the t-distribution, the F-distribution is symmetric.

7. The total area under some F-distribution curves equals 1.

8. Because the test statistic for the F-distribution is always greater than or equal to 1, all one-tailed tests are right-tailed tests.

Skill Building

9. How many parameters are needed for an F-distribution? What is/are the parameter(s)?

10. What type of data are modeled using the F-distribution?

11. Compute the area to the right of the F-statistic based on the following information:

    a. $F(2,8) = 15$

    b. $F(8,2) = 15$

    c. $F(8,8) = 15$

    d. $F(100,100) = 15$

    e. $F(1,1) = 15$

12. Provide a graph for each of the F-distributions in problem 2. Describe the properties of the F-distribution.

Use the data in the table below to answer questions 13–19:

SAMPLE 1	40	46	10	32	38	45
SAMPLE 2	2	2	5	18	9	0

13. Compute the standard deviation and variance for each sample.

14. Do the variances seem to be equal? Explain.

15. What are the null and alternative hypotheses to test for equal variances?

16. What is the test statistic to test for equal variances?

17. What are the degrees of freedom associated with the test statistic to test the hypotheses in problem 7?

18. Perform the test of equal variances. What is the *P*-value? Interpret the result.

19. Provide a histogram or Q-Q plot of the data. Was the normality assumption of the data reasonably met to perform this test? Explain.

Extending Concepts

20. What is the mode of the *F*-distribution?

21. Can you use the *F*-test to compare two populations that have different means?

22. Can the *F*-test be used to decide if two samples came from the same population?

23. Can the *F*-test be used to decide if two populations have the same standard deviation?

24. What is the critical value of *F* when comparing the variance of two normal populations? Assume that both sample sizes are 10, and that the level of significance of significance is .10. Do you use Table 10A, 10B, 10C, or 10D for this?

25. Why is *F*-distribution centered around the value $F = 1$?

10.3 Analysis of Variance (ANOVA)

Analysis of variance (ANOVA) is a hypothesis test that is used to compare the means of three or more populations. Even though the means are compared, it is not called an analysis of means because the variances are used to make inferences about the means.

The variance between the samples is compared to the variance within each sample. If the between variation is much larger than the within variation, then the means of different groups will not be equal. If the between and within variations are approximately equal, then there will not be a statistically significant difference between means.

When sampling from a population, sample means are expected to differ from sample to sample due to chance, which is called sampling error. ANOVA answers the question of whether the observed differences in means among groups are greater than the expected differences due to chance or due to a true difference in the population of means.

When comparing the means of two independent samples, ANOVA is equivalent to using a two-sample *t*-test. If one independent variable is being tested, the procedure is named a one-way ANOVA. If two independent variables are being tested, it is called a two-way ANOVA.

10.3.1 One-Way ANOVA

Autonomous and unmanned technologies continue to develop and become more commercially available. The enhanced safety of these vehicles requires automobile insurance companies to adjust insurance premiums as car accidents plummet (Xu & Fan, 2019).

A consumer protection organization uses a one-way ANOVA to compare the average annual insurance premiums for fully automated vehicles, partially automated vehicles, and traditional vehicles.

To perform a one-way ANOVA test, the following conditions must be satisfied:

- Each of the k samples $k \geq 3$, are randomly selected from a normal or approximately normal population.
- The samples are independent of each other.
- Each of the k populations has the same variance.

The null and alternative hypotheses are:

H_0: All population means are equal.

$$\mu_1 = \mu_2 = \mu_3 = \ldots = \mu_k$$

H_a: At least one mean is different from the others.

The alternative hypothesis states only that at least two population means are different from each other. It does not state which ones. To answer the question of which population means differ, a post-hoc test can be used (Kucuk, 2016).

FIGURE 10.14 The Cars of the Future

The sampling distribution of the test statistic is approximated by an *F*-distribution. The test statistic is

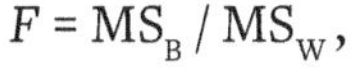

$$F = \mathrm{MS_B} \,/\, \mathrm{MS_W},$$

where MS_B is the variance between samples, and MS_W is the variance within samples.

$$\bar{\bar{x}} = \sum x/N$$
$$MS_B = SS_B / df_N$$
$$MS_W/ = SS_W/df_D.$$

The test has degrees of freedom for both the numerator $df_N = k - 1$ and the denominator $df_D = N - k$. N is the sum of the sample sizes:

$$N = n_1 + n_2 + ... + n_k.$$

The variance between samples measures the differences related to the treatment given to each sample. The variance within samples measures the differences related to entries within the same sample and is usually due to sampling error.

ANOVA Summary Table

VARIATION	SUM OF SQUARES	DEGREES OF FREEDOM	MEAN SQUARES	F
BETWEEN	SS_B	$df_N = k - 1$	$MS_B = SS_B/df_N$	MS_B/ MS_W
WITHIN	SS_W	$df_D = N - k$	$MS_W = SS_W/df_D$	

All one-way ANOVA tests are right-tailed hypothesis tests. Therefore, if the test statistic is greater than the critical value, then the null hypothesis is rejected. Results of a one-way analysis of variance test are usually summarized in an ANOVA summary table as illustrated above.

Example:

A consumer protection organization wants to determine whether there is a statistically significant difference in the average annual insurance premiums for fully automated vehicles, partially automated vehicles, and conventional vehicles.

At the $\alpha = 0.01$ level of significance, can they conclude that at least one mean premium is different from the others? Assume that each population of average annual insurance premiums is normally distributed and that the population variances are equal. The results are shown in the table.

FIGURE 10.15 Consumer World

FULLY AUTOMATED	PARTIALLY AUTOMATED	CONVENTIONAL
1,200	1,600	1,400
1,500	1,400	1,700
1,700	2,100	2,000
1,200	1,500	1,500
	1,900	
$n_1 = 4$	$n_2 = 5$	$n_3 = 4$
$\bar{x}_1 = 1{,}400$	$\bar{x}_2 = 1{,}700$	$\bar{x}_3 = 1{,}650$
$s_1^2 = 60{,}000$	$s_2^2 = 85{,}000$	$s_3^2 = 70{,}000$

Solution:

The null and alternative hypotheses are:

H_0: All population means are equal.

$$\mu_1 = \mu_2 = \mu_3$$

H_a: At least one mean is different from the others.

Because there are $k = 3$ samples, $df_N = k - 1 = 3 - 1 = 2$, and the denominator $df_D = N - k = 13 - 3 = 10$. The critical value is $F_{crit} = 7.56$. The critical value is obtained from the R command:

```
> qf(.99,2,10)
```

The rejection region is $F > 7.56$. The test statistic is calculated by finding

$$\bar{\bar{x}} = \sum x / N$$
$$\bar{\bar{x}} = \sum x / N$$
$$= (5{,}600 + 8{,}500 + 6{,}600)/13$$
$$= 1{,}592.31.$$

MS_B and MS_W are:

$$MS_B = SS_B / df_N = [4(1{,}400 - 1{,}592.31)^2 + 5(1{,}700 - 1{,}592.31)^2 + 4(1{,}650 - 1{,}592.31)^2] / (3 - 1)$$
$$= 2{,}19230.77/2$$
$$= 109{,}615.385$$

$$MS_W = SS_W / df_D = [(4 - 1)(60{,}000) + (5 - 1)(85{,}000) + (4 - 1)(70{,}000)] / (13 - 3)$$

$$= 730{,}000 / 10$$
$$= 73{,}000.$$

The test statistic is

$$F = MS_B / MS_W$$
$$= 109{,}615.385 / 73{,}000$$
$$= 1.50.$$

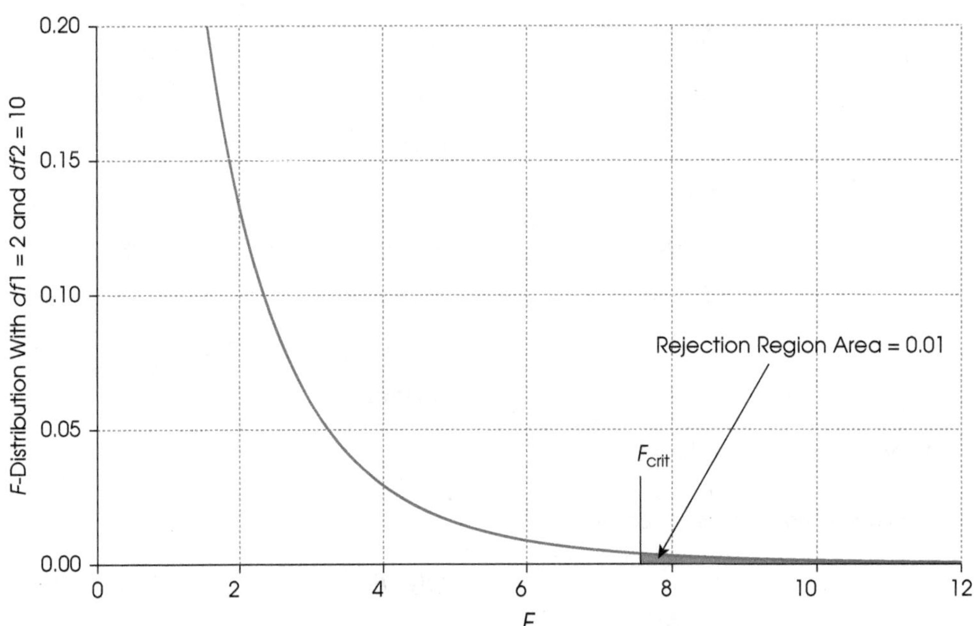

FIGURE 10.16 Rejection Region for *F*-Statistic

The figure shows the location of the rejection region. Because $F = 1.50$ is not in the rejection region, the consumer protection organization fails to reject the null hypothesis at the $\alpha = 0.01$ level of significance.

Interpretation:
There is not enough evidence at the 1% level of significance to conclude that there is a difference in the mean annual insurance premiums of fully automated, partially automated, and conventional vehicles.

10.3.2 Two-Way ANOVA

Garden peas (*Pisum sativum* L.) are valuable crops for many reasons both economically and nutritionally (Palcu et al., 2019). When early humans shifted from being hunter-gatherers, peas were one of the first crops cultivated. Peas were cultivated dating back to 9000 BC in the Crescent Fertile area. There are currently many varieties of peas. One such variety is the garden pea called the Bördi. Biologists want to determine the effects of seed bacterization and soil fertilization on production parameters (dependent variable) of the Bördi variety of pea.

Palcu, et al. (2019) randomly planted garden peas on 36 plots which formed 12 experimental variants, labeled V1, V2, ..., V12. The variants labeled V1 to V6 were

FIGURE 10.17 The Garden Pea

unbacterized, while those labeled V7 to V12 were bacterized (factor A). The control consisted of the unfertilized variants V1 and V7. The substance Universol was used as a fertilizer for variants V2, V3, V4, V8, V9, and V10. The variants that were fertilized with the substance Ferticare (factor B) were V5, V6, V11, and V12, while the second set of six variants were bacterized. This second set of variants is referred to as factor A. The unfertilized controls were variant one and variant seven. Six of the variants were fertilized with a substance called Universol. This is an illustration of a two-way ANOVA where the two factors are factor A and factor B, and the dependent variable is the production parameter.

A two-way ANOVA is used to test the effect of two factors or two independent variables on one dependent variable. A two-way ANOVA has three null hypotheses, one for each main effect and one for the interaction effect.

A main effect is the effect of one independent variable on the dependent variable. The interaction effect is the effect of both independent variables on the dependent variable.

Hypotheses for main effects are:

H_0: Bacterization has no effect on production parameters of the garden pea.

H_a: Bacterization has an effect on production parameters of the garden pea.

H_0: Fertilization has no effect on production parameters of the garden pea.

H_a: Fertilization has an effect on production parameters of the garden pea.

Hypotheses for interaction effects:

H_0: There is no interaction effect between bacterization and fertilization on production parameters of the garden pea.

H_0: There is an interaction effect between bacterization and fertilization on production parameters of the garden pea.

The assumptions of the two-way ANOVA test are the same as those of a one-way ANOVA test with the additional condition that all samples must be of the same size when conducting a two-way ANOVA test. An *F*-test statistic is calculated for each hypothesis. Therefore, it is possible to reject none, one, two, or all of the null hypotheses.

Hand computation of the two-way ANOVA is beyond the scope of this book. However, it is possible to do a two-way ANOVA in R using the R command:

```
summary.aov()
```

10.3.3 Exercises

Understanding Concepts

1. What does the acronym "ANOVA" represent?

2. What is the purpose of an ANOVA test?

3. When sampling from any population, sample averages are expected to differ from sample to sample due to chance. What is this called?

4. If you used ANOVA to compare the means of two independent samples, what type of hypothesis test would this be equivalent to?

True or false? In Exercises 5–10, determine whether the statement is true or false. If it is false, rewrite it as a true statement.

5. ANOVA is used to compare the variances of three or more populations.

6. In ANOVA, the variances are used to make inferences about means.

7. In ANOVA, the variance between samples is compared to the variances within each sample.

8. If the between variation is much larger than the within variation, then the means of different groups will be equal.

9. If the between and within variations are approximately equal, then there will not be a statistically significant difference between the means.

10. A statistically significant difference implies that the difference does not occur by chance.

Skill Building

11. Compute the p-values for the ANOVA F-test based on the following information:

a. There are 5 groups in a study with 6 observations per group. The F-statistic is 10.

b. The F-statistic is 5 with 3 with 5 degrees of freedom.

12. What is the difference between a one-way ANOVA and a two-way ANOVA? Provide an example of each.

Use the following to answer questions 13–17:

Consider the ANOVA table below that is based on an experiment.

Score

	SUMS OF SQUARES	DF	MEAN SQUARE	F
Group	3564	2		
Error	1991			
Total	5555	24		

13. Based on the table, how many total observations are there for this experiment? How many treatment groups? Explain.

14. How many degrees of freedom are there for error?

15. What is the value of the F-statistic to test for differences in population means?

16. What are the degrees of freedom of the F-statistic in problem 5?

17. What is the p-value for this example? Is it significant at the 0.05 level?

18. Consider the data below that are based on an experiment with two factors, A and B. Each factor has two levels. The value of the mean response is included. Provide a graph of the means and determine visually if there is an interaction. Explain.

LEVEL OF FACTOR A	LEVEL OF FACTOR B	MEAN RESPONSE
1	1	10
1	2	20
2	1	35
2	2	40

19. Fill out the degrees of freedom based on the source of variations listed below for the two-way ANOVA that would test for differences in population means based on the data in problem 18.

SOURCE OF VARIATION	DEGREES OF FREEDOM
Factor A	
Factor B	
Error	
Total	

20. Why is it not possible to test for interactions in problem 19?

Extending Concepts

21. Is ANOVA a test for comparing variances or means of populations?

22. In an ANOVA test with nine groups and a total sample of size of 24, the computed statistic is $F = 4.00$. Find the best p-value corresponding to this case from Tables 10A–10D.

23. In which way is ANOVA related to a t-test?

24. What is the result of the ANOVA tests if the statistic F is very close to 1?

25. What is the interaction effect in a two-way ANOVA?

10.4 R and RStudio

10.4.1 Programming Assignments

Exercise 10.1

A sum of squared normal random independent and identically distributed (i.i.d) random variables has a chi-square distribution. If Z_i are i.i.d `normal(0, 1)` random numbers, and

$$\chi^2 = \sum_{i=1}^{n} Z_i^2,$$

then χ^2 has a chi-square distribution with n degrees of freedom.

Let's do an R experiment to explore the chi-square distribution. First, generate many normal distributed numbers and break them into five groups. Here the `matrix` command is used to transform a vector of 50,000 random normal numbers generated by the command `rnorm` into a 10,000 rows x 5 column matrix

```
G = matrix(rnorm(50000), ncol=5)
```

Each resulting column vector is squared, and all added up to a new vector H:

```
H = G[,1]^2 + G[,2]^2 + G[,3]^2 + G[,4]^2 + G[,5]^2
```

We prepare a list of numbers representing the probability density function (PDF) for the chi-square distribution calculated for a list of values in a range from 0 to 20.0. Note that the chi-square random variable is always positive, being a sum of squares. The command `dchisq(q, 5)` is used for a chi-square distribution with 5 degrees of freedom.

```
q = seq(0, 20, 0.1); c2 = dchisq(q,5)
```

Next we plot a histogram of the numbers in vector H, with the bin height normalized such that the sum of areas of all bars sums up to unity, as opposed to the default when the bin height represents the bin frequency, by setting `freq = FALSE`. The number of bins in the histogram is set by the parameter `breaks = 20`. On the same graph we also plot the expected PDF as a set of orange lines with a line width of 2 pixels.

```
hist(H, breaks=20, freq=FALSE, main="chi-square distribution");
lines(q, c2, col = 'orange', lwd=2)
```

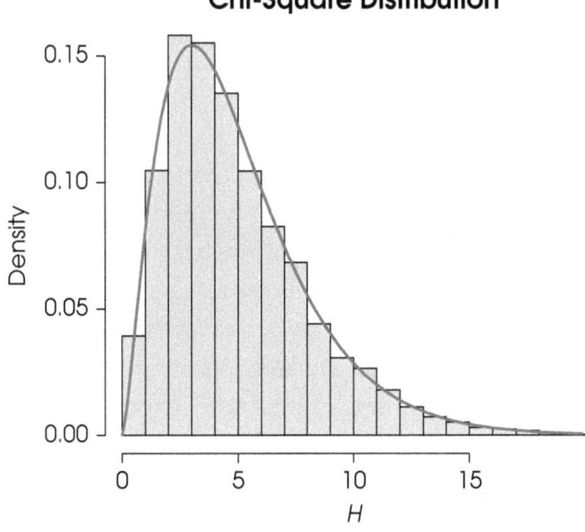

FIGURE 10.18 Chi-Square Distribution

Does this graph confirm the idea that a sum of squares of 5 i.i.d normal random variables are distributed according to the chi-square pdf? Explain your answer

Exercise 10.2

What can you tell about the mode, the median, and the mean values of the distribution you obtained for Exercise 10.1?

Exercise 10.3

Repeat Exercise 10.1. How do the mode, median, and mean value change when the number of degrees of freedom of the chi-square distribution changes? Run the program and observe the results for $df = 3$, $df = 4$, and $df = 5$.

Exercise 10.4

What will happen when *df* increases in Exercise 10.1? Is it true that the distribution start to look normal? Can you guess the mean and standard deviation?

Exercise 10.5

In a goodness-of-fit test, we seek to compare a set of categorical data against an expected set of probabilities associated with each categorical outcome associated with the data.

A die is tossed 200 times and we find the following distribution of rolls, when each face of the die represents a category label by the value of that face.

FACE	1	2	3	4	5	6
Number of rolls	32	31	32	30	33	42

The expected probability of each face is 1/6 if the die is fair. However, face 6 comes up 42 times, which is a little suspicious. Is this just a coincidence or perhaps a manufacturing defect?

The χ^2 statistic defined by

$$\chi^2 = \sum \frac{(f_i - e_i)^2}{e_i}$$

will be large when there is a big discrepancy between the actual frequencies f_i and the expected (model) frequencies e_i.

The inference will be accurate providing that the data is i.i.d and has a multinomial distribution specified by a set of probabilities. Also, the χ^2 test works well when the expected counts are larger than 5. Otherwise, a division by a small number distorts the results. Under these assumptions, the χ^2 statistic is approximately distributed according to a $n - 1$ degrees of freedom chi-square distribution. This means that if other experiments of 200 die tossing would be executed, then the results for their χ^2 scores would have a chi-square distribution. But what can we say when we have the results of only one experiment?

The null hypothesis for this test is that the evidence supports the prescribed probabilities, while the alternative is that the measured frequencies contradict the prescribed probabilities. The question we are asking is: How many experiments would have a worse χ^2 score than the one at hand? If there are fewer than 5%, there is a good justification to reject the null hypothesis because of the data. In other words, if the area under the density distribution curve at the right of the χ^2 score is less than 0.05 (that is p-value < 0.05), then we infer that the case we have is so extreme that it is unlikely to be obtained by chance under the null hypothesis.

The R command for the χ^2 test is `chisq.data`, and requires two vectors: one to specify the measured frequencies and another one to specify the expected values, indicated by parameter `p = expect`. Of course, the two vectors have the same size.

```
data = c(32, 31, 32, 30, 33, 42);
expect = c(1,1,1,1,1,1)/6;
chisq.test(data, p = expect)

##  Chi-square test for given probabilities

## data: data
## X-squared = 2.86, df = 5, p-value = 0.7216
```

The null hypothesis here is that the die is fair and the probability for any face is equal to 1/6. The alternative is that at least one category does not have the 1/6 probability.

The results show that $\chi^2 = 2.86$, the number of degrees of freedom is 6 − 1=5, and the p-value = 0.7216. This is a fairly large value, so we fail to reject the hypothesis. We have no reason to reject the hypothesis that the die is fair. More experiments will be required to give a more definitive answer. At what confidence level would the null hypothesis be rejected?

Exercise 10.6

Can you use the X^2 value and the chi-square distribution function `dchisq` to calculate the p-value for the data in Exercise 10.5?

Exercise 10.7

The most encountered letters in the English language have the following distribution

LETTER	E	T	N	R	O
FREQUENCY	29	21	17	17	16

which means that out of 100 letters in a piece of text, on average, the letter E appears 29 times, for example.

In a piece of text, written in an unidentified language, there are 100 letter Es, 110 letter Ts, 80 letter Ns, 55 letter Rs, and 14 letter Os.

Complete the R code below, and run it, and decide whether or not the text is written in English.

```
data =
expect = c(29, 21, 17, 17, 16)/100;

chisq.test
```

How much is X^2 and the p-value, in this case? Can you reject the null hypothesis that this piece of text is written in English, based on the evidence provided? Explain.

Exercise 10.8

The question here is: Why does the chi-square statistic have a X^2 distribution? One way to look at this is to assume that the error $f_i - e_i = Z_i\sqrt{e_i}$ is somewhat proportional to the square root of the expected number, and if Z_i are normal with mean 0 and variance 1, then the statistic would be exactly χ^2. We can set up R code to run simulations with multinomial distribution, and verify experimentally that asymptotically the differences from the expected count are indeed roughly this large.

We want to simulate colors of M&Ms in four bags. Each bag has 57 candies. For each experiment, we generate random numbers with a multinomial distribution according to our expectation of color probabilities `p = (.24, .20, .16, .14, .13, .13)`. The expected number for each color will then be $N \times p$.

```
N = 4*57
ne = 100000
probs = c(.24, .20, .16, .14, .13, .13)
colors = c('blue','orange','green', 'yellow', 'red', 'brown')
expected = round(N*probs)
```

We run the experiment 100,000 times, with the generator function for the multinomial distribution `rmultinom`, and collect the results in a 5×100000 matrix:

```
X = rmultinom(ne, N, probs)
```

For each column we find the scaled errors $(f_i - e_i)/\sqrt{e_i}$, by applying a function to each column, as indicated by the second parameter 2. If 1 is used instead of 2, then the indicated function is applied to each row, instead of column:

```
Z = apply(X, 2, function(x) (x-expected)/sqrt(expected))
```

To test the assumption that the Z numbers for each color are normal with mean 0 and variance 1, we plot the histogram and compare it with the standard normal density distribution. For that we set a vector for the x values on which we want to calculate the normal distribution density with the function `dnorm` and arrange the graphics space in three rows and two columns with graphical parameter `mfrow`, so that the histogram for all six colors appear in one graph:

```
xvals=seq(-4,4,0.01)
par(mfrow=c(3,2))
for(k in 1:6){
  hist(Z[k,],breaks=20, freq=FALSE, main=colors[k])
  lines(xvals, dnorm(xvals), lw = 2)
  }
```

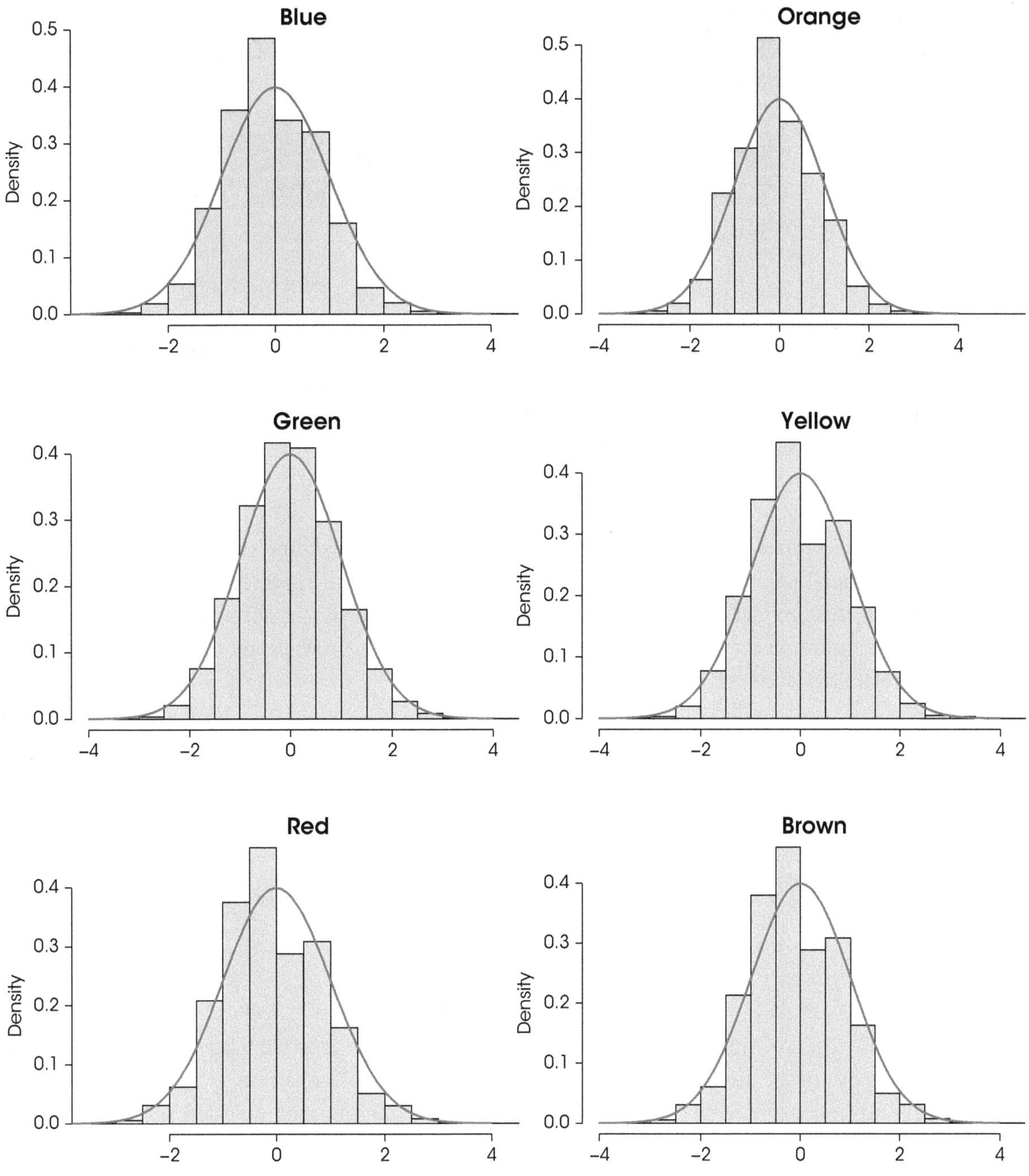

FIGURE 10.19 Histograms of Scaled Errors $(f_i - e_i)/\sqrt{e_i}$

Do the histograms support our assumption that the scaled errors are normal variates? Explain your reasoning.

Exercise 10.9

The same statistic can also be used to study if two rows in a contingency table are "independent." That is, the null hypothesis is that the rows are independent, and the alternative hypothesis is that they are not independent. For example, suppose you find the following data on the severity of car crashes tabulated for the cases in which the passenger wore a seat belt, or did not, for a total of n = 86,769 cases:

		INJURY LEVEL			
		NONE	MINIMAL	MINOR	MAJOR
Seat belt	Yes	12,813	647	359	42
	No	65,963	4,000	2,642	303

Are the two rows independent, or does the seat belt make a difference? Again, the chi-square statistic makes an appearance. But what are the expected counts? Under a null hypothesis assumption of independence, we can use the marginal probabilities to calculate the expected counts. For example,

$$P(\text{none and yes}) = P(\text{none})P(\text{yes}),$$

which is estimated by the proportion of all "none" (the first column sum divided by n) and the proportion of all "yes" (the first-row sum divided by n). The expected frequency for this cell then is this product times the total number of cases. Or, after simplifying, the row sum times the column sum divided by n. We need to do this for each entry. Better to let the computer do so. Here it is quite simple.

```
yesbelt  = c(12813,647,359,42)
nobelt  = c(65963,4000,2642,303)
chisq.test(data.frame(yesbelt,nobelt))

##   Pearson's Chi-square test

## data: data.frame(yesbelt, nobelt)
## X-squared = 59.224, df = 3, p-value = 8.61e-13
```

This tests the null hypothesis that the two rows are independent against the alternative that they are not. In this example, the extremely small p-value leads us to believe the two rows are not independent (we reject the null hypothesis). Notice that we needed to make a data frame of the two values. Alternatively, we can just combine the two vectors as rows using the command `rbind`.

Exercise 10.10

The test for independence checks to see if the rows are independent. A test for homogeneity tests to see if the rows come from the same distribution or appear to come from different distributions. Intuitively, the proportions in each category should be about the same if the rows are from the same distribution. The χ^2 statistic will again help us decide what it means to be "close" to the same.

The test for homogeneity tests categorical data to see if the rows come from different distributions. How good is it? Let's find out by taking data from different distributions and seeing how it does. We can easily roll a die using the *sample* command. This command chooses randomly from a vector of options, a given number of times, and eventually with a specified set of probabilities, as indicated by the parameter p. Let's roll a fair one and a biased one and see if the chi-square test can decide the difference. First, roll the fair die 200 times and the biased one 100 times, and then tabulate:

```
die.fair = sample(1:6,200,p=c(1,1,1,1,1,1)/6,replace=T)
die.bias = sample(1:6,100,p=c(.5,.5,1,1,1,2)/6,replace=T)
res.fair = table(die.fair);res.bias = table(die.bias)
rbind(res.fair,res.bias)
```

Do these appear to be from the same distribution? We see that the biased die has more sixes and far fewer twos than we should expect. So, it clearly doesn't look so. The χ^2 test for homogeneity does a similar analysis as the χ^2 test for independence. For each cell it computes an expected amount and then uses this to compare to the frequency. What numbers should we expect? Consider how many twos the fair die should roll in 200 rolls. The expected number would be 200 times the probability of rolling a two. This we don't know, but if we assume that the two rows of numbers are from the same distribution, then the marginal proportions give an estimate. The marginal total is 49/300 = (37 + 12)/300 = 0.163. So, we expect 200*0.163 = 33. And we had 37. As before, we add up all these differences squared and scale by the expected number to get a statistic:

$$\chi^2 = \sum_{i}^{n} \frac{(f_i - e_i)^2}{e_i}.$$

Under the null hypothesis that both sets of data come from the same distribution (homogeneity) and a proper sample, this has the chi-square distribution with (2 − 1)(6 − 1) = 5 degrees of freedom. That is the number of rows minus 1 times the number of columns minus 1.

The heavy lifting is done for us as follows with the `chisq.test` function.

```
chisq.test(rbind(res.fair,res.bias))

##  Pearson's Chi-square test

## data: rbind(res.fair, res.bias)
## X-squared = 14.743, df = 5, p-value = 0.01152
```

The small number in this case allows us to reject the null hypothesis. Run the experiment again, and we might see larger p-values.

If we wish to see some of the intermediate steps, we may use options to have a more complete report. For example, to print the expected counts, we can extract that part like this:

```
chisq.test(rbind(res.fair,res.bias))[['expected']]
```

Load the R data set `UCBAdmissions` that contains data on admissions to some UC Berkley departments by gender. The command is `data(UCBAdmissions)`. The command `x = ftable(UCBAdmissions)` will show a nice tabulation of the data. To extract the first rows, admitted male and female students, use the command `u[1 : 2,]`. Do a test of homogeneity between these rows, and infer a conclusion. Repeat the analysis for rejected students.

10.4.2 Group Experiments

M&M Candies

Perform a statistical hypothesis test to determine whether a bag of M&Ms contains the advertised number of each color. Each student will need one bag of plain M&Ms (1.69 oz), and each group will need one paper plate.

FIGURE 10.20 Colorful M&Ms

In this section we are going to use R to explore the χ^2-distribution (chi-square) and its use as a goodness of fit test. This distribution allows us to have statistical tests of categorical data. For example, we want to compare frequency of the color of candy in a jar with the expected proportions as specified by the manufacturer. Are the results compatible with a random sample? Or maybe somebody has a favorite candy color?

The key to answering this question is to look at how far off the data are from the expected. If we call f_i the frequency of category (color) i, and e_i the expected count of category i, then the χ^2 statistic is defined to be

$$\chi^2 = \sum_{i=1}^{n} \frac{(f_i - e_i)^2}{e_i}.$$

For a perfect match χ^2 should be zero and a positive number for a serious discrepancy.

Type the R command: `curve(dchisq(x, df=5), col='red', main = "Chi-Square Density Graph", from=0,to=20)` in the cell below to see the shape of probability distribution of χ^2 with 5 degrees of freedoms (six M&M colors). What is the mode of the distribution?

```
curve(dchisq(x, df=5), col='red', main = "Chi-Square Density Graph",
   xlab = expression(chi^2), from=0, to=20)
```

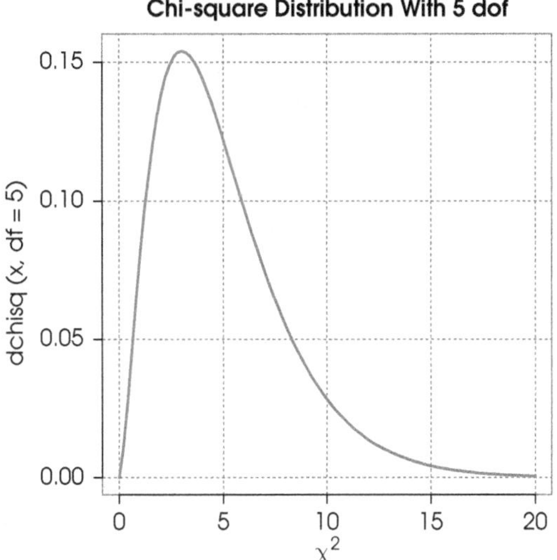

FIGURE 10.21 Chi-Square Density Graph

If the area of the probability density curve from the value of X^2 obtained to infinity is less than an established threshold (normally 0.05), the discrepancy between the measured and expected data is significant, and we need to reject the null hypothesis, because it is very unlikely that the result of the test can be simply explained by random variability or pure coincidence.

Procedure:

1. Make sure your hands are clean. You will be handling food that you may want to eat at the end of this activity.
2. Separate into groups of four students. Each student receives one bag of M&Ms.
3. Open all bags of M&Ms, and pour them onto the paper plate. *DO NOT EAT ANY OF THE M&Ms YET!*
4. Separate the M&Ms into color categories, and count the number of each color your group has.
5. Record your counts in the row 1 "Observed: (O)" of a table. In row 2, record the expected count by multiplying the probability for each color with the total number of M&Ms in the group.
6. Create two vectors: `data = c(....)` and `expected = c(...)` with the data from the two rows.
7. Calculate the X^2 score with the formula: `X = (data - expected)^2/expected`.
8. Assign the degrees of freedom variable: `df = 6 - 1`.
9. Find the p-value as `1 - dchisq(X, df)` by using the distribution function for the X^2 distribution.
10. Calculate the statistic by using the `chisq.test` function: `chisq.test(data, expected, df)`.

11. Calculate the critical value for confidence level of 95% by using the quantile function for the χ^2 distribution and compare it with your χ^2 value: `cv = qchisq(0.95, 5)`.

Question 1: What is the null hypothesis?
Question 2: What is the alternate hypothesis?
Question 3: What is your conclusion?
Question 4: What p-value did you find?
Question 6: What critical value did you find?

10.4.3 Case Scenarios

CASE SCENARIO

Pizza Crust

FIGURE 10.22 Late Night Snacks

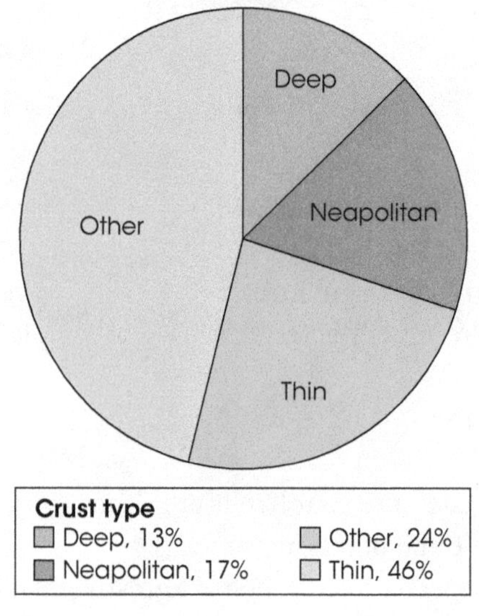

FIGURE 10.23 Crust Type

A popular late-night snack among college students in the United States is pizza. Zagat recently researched this question: Is your favorite pizza deep dish, thin crust, Neapolitan, or something else (Dobkin, 2014)? The distribution of responses is shown in the pie chart. Students from three different institutions in two different regions of the country, namely the Midwest and East Coast, conducted surveys to find out the favorite type of crust on their campus. The frequencies are shown in the following table.

CRUST TYPE	PERCENT	EAST COAST	MIDWEST	TOTALS
Thin	46	97	27	124
Deep	13	35	56	91
Neapolitan	17	44	2	46
Other	24	24	15	39

Source: Dobkin, K. (2014, December 2). Zagat's 2014 pizza survey: Favorite toppings, trends and more. Zagat. https://www.zagat.com/b/zagats-2014-pizza-survey-favorite-toppings-trends-and-more

1. State the null and alternative hypotheses for the chi-square goodness-of-fit test to determine if the students total observed frequency compares to the expected distribution found by Zagat. Compute and compare the expected frequencies for the students that prefer thin crust pizza, as if students who lived on the East Coast had the same preferences as students who lived in the Midwest.
2. Utilizing the chi-square goodness of fit statistics, test your null hypothesis from question 1. Using a significance level of .05 and state your conclusions.
3. Is there a relationship among the favorite types of pizza crust between regions? Using a significance level of .05, determine if there is a statistically significant relationship between each region pair using the test of independence.
4. Based on the information you gained from the statistical analysis you performed, what did you learn about pizza preferences? For example, if you were developing a pizza restaurant chain, would you serve the same type of pizza in each region? What led you to your conclusion?

CASE SCENARIO

Total Dissolved Solids

FIGURE 10.24 Water and Humans

Does the type of water purification impact the quality of water? Suppose the question was considered by a small team of researchers. A popular variable used to measure water quality is the total dissolved solids (TDS). The lower the TDS, the better the water quality. The researchers investigated whether boiling, distilling, filtering water, or doing nothing (i.e., the control) produced a lower TDS. The data are shown in the table below.

	TOTAL DISSOLVED SOLIDS (MG/L)					
TECHNIQUE	OBS 1	OBS 2	OBS 3	OBS 4	OBS 5	OBS 6
NONE	105	327	295	52	342	328
BOILED	326	496	40	234	335	326
DISTILLED	43	38	27	23	35	39
FILTERED	71	55	124	79	116	89

1. What is the ANOVA model that would be used to analyze these data? Define all variables.
2. Make a normal quantile plot for the data in each of the four treatment groups. Summarize the information in the plots, and draw a conclusion regarding the normality of these data.

3. Summarize the data with a table containing the sample size, mean, standard deviation, and standard error for each group.
4. Is the assumption of equal variances reasonable here? Explain why or why not.
5. Run a one-way ANOVA. Give the hypothesis tested, the test statistic with degrees of freedom, and the p-value. Summarize your conclusion.

CASE SCENARIO

Tomato Plant Yield

FIGURE 10.25 Tomato Plants at Sunset

Tomato plants are commonly grown in community gardens in cities around the United States. A garden club in a local neighborhood wanted to find out the best way to achieve the highest yield of tomatoes. They considered two variables that are important to tomato growth: fertilizer type (organic versus non-organic) and the number of times watered per week (one, two, or three). The data are in the table below.

	TIMES WATERED PER WEEK		
FERTILIZER	ONCE	TWICE	THRICE
Organic	A	B	C
Nonorganic	D	E	F

TECHNIQUE	OBS 1	OBS 2	OBS 3	OBS 4	OBS 5
A	82	70	65	75	87
B	94	85	105	92	72
C	87	98	115	88	84
D	69	51	65	59	55
E	54	68	59	52	51

1. What are the hypotheses being tested?
2. Perform a preliminary analysis of the data (e.g., make mean plots, check for homogeneity of the variances, determine whether any ANOVA assumptions are violated, including whether the model is additive).
3. Run a two-way ANOVA to determine whether the two factors have an impact on the tomato yield. What are your conclusions? What is your recommendation to the garden club?
4. Check the residual plots for any issues with the design or data.
5. Use the internet to learn about gardening. What are some other factors that could have been considered that you could let the garden club know that might impact the tomato yield?

Use these questions as a self-assessment checklist for this chapter:

1. Do you know the purpose of a goodness-of-fit test?
2. Do you know how to use the chi-square distribution to conduct a goodness-of-fit test?
3. Do you know how to use the chi-square distribution to test for independence?
4. Do you know how to use the *F*-distribution to compare two population variances?
5. Do you know that the acronym ANOVA represents?
6. Do you know the definition of a one-way analysis of variance test?
7. Do you know how to use a one-way analysis of variance hypothesis test that involves there or more means?
8. Do you know how to perform the following tests with R: chi-square goodness-of-fit test, chi-square test of independence, *F*-test for equality of population variance, and analysis of variance?

References

American Addiction Centers. (2020, May 19). *What is the success rate of AA?* https://americanaddictioncenters.org/rehab-guide/12-step/whats-the-success-rate-of-aa

Boutros, S. (2013). Double venous system drainage in deep inferior epigastric perforator flat breast reconstruction: A single-surgeon experience. *Plastic Reconstructive Surgery, 131*, 671–676.

Brattain, M. (2007). Race, racism, and antiracism: UNESCO and the politics of presenting science to the postwar public. *The American Historical Review, 112*(5), 1386–1413. https://doi.org/10.1086/ahr.112.5.1386

Daniel, C. (2012, August 3). Why juries don't reflect the demographics of Harris County. *Houston Chronicle.* https://www.chron.com/opinion/outlook/article/Why-juries-don-t-reflect-the-demographics-of-3761368.php

Kim, M. K., Han, K., Kim, H., Park, Y., Kwon, H., Yoon, K., & Lee, S. (2017). Cholesterol variability and the risk of mortality, myocardial infarction, and stroke: A nationwide population-based study. *European Heart Journal, 38*(48), 3560–3566. https://doi.org/10.1093/eurheartj/ehx585

Kucuk, U., Eyuboglu, M., Kucuk, H. O., & Degirmencioglu, G. (2016). Importance of using proper post hoc test with ANOVA. *International Journal of Cardiology, 209*, 346. https://doi.org/10.1016/j.ijcard.2015.11.061

Palcu, S. E, Mureşan, C., Popa, N. C., & Tamba-Berehoiu, R. M. (2019). Variability assessment of garden pea *Pisum sativum*) production by using two-way ANOVA analysis. *Romanian Biotechnological Letters, 24*(5), 913–921. https://doi.org/ 10.25083/rbl/24.5/913.921

SCORE. (2016, December 2). *Infographic: Small business credit, capital and cash flow.* https://www.score.org/resource/infographic-small-business-credit-capital-and-cash-flow

Siegel, R. L., Miller, K. D., Fuchs, H. E., & Jemal, A. (2022). Cancer statistics, 2022. *CA: A Cancer Journal for Clinicians, 72*(1), 7–33.

Tharu, B., & Tsokos, C. (2017). A statistical study of serum cholesterol level by gender and race. *Journal of Research in Health Sciences, 17*(3), 386. https://www.ncbi.nlm.nih.gov/pmc/articles/PMC7189954/

12 Step Cult Religion Exposed. (2015, September 11). *Alcoholics Anonymous—Destroying relationships one step at a time.* https://12stepcultreligionexposed.wordpress.com/2015/09/11/alcoholics-anonymous-destroying-relationships-one-step-at-a-time/

Xu, X., & Fan, C. (2019). Autonomous vehicles, risk perceptions and insurance demand: An individual survey in China. *Transportation Research Part A: Policy and Practice, 124*, 549–556. https://doi.org/10.1016/j.tra.2018.04.009

Figure Credits

Fig. 10.1: Copyright © 2020 by Melpomeni Kalliri. Reprinted with permission.
Fig. 10.4: Copyright © Unsplash/Tim Mossholder.
Fig. 10.5: Copyright © Unsplash/Remy Baudouin.

Fig. 10.7: Copyright © Unsplash/Jordan Whitt.
Fig. 10.11: Copyright © Unsplash/Lucas Vasques.
Fig. 10.12: Copyright © Unsplash/Ritika S.
Fig. 10.14: Copyright © Unsplash/Paul Hoenhorst.
Fig. 10.15: Copyright © Unsplash/Ryoji Iwata.
Fig. 10.17: Copyright © Unsplash/Jessica Ruscello.
Fig. 10.20: Copyright © Unsplash/Patrick Fore.
Fig. 10.22: Copyright © Unsplash/Nicolás Perondi.
Fig. 10.24: Copyright © Unsplash/Johnny McClung.
Fig. 10.25: Copyright © Unsplash/Chad Stembridge.

PART V

Statistical Inference Assumptions

CHAPTER

11

Correlation and Regression

CHAPTER OUTLINE

CHAPTER OBJECTIVES

Upon completion of this chapter you will be able to:

1. Distinguish between correlation and causation.
2. Understand simple linear regression.
3. Understand multiple linear regression.
4. Interpret regression model diagnostics.
5. Use R and RStudio to calculate correlation coefficients, regression parameters, and to perform regression model diagnostics.

Myrtle Beach is a city on the Atlantic coast of South Carolina, USA. It is a resort city that is well known by tourists for its beautiful 60-mile string of beaches as well as its many golf courses. Due to the COVID-19 pandemic, South Carolina's state of emergency declaration in March 2020 and subsequent work-from-home order in April 2020 resulted in a decrease in human mobility and in tourism coming to a standstill. As these declarations were lifted, mobility increased. As mobility increased, so did the daily new COVID-19 cases. To quantify the increase, scientists conducted a correlation study to investigate the relationship between daily new COVID-19 cases and the average travel distance in South Carolina. They found a positive correlation coefficient of .7681 (Li, et al., 2020). In this chapter you will learn how to calculate and interpret this value. Additionally, you will learn about one of the most widely used statistical methodologies. Correlation shows the relationship between two variables, while regression allows one to see how one variable affects the other.

FIGURE 11.1 Myrtle Beach, South Carolina, USA

Chapter Vocabulary

- When a numerical data set consists of ordered pairs, it is called a bivariate data set.
- Pearson's correlation coefficient quantifies the strength and the direction of the linear relationship between two quantitative random variables X and Y.
- A lurking variable is a third variable that is known to the researcher, but not accounted for in the study.
- A regression line is a linear model that best fits the data.
- Multiple linear regression is a statistical technique that uses several independent (explanatory) variables to predict the outcome of a dependent (response) variable.
- Multicollinearity is defined as the occurrence of high intercorrelations among two or more independent variables in a multiple linear regression model.
- The coefficient of determination is the proportion of total variability explained by the regression model.
- Multicollinearity is the occurrence of high intercorrelations among two or more independent (response) variables in a multiple linear regression model.

11.1 Correlation

When a numerical data set consists of ordered pairs, it is called a bivariate data set. A scatterplot is a commonly used descriptive statistical tool for graphing bivariate data. The scatterplot allows us to eyeball the data for visual interpretation of the relationship between variables. Questions about relationships between two or more variables arise frequently in business, science, medicine, and other applications.

For example, researchers study the relationship between a chest computed tomography (CT) scan and reverse-transcription polymerase chain reaction (RT-PCR) tests in the diagnosis of COVID-19 (Ai et al., 2020). One way to quantify the relationship specifically is to calculate the correlation coefficient.

11.1.1 Pearson's Correlation Coefficient

There are several types of correlation coefficient. We will discuss the one by English mathematician and biostatistician Karl Pearson as he was a pioneer in this area. Pearson's correlation coefficient quantifies the strength and the direction of the linear relationship between two quantitative random variables X and Y. The correlation coefficient is a dimensionless quantity. The following assumptions must be met:

- The sample is a random sample.
- The ordered pairs of data can be approximated by a straight line.
- The data are measured at the interval or ratio level of measurement.
- Both variable X and Y have a normal distribution.

The correlation coefficient ranges from –1 to 1. A correlation of –1 indicates a perfectly negative linear relationship between the two random variables. That is, as values of X increase, values of Y decrease, or vice versa. A correlation equal to 1 indicates a perfectly positive linear relationship between the two random variables. As values of X increase, so do the values of Y. When there is no linear relationship between the random variables or if there is a weak relationship, the value of the correlation coefficient will be approximately 0.

There are several ways to compute the correlation by hand. One such formula is

$$r = \frac{n\left(\sum xy\right) - \left(\sum x\right)\left(\sum y\right)}{\sqrt{\left[n\left(\sum x^2\right) - \left(\sum x\right)^2\right]\left[n\left(\sum y^2\right) - \left(\sum y\right)^2\right]}}.$$

However, the correlation coefficient is typically computed with software.

11.1.2 *t*-Test for Correlation Coefficient

The *t*-Test for the correlation coefficient refers to the hypothesis test to determine if the population correlation coefficient is equal to zero or not. The population correlation coefficient is typically represented with the Greek letter rho, ρ (pronounced "row"). The null and alternative hypotheses tests are

$$H_0 : \rho = 0$$

$$H_a : \rho \neq 0.$$

The standardized test statistic for the *t*-test for the correlation coefficient is

$$t = r\sqrt{\frac{n-2}{1-r^2}},$$

with degrees of freedom equal to $n - 2$, where n is the number of ordered pairs.

Example:

Researchers studied the correlation between the symptoms of post-traumatic growth and post-traumatic stress disorder (Liu et al., 2017). In a random sample of $n = 63$ studies, the correlation was 0.22. Assume that the sample is a random sample, the data pairs follow approximately a straight line, the data are measured at the interval or ratio level, and the variables have a joint normal distribution. Test the significance of the correlation coefficient at the $\alpha = 0.05$ level of significance.

FIGURE 11.2 Stress

Answer:

The null and alternative hypotheses are

$$H_0 : \rho = 0$$

$$H_a : \rho \neq 0.$$

The standardized test statistic for the *t*-test for the correlation coefficient is

$$t = r\sqrt{\frac{n-2}{1-r^2}}$$

with degrees of freedom equal to $n - 2$, where n is the number of ordered pairs, and r is the sample correlation coefficient. The value of the test statistic is

$$t = 0.22\sqrt{\frac{63-2}{1-(0.22)^2}}$$

$$t \approx 1.76.$$

Since this is a two-tailed test, based on the not-equaled sign in the alternative hypothesis, there are two critical values. The critical values are $t_{0.05/2,\,4} = 2.7764$ and $-t_{0.05/2,\,4} = -2.7764$ are found in Appendix A, Table 8. Because the test statistic does not fall in the rejection region, we do not reject the null hypothesis at the $\alpha = 0.05$ level of significance. We conclude that there is not a correlation between the symptoms of post-traumatic growth and post-traumatic stress disorder.

11.1.3 Correlation and Causation

When two variables are correlated, it does not necessarily mean that one variable causes the other variable. That is, correlation does not mean causation. There are other possibilities such as lurking variables. A lurking variable is a third variable that is known to the researcher, but not accounted for in the study.

Example:

The vocabulary of a group of young children was observed, and it turned out that the children who had bigger shoes had a larger vocabulary. Are large shoes and vocabulary correlated? Do large shoes cause a larger vocabulary?

Answer:

Large shoes and large vocabulary are correlated. However, large shoes do not cause a large vocabulary. Age is a confounding variable in this example as age is related to both shoe size and vocabulary in children.

FIGURE 11.3 Are Large Shoes and Vocabulary Related?

11.1.4 Exercises

Understanding Concepts

1. What is a bivariate data set?
2. What is another name for an independent variable?
3. What is another name for a dependent variable?
4. What is the range of values for a correlation coefficient?
5. What is standard notation for the sample correlation coefficient?

True or false? In Exercises 6–11, determine whether the statement is true or false. If it is false, rewrite it as a true statement.

6. A scatterplot can be used to determine if a linear relationship exists between two variables.
7. Interpreting correlation using a scatter plot is objective.
8. When two variables have a weak positive linear correlation, the correlation coefficient is close to 1.
9. When the correlation coefficient is close to 0, it does not mean that there is no relationship between the two variables.
10. A *t*-test can be used to test whether the correlation between two variables is significant.
11. The null and alternative hypotheses for the correlation coefficient are "no correlation" and "significant correlation," respectively.

Skill Building

12. Explain the type of relationships that can be explained by the Pearson correlation coefficient.
13. The Pearson correlation coefficient provides a range of values between what two numbers?
14. If there is no relationship between two variables, what value would you expect for the Pearson correlation coefficient? Draw a scatterplot with this correlation.
15. Create a graph of a scatterplot with a strong negative correlation that could be measured with the Pearson correlation coefficient.

16. Compute the Pearson correlation coefficient, r, for the data below. Describe the correlation.

X	5	7	9	12	10
Y	10	7	8	2	1

17. Use the data in Exercise 16 to determine whether the correlation coefficient is significantly different from zero. Provide the test statistic, p-value, and state conclusions.

18. Would your answers in Exercises 16 or 17 change if the independent variable x and the dependent variable y values were switched (i.e., replace the values with the values and replace the values with the values)? Explain.

19. One example of data in which a strong, positive correlation is often found is the number of fire trucks sent to a fire and the amount of damage caused by the fire. The strong, positive correlation often found in these data may indicate that the more fire trucks that are sent to a fire, the greater the property damage by the fire. Explain how this interpretation may be incorrect and what could cause the high correlation.

20. Suppose the data point $(x = 9, y = 8)$ in Exercise 16 was changed to $(x = 9, y = 20)$. How would this impact the values of the correlation coefficient?

Extending Concepts

21. What does Spearman's correlation coefficient quantify?

22. Shark attacks are uncommon, but there is a well-known relationship between ice cream sales and shark attacks. What is a possible lurking variable in this example?

23. After conducting a t-test for correlation coefficient, which hypothesis test would it be logical to conduct next? Explain your answer.

24. The correlation coefficient obtained in an experiment was 0.23. What can we say about any possible relationship between the two variables?

25. What is the difference between the correlation coefficient r and the population coefficient?

11.2 Simple Linear Regression

In studying relationships between two variables, we collect data and then construct a scatterplot. The purpose of the scatterplot is to determine the nature of the relationship between the variables. After the scatterplot is constructed and a linear relationship is determined, the next steps are to compute the value of the correlation coefficient and to test the significance of the relationship using a hypothesis test for the correlation coefficient. If the value of the correlation coefficient is significant. If prediction is the goal, then the next step is to determine the equation of the regression line. Regression is one of the most widely used statistical methods. The primary use of regression is prediction, which is accomplished with a regression line.

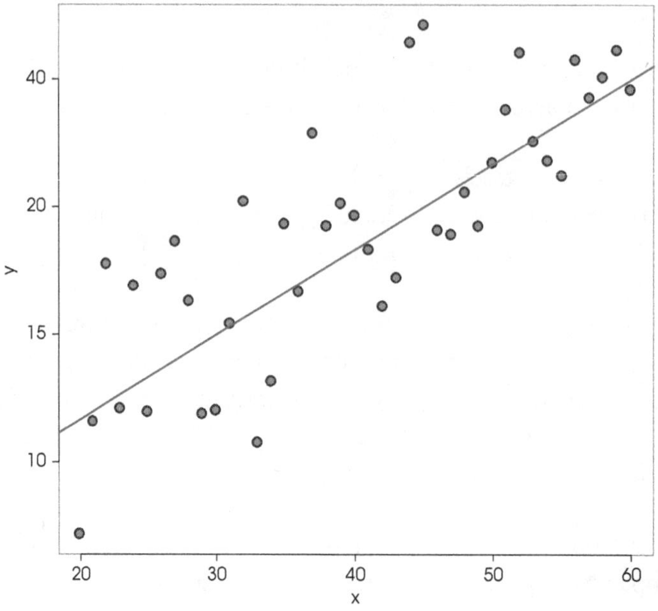

FIGURE 11.4 Linear Regression Graph

11.2.1 Equation of a Regression Line

Many people have some familiarity with linear regression from reading news blogs in which scatterplots are overlaid with a regression line. A regression line is a linear model that best fits the data. Hence, the regression line is called the line of best fit. There are many types of regression models. In fact, both undergraduate and graduate students who major in statistics typically start their studies with a year of linear regression courses. There are several other required nonlinear regression courses as well.

We will cover simple linear regression as it is the basic linear model that assumes the existence of a linear relationship between variables *X* and *Y*. The equation of a regression line allows us to use the independent (explanatory) variable x to make predictions for the dependent (response) variable y. Recall from algebra, the slope-intercept form of an equation of a line

$$y = mx + b,$$

where m represents the slope and b represents the y-coordinate of the intercept. Similarly, the equation of a regression line for an independent variable x and a dependent variable y is

$$\hat{y} = mx + b,$$

where $\hat{y}$ is the predicted y-value for a given x-value. The slope m and y-intercept are given by equations determined by a method called *least squares*,

$$m = \frac{n\sum \mathrm{xy} - (\sum x)(y)}{n\sum x^2 - (\sum x)^2} \text{ and } b = \bar{y} - m\bar{x} = \frac{\sum x}{n} - m\frac{\sum x}{n}.$$

Note that the regression line always passes through the point that represents the mean of the x-values and y-values, $(\bar{x}, \bar{y})$.

A line of best fit is a line that overall minimizes the differences between an observed y-value and its predicted value. These differences are called *residuals*. For a given x-value, a residual is

$$d_i = y_i - \hat{y}_i.$$

The method of least squares, which is used to predict m and b in the equation $\hat{y} = mx + b$, minimizes the sum of the squared residuals.

$$\sum d_i^2.$$

The values m and b are typically not computed by hand. Instead software is used to determine these values.

11.2.2 Using R to Find a Linear Regression Equation

The concept of *regression* in statistics has many specialized varieties, and consequently navigating all of R's powerful features and options relating to regression can get confusing. There are more than 200 functions in R listed in this "regression reference card" (https://cran.r-project.org/doc/contrib/Ricci-refcard-regression.pdf).

QR Code Sidebar 11.1

https://cran.r-project.org/doc/contrib/Ricci-refcard-regression.pdf

The most basic function in R for fitting a linear model is `lm()` and is used in the following way:

```
myfit <- lm(formula, data)
```

where `formula` describes the model believed to be applicable and `data` is a data frame holding the recorded values to be used in fitting the model. The result `myfit` is an object, a simple list with the class attribute "*lm*," that contains various information pertaining to the this model.

In R, a *formula* is used to inform the model about the relationships between variables in the model. For example:

```
Y ~ X1 + X2
```

describes a model in which the response, or dependent, variable is supposed to vary according to two predictor, or independent, variables, X_1 and X_2. There are other symbols used to modify the formula in various ways.

Once the model is build with function `lm()` we can use several other functions that have a "*lm*" object as an argument and calculate various quantities associated with the model. For example, the function `coefficients()` will produce a list of fitting coefficients, the intercept and slopes, while function `predict()` is used to employ the fitted model to predict response values for a new set of predictors.

In the following example we create an artificial data set based on the line $y = 5 + 3x$ on which we add some normal random errors.

```
x <- 4:20
y <- 5 + 3*x + 10*runif(17)
xy.data <- data.frame(x,y)
fit <- lm(y ~ x, xy.data)
```

The function `summary()` collects several important quantities that can help us judge the quality of the model `fit` for the given data.

```
summary(fit)
```

```
##
## Call:
## lm(formula = y ~ x, data = xy.data)
##
## Residuals:
##     Min      1Q  Median      3Q     Max
## -5.1766 -1.9822  0.5032  2.7096  3.1500
##
## Coefficients:
##             Estimate Std. Error t value Pr(>|t|)
## (Intercept)   11.390      1.750   6.509 9.88e-06 ***
## x              3.012      0.135  22.310 6.44e-13 ***
## ---
## Signif. codes:  0 '***' 0.001 '**' 0.01 '*' 0.05 '.' 0.1 ' ' 1
##
## Residual standard error: 2.727 on 15 degrees of freedom
## Multiple R-squared:  0.9707, Adjusted R-squared:  0.9688
## F-statistic: 497.7 on 1 and 15 DF,  p-value: 6.439e-13
```

Among many other details, this result tells us that the fitted slope is very accurate since it is marked with the significance code `***`, which refers to the p-value. However, the intercept has not been captured at the same level of significance; instead of the expected 5, we obtained 11.39.

One way to validate the model is to use a graphical representation. In the present example, this was very easy because we only have two variables, but in models with many dimensions graphical representations might be more difficult.

```
plot(x, y, type="n",xlim=c(0,21), ylim=c(0,75))
rect(par("usr")[1], par("usr")[3], par("usr")[2],
     par("usr")[4], col="lightgrey")
points(x, y, col="dodgerblue3", xlim=c(0,21), ylim=c(0,75), pch=19)
grid(col="white")
abline(coef=fit$coefficients,col="orange")
text(6, 60,
sprintf("y = %4.2f + %4.2f x",
          fit$coefficients[1], fit$coefficients[2]))
```

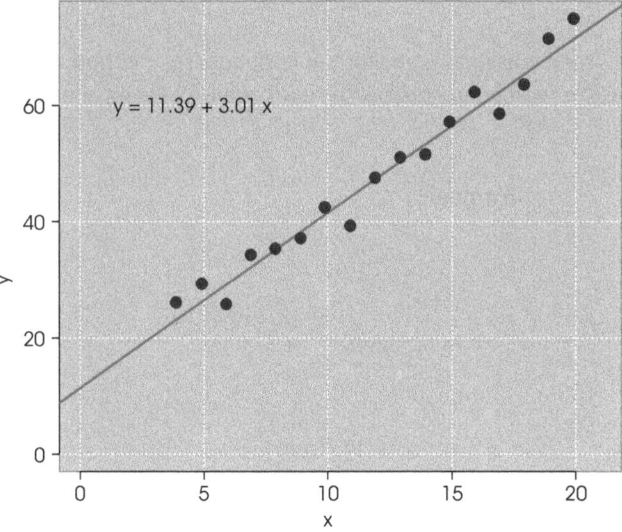

FIGURE 11.5 Worked Example of Linear Regression

11.2.3 Applications of Regression Lines

Because regression analysis is one of the most important statistical techniques, it has applications in almost every aspect of life. These are some of the many examples of using an equation of a regression line for prediction. An economist can use a regression equation to predict consumption expenditures (dependent variable) from personal disposable income (independent variable). An environmentalist can use a regression equation to predict the number of days the ozone levels exceeded 0.20 ppm (dependent variable) from the seasonal meteorological index (independent variable). A meteorologist can use a regression equation to predict average monthly precipitation (dependent variable) from average daily temperature (independent variable).

Example:

Ambient ultrafine particles (UFPs) occur in the environment both naturally and artificially. These particles, less than 0.1 μm (micrometer) in diameter, have been shown to be a likely contributor to cardiovascular morbidity (Weichenthal et al., 2016). To further investigate this research hypothesis, scientists developed a land-use simple linear regression model for UPFs in Montreal, Canada. The independent and dependent variables of the model are annual average NO_x emissions (measured in grams) and UFP, respectively. NO_x is an atmospheric chemistry term for the nitrogen oxides that

FIGURE 11.6 Montreal, Canada

are most relevant to air pollution such as greenhouse gases. Using the least squares method, they determined that $m = 4.7$ and $b = 25{,}583.10$. Determine the regression equation. Predict the UFP for an annual NO_x emission of 2,000 g.

Answer:

The land-use regression equation is

$$\hat{y} = mx + b,$$
$$\hat{y} = 4.7x + 25{,}583.10.$$

For an annual NO_x emission of 2,000 g,

$$\hat{y} = 4.7(2000) + 25{,}583.10$$
$$\hat{y} = 34{,}983.10 \text{ count/cm}^3.$$

Therefore, the predicted average level of ultrafine particles is 34,983.10 *count/cm*^{3} for an annual NO_x emission of 2,000 g.

11.2.4 Exercises

Understanding Concepts

1. What is another name for a regression line?
2. In linear regression, what are the residuals?
3. How are y-values predicted using regression?
4. In the field of statistics, how many points in the data set are used to determine the equation of a regression line?

True or false? In Exercises 5–10, determine whether the statement is true or false. If it is false, rewrite it as a true statement.

5. A regression line is the line for which the sum of the squares of the residuals is a minimum.
6. When the correlation between the variables x and y is significant, the equation of a regression line can be used to predict y-values for certain x-values.
7. When two variables have a positive linear correlation, the slope of the regression line is always positive.
8. You can use a regression line to predict y-values for x-values that are not in or close to the range of the x-values found in the data.

9. When the correlation between x and y is not significant, you should not use linear regression. Instead, use the mean of the y-values.

10. When determining the equation of a regression line, it is helpful to construct a scatter plot of the data to check for outliers.

Skill Building

Use the following data to answer questions 11–17:

Oliver and Tony work at a dentist office. They had a conversation one day about how much time it took to complete a routine cleaning for each patient. Tony wondered if the time since the last visit to the office was related to the length of a cleaning. Oliver went to the filing cabinet and came up with the following data:

x = Months since last visit	6	13	6	8	9	10	14	7	11	9
y = Length of cleaning (mins)	20	49	15	33	35	42	52	29	55	36

11. Find the equation of the least squares regression line for predicting y from x.

12. Would the equation of the regression line change in Exercise 11 if you wanted to predict x from y? Explain.

13. Use the equation of the regression line you found in Exercise 11 to predict the value of y when $x = 12$.

14. From Exercise 13, could you use the same equation to predict the value of y when $x = 36$? Explain.

15. Now imagine if Tony discovered an additional patient's file, who last visited the dentist 3 months ago and whose cleaning took 120 minutes. How would this impact the correlation coefficient?

16. In Exercise 15, an outlier was introduced to the data. What is the impact of outliers on regression lines?

17. Use the data with the outlier mentioned in the previous exercises to compute the regression line for predicting y from x. What is the difference in this regression line compared to the one you computed in Exercise 11?

Use the following for questions 18–20:

The data file "HIV" contains data on HIV cases and socioeconomic factors based on the geographic, level known as census tracts, in Washington, DC, from 2010. Use the data to determine whether there is a correlation between HIV cases and unemployment rates.

QR Code Sidebar 11.2

https://DataAnalysisUsingR.com/datasets/hiv.dat

(Note: The HIV cases are in the variable *HIVcase*. The unemployment rates are in the variable *unemployRate*.) Describe the correlation.

18. What is the equation of the regression line that predicts HIV cases from unemployment rates?

19. Provide a scatterplot of the data with the regression line.

20. Predict the HIV cases for a census tract that has an unemployment rate of .10.

Extending Concepts

21. What does the word *simple* indicate in the phrase *simple linear regression*?

22. What is the relationship between an equation of a regression line and an algebraic equation of a line that is in slope-intercept form?

23. Given a data set with 40 ordered pairs, which command in R would you use to find a line of best fit?

24. Explain why the point made of the mean of x-values and the mean of y-values lies on the line of best fit.

25. The R function `summary()` provides a model fit with coefficients listed as follows: `(Intercept) 4.3` and `x-coefficient -1.2`. Use this model to predict the dependent variable when the independent variable is 0.5.

11.3 Multiple Linear Regression

In previous sections we explained the concepts of simple linear regression and correlation. In simple linear regression, the regression equation contains one independent variable x and one dependent variable y. However, in many instances, a better regression equation model contains more than one independent variable.

11.3.1 Determining a Multiple Linear Regression Equation

In multiple regression, there are several independent variables and one dependent variable. The equation is

$$\hat{y} = m_1 x_1 + m_2 x_2 + m_3 x_3 + \ldots + m_k x_k + b,$$

where $\hat{y}$ is the predicted y-value for a given x_i, and b is the y-intercept. Each coefficient m_i is the amount of change in $\hat{y}$ when the independent variable x_i is changed by one unit and all other independent variables are held constant.

The assumptions of multiple regression are:

1. The normality assumption: For any specific value of the dependent variable, the values of the dependent variable are normally distributed.
2. The equal variance assumption: The variances and standard deviations for the dependent variables are the same for each value of the independent variable.
3. The linearity assumption: There exists a linear relationship between the dependent variable and the independent variables.
4. The nonmulticollinearity assumption: The independent variables are not correlated.
5. The independence assumption: The values for the dependent variables are independent of each other.

Because the mathematics needed to determine a multiple regression equation is beyond the scope of this book, we will use software to find multiple regression equations.

11.3.2 Using R to Find a Multiple Linear Regression Equation

The same function `lm()` that we used for simple regression can also be used to model a multiple regression situation. This information is reflected in the formula used to describe the model. For example,

```
z ~ x + y
```

assumes a model in which the dependent variable z depends linearly on both x and y, in an independent way such that the variation in z due to change in x is not influenced by variation in y. If we suspect such an interdependence, we can add an interaction term in the formula

```
z ~ x + y + x:y
```

which means that a slope for the product of the independent variables $x \times y$ is introduced in the mathematical formula, in addition to slopes for x and y.

To illustrate this point, consider the automobile data in the `mtcars` data frame. Suppose that we are interested in the impact of automobile weight and horse power on mileage. We fit a regression model that includes an interaction term:

```
fit <- lm(mpg ~ hp + wt + hp:wt, data=mtcars)
summary(fit)
##
## Call:
## lm(formula = mpg ~ hp + wt + hp:wt, data = mtcars)
##
## Residuals:
##      Min       1Q  Median       3Q      Max
## -3.0632 -1.6491 -0.7362  1.4211  4.5513
##
```

```
## Coefficients:
##              Estimate Std. Error t value Pr(>|t|)
## (Intercept) 49.80842    3.60516  13.816 5.01e-14 ***
## hp          -0.12010    0.02470  -4.863 4.04e-05 ***
## wt          -8.21662    1.26971  -6.471 5.20e-07 ***
## hp:wt        0.02785    0.00742   3.753 0.000811 ***
## ---
## Signif. codes:  0 '***' 0.001 '**' 0.01 '*' 0.05 '.' 0.1 ' ' 1
##
## Residual standard error: 2.153 on 28 degrees of freedom
## Multiple R-squared:  0.8848, Adjusted R-squared:  0.8724
## F-statistic: 71.66 on 3 and 28 DF,  p-value: 2.981e-13
```

Results show that the model finds significant contribution to all factors involved. The mileage decreases with both the power and weight of the car, but also increases with the product of these two independent variable. What does it mean? We can understand this in the sense, for example, that the relationship between miles per gallon and power is influenced by car weight.

Sometimes we expect that the dependent variable changes in more complicated ways with the dependent variable. For example the height to which a baseball will go when thrown straight up depends quadratically with the time it takes to catch the falling ball. If the time was doubled, the height was four times greater. Technically, fitting a polynomial model $y = m_0 + m_1 x + m_1 x^2 + \ldots$ is also a multiple regression problem if we use, for example, the formula

```
y ~ x + x2 + x3
```

where x2 $= x^2$ and x3 $= x^3$ are the squared and cubed versions of vector x, respectively.

FIGURE 11.7 Multiple Linear Regression and World Prediction

11.3.3 Applications of Multiple Linear Regression

These are some of the many examples of using multiple regression for prediction. An economist can use a regression equation to predict consumption expenditures (dependent variable) from several independent variables such as personal disposable income, purchase intentions expressed on social media, and amount of available credit. An environmentalist can use a regression equation to predict the number of days the ozone levels exceeded 0.20 ppm (dependent variable) from several independent variable such as seasonal meteorological index, population density, and amount of public funds devoted to environmental awareness.

Example:

In the land-use regression example above, researchers also considered a multiple regression model (Weichenthal et al., 2016). They determined that several factors contribute to ambient ultrafine particles (UFPs)($< 0.1\,\mu m$). The contributors are temperature, wind speed, amount of park space, amount of open space, local roads, length of rail, and population density. What is the dependent variable? What are the independent variables?

Answer:

The dependent variable is the ambient ultrafine particles (UFPs)($< 0.1\,\mu m$). There are several independent variables: temperature, wind speed, amount of park space, amount of open space, local roads, length of rail, and population density.

How did the researchers decide which independent variables to include in the model? A course in regression presents several methods. We will explain how to use output from R and other technology.

It is pretty straightforward. The regression output from R and other technology provides a p-value for the coefficient of each independent variable, x_i. If the corresponding p-value is less than the level of significance, typically $\propto = 0.05$, then the coefficient m_i of the independent variable x_i is significant. When the independent variable x_i is significant, the independent variable is included in the model.

11.3.4 Exercises

Understanding Concepts

1. What are the differences between simple linear regression and multiple regression regarding the independent and dependent variables?

2. What is the normality assumption of multiple regression?

3. What is the linearity assumption of multiple regression?

4. In multiple regression, how is the strength of the relationship between the independent variables and the dependent variable measured?

True or false? In Exercises 5–10, determine whether the statement is true or false. If it is false, rewrite it as a true statement.

5. A multiple linear regression may have two or more independent variables.

6. A multiple regression equation with two independent variables represents the equation of a line.

7. In a multiple regression equation, each coefficient of an independent variable, x, represents the amount of change in the dependent variable for one unit of change in the corresponding x-value when all other x-values are held constant.

8. In multiple regression, the strength of the relationship between the independent variables and the dependent variable is measured by a multiple correlation coefficient.

9. The value indicating the strength of the relationship between the independent variables and the dependent variable in multiple regression varies from 0 to 1 and can never be negative.

Skill Building

Use the following to answer questions 10–12:

Assume we have a fitted multiple regression equation that is $\hat{y} = 10x_1 + 5x_2 + 7$.

10. If $x_1 = 3$ and $x_2 = 4$, what do you estimate as the predicted value of $\hat{y}$?

11. If the true value for y is 60 when $x_1 = 3$ and $x_2 = 5$, what is the value of the residual?

12. Explain why it is not necessary that the true value of y match the predicted value of y when $x_1 = 3$ and $x_2 = 4$.

Use the following to answer questions 13–19:

The data file "HIV" contains data on HIV cases and socioeconomic factors based on the geographic level, known as census tracts, in Washington, DC, from 2010. The variables are defined as follows:

HIV Cases (*Hivcase*) = The number of reported HIV cases in each census tract.

Education Index (*EducIndex*) = The index ranges from 1 to 7, where the higher the value indicates the higher the level of education obtained. For example, 4 is assigned to a bachelor's degree, and values greater than 4 indicate a general population that has obtained a higher degree than a bachelor's, on average.

QR Code Sidebar 11.3

https://DataAnalysisUsingR.com/datasets/hiv.dat

Total Crime Index (*TotCrimeIndex*) = It is a measure that compares the local crime rates of each census tract in Washington, DC, to that of the United States. Thus, an index value of 100 is average, and each unit increase or decrease is a percentage higher or lower than that of the United States in 2013.

Unemployment rate (*UnemployRate*) = The unemployment rate is calculated by the reported number of unemployed as a percentage of the civilian labor force that is 16 years or older.

Adult poverty (*AdultPov*) = The adult poverty rate is calculated by taking those 18 to 64 years of age who are living below the poverty line and dividing by the whole adult population per census tract.

FIGURE 11.8 Poverty, Unemployment, Uncertainty

Median housing income (*HousingIncome*) = Median housing income includes those with no income and individuals who are 15 years or older living in the same household.

Median age (*MedAge*) = The median age is obtained for each census tract and is based on the distribution of the population by single years of age.

Health care expenditure (*HealthCare*) = This is the total dollars spent from all the individuals within each census tract. Health care expenditure rate is calculated by dividing by the population within each census tract.

13. Determine a multiple linear regression equation that predicts HIV cases for a census tract.

14. Which of the explanatory variables are significant predictors of HIV cases, when all the variables are in the model?

15. If all variables were held constant, interpret the estimate of the education index variable on the predicted HIV cases.

16. Examine the residuals for the predicted multiple regression equation computed in Exercise 13. Is the assumption that the residuals are normally distributed reasonably met? Provide the graphs or statistics you used to assess this assumption.

17. Use a scatterplot and correlation test to examine all pairwise relationships between the variables to check for multicollinearity. In a multiple linear regression model, multicollinearity is defined as the occurrence of high intercorrelations among two or more independent variables. Provide your scatterplot and correlation test. Which variables are highly correlated?

18. Would you modify your model based on your results in the previous exercise? If so, how would this change the multiple regression equation?

19. What is the predicted number of HIV cases in a census tract that has a total crime index of 110, a health care expenditure of $100 million, a median age of 35, an education index of 4.2, an unemployment rate of .01, a median household income of $100,000, and an adult poverty rate of .02?

Extending Concepts

20. What does the term *multiple* indicate in the phrase *multiple linear regression*?

21. Give an example where a multiple linear regression model would be more appropriate than a simple linear regression model.

22. Describe a real-life example where a multiple linear regression equation would be an appropriate model.

23. What do you expect for a multilinear regression model that has an interaction term?

24. Explain how multilinear regression can be used to fit variables that seem to have a quadratic dependence, in the sense that the dependent variable quadruples when the independent variable doubles.

11.4 Regression Model Diagnostics

"Great-grandfather" statistician John Tukey would often say to his students that all models are wrong. One of Tukey's students was both Dr. Glenn Griesinger's professor and the advisor of her dissertation advisor. That is why those in the field refer to John Tukey as "great-grandfather." According to Tukey, no model is perfect. Therefore, the goal is to choose the model that is the least wrong. We should never use a regression model without first conducting model diagnostics. Analyzing the model addresses whether the dependent variable really does depend on the specific independent variables contained in the model.

11.4.1 Variation About a Regression Line

There are three types of variation about a regression line—total variation, explained variation, and unexplained variation.

Total variation is the sum of the squared total deviation:

$$\text{total deviation} = y_i - \bar{y}$$

$$\text{variation} = \sum (y_i - \bar{y})^2.$$

Explained variation can be explained by the relationship between x and y. It is the sum of the squared explained deviation:

$$\text{explained deviation} = \hat{y}_i - \bar{y}$$

$$\text{explained variation} = \sum (\hat{y}_i - \bar{y})^2.$$

Unexplained variation cannot be explained by the relationship between x and y because this is the type of variation that is due to factors such lurking variables, error, or even coincidence. Unexplained variation is the sum of the squared unexplained deviation:

$$\text{unexplained deviation} = y_i - \hat{y}_i$$

$$\text{unexplained variation} = \sum (y_i - \hat{y}_i)^2.$$

Variation plays an important role in model diagnostics. It is used to compute the coefficient of determination, r^2.

11.4.2 Coefficient of Determination, r^2

Recall the correlation coefficient r measures the strength and magnitude of the linear relationship between two variables. To determine the coefficient of determination, simply compute the square of r.

The coefficient of determination uses the relative sizes of the variability explained by the regression equation and the total variability to measure the overall adequacy of the model. That is, the coefficient of determination, r^2, $0 < r^2 < 1$, is the proportion of total variability explained by the regression model. In other words, it is the ratio of the explained variation to the total variation.

$$r^2 = \frac{\text{explained variation}}{\text{total variation.}}$$

Example:

In a regression output, we receive a value $r^2 = 0.7257$. Interpret this result.

Answer:

This means that 72.57% of the variation in y can be explained by the relationship between x and y. The remaining 27.43% of the variation is unexplained and is due to other factors such as lurking variables, error, or coincidence.

Technology also outputs an adjusted r^2. This is an r^2 value that has been corrected for the number of independent variables present in the model. What is a good r^2 value? A rule of thumb is that any $r^2 \geq 0.80$ indicates a very good model. However, one should not worship r^2. There are other model diagnostics as well such as the testing for the slope of the regression equation.

11.4.3 Testing the Slope

Trying to predict or control the dependent variable by the independent variables(s) makes sense only if the two variables are related. The regression equation is

$$\hat{y} = mx + b,$$

and the slope is m. If $m = 0$, then the dependent variable does not depend on the independent variable. Recall from algebra that the slope of horizontal line is 0. Therefore, if the scatterplot indicates, for example, a positive relationship and model diagnostics indicate that the slope of the regression line is zero, then this model will probably not be a good model. However, we would consider the r^2 value as it carries more weight than the test for the slope.

To perform model diagnostics using a hypothesis test for the slope, write the null and alternative hypotheses:

$$H_0 : m = 0$$

$$H_a : m \neq 0$$

Using software, if the p-value associated with m is less than the level of significance, then we reject the null hypothesis. We conclude that the slope does not equal 0. This provides evidence for the model being a good model for prediction, but we always consider all model diagnostic tests before making a decision. This test uses a t-test for determining the critical value (again using software).

11.4.4 Overall *F*-test

The overall F-test another model diagnostic that uses the null and alternative hypotheses:

$$H_0 : m = 0$$

$$H_a : m \neq 0.$$

However, instead of using the t-test for determining the critical value, this model diagnostic uses a skewed distribution, the F-distribution. The F-distribution is the ratio of two χ^2-distributions, each divided by their respective degrees of freedom.

The overall F-test is a formal procedure for testing the overall adequacy of the model. In general, the test considers the question of whether there is some relationship between the independent and dependent variable in the model.

We have discussed three model diagnostic techniques—the coefficient of variation, the t-test for the slope, and the overall F-test. There are also other model diagnostics that can help to determine when a regression model is an adequate model. It is extremely important that one should do more than r^2 for diagnostics before using any linear regression model for prediction.

11.4.5 Exercises

Understanding Concepts

1. What does the phrase "all models are wrong" imply?

2. When are model diagnostics performed?

3. How many types of variation about a regression line are there? Name them.

4. What does the coefficient of determination r^2 measure?

5. What is the ratio of the explained variation to the total variation called?

6. What is the null hypothesis of the overall F-test?

True or false? In Exercises 7–12, determine whether the statement is true or false. If it is false, rewrite it as a true statement.

7. You should always conduct model diagnostics before using a regression model for estimation.

8. Regression model diagnostics are a substitute for ensuring the regression assumptions are satisfied.

9. Checking that regression assumptions are satisfied should always be carried out as a first step.

10. When conducting regression model diagnostics, it is only necessary to calculate the coefficient of determination and use it to diagnose your regression equation.

11. To determine the coefficient of determination, r^2, one can compute the correlation coefficient, then square it.

12. The overall F-test is used for regression model diagnostics.

Skill Building

Use the HIV data set described in section 11.3 (Exercises 13–19) to answer questions 13–15:

13. What is the r^2 value for the model you found in Exercise 13, Section 11.3? Explain the meaning.

14. What are the degrees of freedom and error for the model from Section 11.3?

15. What does the overall F-test for these data tell us? State the null and alternative hypotheses being tested for the model you found in Exercise 13, Section 11.3.

Use the following to answer questions 16–20:

FIGURE 11.9 Injuries During Cheerleading

The sport of cheerleading involves teams cheering at a sporting event by performing various dances, cheers, stunts, jumps, and so forth. Student researchers at Morgan State University studied how the number of injuries experienced by cheerleaders was impacted by the age of the cheerleader and how long they were a cheerleader at their university. The results of a multiple regression analysis of the student survey are shown below:

Model Summary (Number of injuries)

R	*R Square*	*Adjusted R Square*	*Std. Error of the Estimate*
.38	.14	.07	2.12

ANOVA (Number of injuries)

	Sum of Squares	*df*	*Mean Square*	*F*	*Sig.*
Regression	18.64	2	9.32	2.08	.146
Residual	112.04	25	4.48		
Total	130.68	27			

Coefficients (Number of injuries)

	Unstandardized Coefficients		*Standardized Coefficients*		
	B	*Std. Error*	*Beta*	*t*	*Sig.*
(Constant)	-12.51	7.42	.00	-1.68	.104
How old are you?	.85	.42	.61	2.03	.053
How long did you cheer for your university?	-.81	.55	-.44	-1.47	.154

FIGURE 11.10 Regression Analysis Results

16. What percent of variation in number of injuries can be explained by age and the length of time cheering?

17. What is the value of the correlation between the number of injuries and the explanatory variables?

18. Based on the results, provide a 95% confidence interval for b_1, the coefficient of the age variable.

19. What is the value of the test statistic to test the hypotheses H_0: $b_1 = b_2 = 0$ versus H_a: $b_1 \neq 0$ and/or $b_2 \neq 0$. Provide the distribution along with the relevant parameters.

20. What is the p-value for the overall F-test in Exercise 19? Is it statistically significant at the 0.05 level? What does this tell you about your model?

Extending Concepts

21. In regression analysis, at what point should you perform model diagnostics, and why?

22. This chapter discusses several procedures for regression model diagnostics. Explain how to conduct and interpret each procedure.

23. In addition to the regression model diagnostics covered in this textbook, are there additional regression model diagnostic procedures?

24. Explain why the coefficient of determination cannot be negative.

25. Show that the coefficient of determination is the square of the correlation coefficient.

11.5 R and RStudio

11.5.1 Programming Assignments

Exercise 11.1

Scatterplots are very useful to identify and display relationships between numerical variables. They can show in a qualitative way both the direction and strength of their correlation.

In the four scatterplot examples below, look at the overall pattern and also identify any deviations from the pattern.

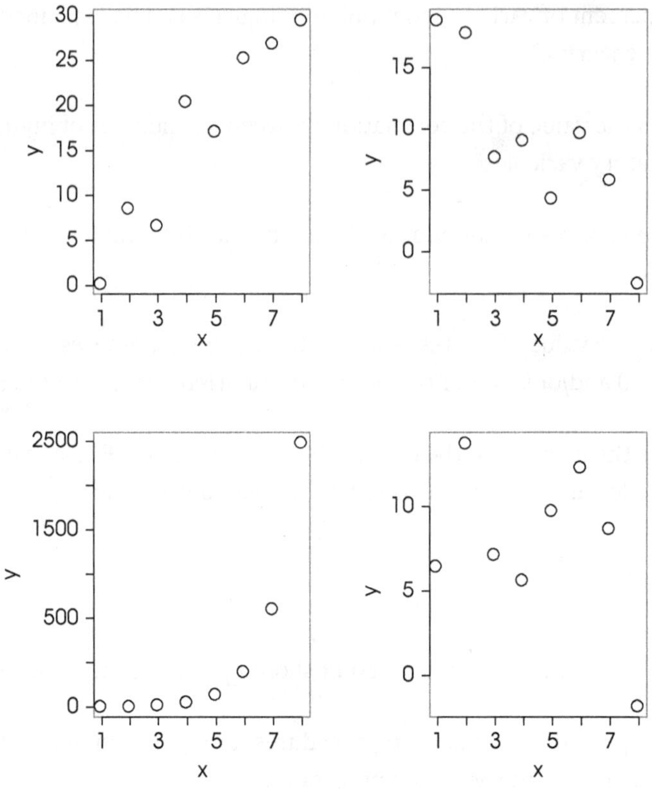

FIGURE 11.11 Scatterplots Show Data Correlation

QR Code Sidebar 11.4

Use the government website https://www.usinflationcalculator.com/monthly-us-inflation-rates-1913-present to collect the CPI data from 1960 to 2016 for the month of June in increments of 4 years and record its two variables (vectors) called `year` and `cpi`.

The first plot shows a strong positive pattern affected by some deviations. The second plot shows a negative association between the variables. As the independent variable x decreases, the dependent variable y decreases. The third plot also shows a strong positive pattern, but is not at all linear, it could show an exponential growth pattern. The last plot does not show any visible patterns

Discuss the pattern for the car mileage versus the car weigth from the `mtcars` data set by plotting the data

```
plot(mtcars$wt, mtcars$mpg)
```

Exercise 11.2

A measure of inflation is the Consumer Price Index (CPI) that measures the average prices paid by consumers for the goods and services.

Make a scatterplot and discuss the relation be the two variables. Use function `cor()` to calculate the correlation coefficient *r*. Based on this value discuss and compare the relation between variables, also in reference to the scatterplot.

Exercise 11.3

Using the data you obtained in Exercise 11.2 formulate a linear model and evaluate and find the coefficients of the best-fit line.

Exercise 11.4

Building up on the work done for Exercise 11.3, use the function `predict()` to predict the CPI for June 2020.

Exercise 11.5

The covariance for two random variables X and Y is defined as the mean of the product of their deviations from their individual expected values.

$$cov(X,Y) = \overline{(X - \bar{X})(Y - \bar{Y})}$$

It is clear that variance of X is just the covariance of the variable with itself: $var(X) = cov(X,Y)$. Show that the correlation coefficient can also be written as

$$r = \frac{cov(X,Y)}{\sqrt{var(X)var(Y)}}.$$

Calculate *r* and the test static coefficient *t* for the data in Exercise 11.2 using the R commands

```
r = cov(year, cpi)/sqrt(var(year)*var(cpi))
t = r*sqrt((n-2)/(1-r^2))
significant.correlation =
                    (qt(0.05/2, df=n-2) < t) && (t < qt(1-0.05/2, df=n-2)
```

The variable `significant.correlation` checks whether the calculated *t* value is between the critical values corresponding to the 0.05 level of significance. If the result is *FALSE*, then we have to reject the hypothesis that data is uncorrelated, which would correspond to null hypothesis that the population correlation $\rho = 0$.

Calculate the coefficient of determination, which is just the square of *r*.

Exercise 11.6

The duration of eruptions and the waiting period between eruptions of the Old Faithful geyser in Yellowstone National Park is recorded in a built-in data set in R. In order to test the hypothesis that the two variables are correlated we apply the function `lm()` to get a linear regression model for the data

```
eruption.lm = lm(waiting ~ eruptions, data=faithful)
summary(eruption.lm)
```

```
##
## Call:
## lm(formula = waiting ~ eruptions, data = faithful)
##
## Residuals:
##      Min       1Q   Median       3Q      Max
## -12.0796  -4.4831   0.2122   3.9246  15.9719
##
## Coefficients:
##             Estimate Std. Error t value Pr(>|t|)
## (Intercept)  33.4744     1.1549   28.98   <2e-16 ***
## eruptions    10.7296     0.3148   34.09   <2e-16 ***
## ---
## Signif. codes:  0 '***' 0.001 '**' 0.01 '*' 0.05 '.' 0.1 ' ' 1
##
## Residual standard error: 5.914 on 270 degrees of freedom
## Multiple R-squared:  0.8115, Adjusted R-squared:  0.8108
## F-statistic:  1162 on 1 and 270 DF,  p-value: < 2.2e-16
```

What conclusions can you derive from this analysis?

Exercise 11.7

For the data in Exercise 11.6 calculate the explained variation: $\sum(\hat{y}_i - \overline{y})^2$, which is the total variation of the predicted value with respect to the mean of the dependent variable. Also calculate the product of the slope square times the variance of the independent variable times number of the degrees of freedom for this variance, and show these two numbers are equal.

```
df = length(faithful$eruptions) - 1
A1 = sum((predict(eruption.lm) - mean(faithful$waiting))^2)
A2 = coefficients(eruption.lm)[2]^2*var(faithful$eruptions)*df
A1 == A2
```

```
## eruptions
##      TRUE
```

Mathematically, this shows that

$$\sum(\hat{y}_i - \overline{y})^2 = m^2\sum((x_i - \overline{x})^2) = m^2 var(x)(n-1).$$

The coefficient of determination is the ratio of the explained variation by the total variation of the dependent variable

```
A3 = coefficients(eruption.lm)[2]^2*var(faithful$eruptions)/
            var(faithful$waiting)
names(A3) <- NULL
r2 = summary(eruption.lm)$r.squared
all.equal(A3, r2)

## [1] TRUE
```

This calculation checks that the ratio *A3* that we just calculated is exactly equal to the square of the correlation coefficient. Why?

Exercise 11.8

You might have observed that the last line in the summary of the eruption data show the results for the overall *F*-statistic. For this test, the hypotheses are:

H_0: All nonconstant coefficients in the regression equation are zero.

H_a: At least one of the non-constant coefficients in the regression equation is non-zero.

The statistic is calculated as the explained variance divided by the unexplained variance with the formula:

$$f = \frac{SSR_H - SSR}{SSR \,/\, (n-2)}$$

where *SSR* is the sum of squared residuals $\sum(y_i - \hat{y}_i)^2$ and SSR_H is the sum of squared residuals under the null hypothesis that the model has only the intercept, which means that $\hat{y}_i = \bar{y}$ for any *i*. To verify

```
n=length(faithful$waiting)
SSR = sum(residuals(eruption.lm)^2)
SSRH = SSRH = var(faithful$waiting)*(n-1)
f = (SSRH - SSR)/(SSR/(n-2))
all.equal(unname(summary(eruption.lm)$fstatistic[1]),f)

## [1] TRUE
```

We should obtain exactly the same value that `summary()` provides.

Calculate the *p*-value for this statistics by using the function `pf()`, which calculates the cumulative distribution for the *F*-distribution with parameters 1, and *n*–2 and option `lower.tail=FALSE` because we need to calculate the probability of *f* values greater than the one from our data.

```
pf(q, 1, n-2, lower.tail = FALSE)
```

If this *p*-value is very small, we have to reject the null hypothesis and assume that the model has at least one significant slope that explains the data.

Exercise 11.9

The data set `stackloss` have observations of a chemical plant in which the loss of ammonia is measured at the same time as other parameters: air flow, water temperature, and acid concentration.

Build a linear multiple regression model by assuming the following regression formula `stack.loss ~ Air.Flow + Water.Temp + Acid.Conc.`

Find the regression equation and predict the stack loss for the following parameters: `Air.Flow=72, Water.Temp=20 and Acid.Conc.=85`. First create a new data frame

```
nd = data.frame(Air.Flow=72,Water.Temp=20,Acid.Conc.=85)
```

and use the function `predict()` to calculate the model value.

Summarize the results and discuss the quality of the model based on the coefficient of determination, the p-values for each predictor and the overall F-statistic test.

Exercise 11.10

Use the `mtcars` data set to investigate the relation between the mileage, horsepowers, and weight for different car model. Contrast and discuss two models, in which the response variable `mpg` depends linearly on `hp` and `wt` with and without the interaction term `hp:wt`. Which model has a better quality? Make a prediction of mileage for a car with 128 hp weighing 3.2 tons.

11.5.2 Group Experiments

Body Measurements

In this experiment students will make a data set with their weight, height, and shoe size and build a linear model that could be used to predict someone's height from their weight and shoe size.

Question 1:
What sampling strategy did you use?

Question 2:
What are the dependent and independent variable?

Question 3:
Is this a multiple linear regression model?

Question 4:
What is the regression equation?

Question 5:
What are the correlation coefficients?

Question 6:
What are the determination coefficients?

Question 7:
Which of the independent variables in the multiple linear regression model of the data set are statistically significant at .05 significance level?

Question 8:
What is the *F*-statistic for the overall quality of the model?

Question 9:
What are the confidence intervals for the model parameters?

Question 10:
Calculate the prediction interval for the prediction of the height of your teacher given his/her weight and shoe size at a 95% confidence level.

11.5.3 Case Scenarios

CASE SCENARIO **Beneath the Surface**

FIGURE 11.12 What's Beneath the Surface?

A group of researchers studying an order of crustaceans known as isopods created a data set. They performed this ecological study in the Negev Desert of Israel. Of particular interest were the isopods' residences, known as burrows.

The researchers were puzzled that some burrows lasted through a generation of the isopods, while others did not. To better understand burrow survival, researchers investigated data on some variables that were thought to impact burrow survival. The data are in the file "burrow." The variables in the data file include:

Y = Burrow survival time.

Dew5/Dew15 = Time in minutes (from 8 a.m.) to evaporation of morning dew 5/15 meters away from burrows.

Shrub5m = Density of shrubs at 5 meters away from the burrows

Rock5m = Density of rocks 5 meters away from burrow

1. Perform a preliminary analysis of the data. Report your findings.
2. Is multicollinearity an issue for any variables? Explain.
3. Are any of the variables individually a significant predictor of burrow survival? Build a simple linear regression model to determine and report the results.

QR Code Sidebar 11.5

https://DataAnalysisUsingR.com/datasets/burrow.dat

4. Build a multiple regression model to determine if the variables *Dew5*, *Dew15*, *Rock5m*, and *Shrub5m* together are significant predictors of burrow survival. Report your results.
5. Are the assumptions reasonably met for the models you built in questions 3 and 4? Explain.
6. How much of the variation of burrow survival can be explained by your variables used in the model in questions 3 and 4?
7. What do you notice about the residuals for your multiple regression model?
8. Write a short paragraph summarizing the results from your analyses.

CASE SCENARIO

Maternal Mortality Ratio

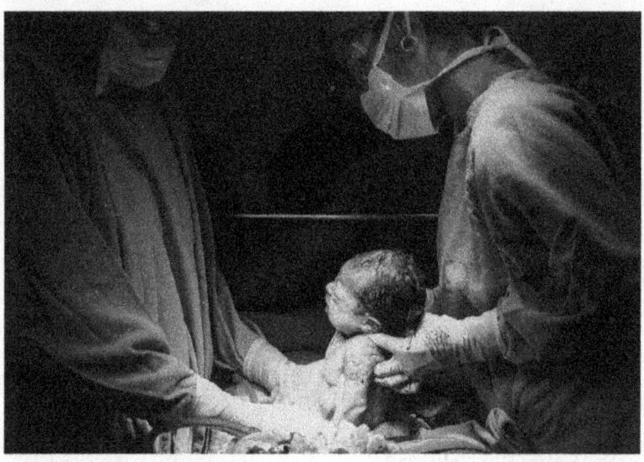

FIGURE 11.13 MMR

A high maternal mortality ratio (MMR) is one of the biggest women's health issues in developing countries. The World Health Organization (WHO) defines MMR as the number of maternal deaths during a given time period per 100,000 live births during the same time period. As a region, Latin America and the Caribbean (LAC) has a relatively low MMR of 85 (Miller et al., 2003). The Dominican Republic (DR), also an LAC country, has an MMR of 100 (Miller et al., 2003). Although the ratio is not the highest in the region, it is puzzling given that many women in the DR receive institutionalized care before, during, and after birth. The rate of institutionalized deliveries is over 97%, and 95% of pregnant women complete at least four antenatal care visits. Researchers investigated several variables related to quality of care and determined the relationship between these variables and the high MMR and the percentage of live births.

The researchers studied this main question: "What is the relationship between quality of maternal care and birth outcomes in the Dominican Republic?"

The variables, at the provincial level, considered were:

LiveBirthPercent = The percent of live births.

BedRate = The number of hospital beds calculated over the population and converted into a rate per 100,000 in the population.

VaginalAvg = Percentage of total vaginal deliveries out of total births.

CesareanDelivery = Percentage of total cesarean deliveries out of total births.

Literacy = Computed as the percentage of people in the population, over the age of 15, that were literate.

SecondaryM = The percentage of men with a secondary education.

Income = Income per capita, in Dominican pesos.

UrbanPercent = Percent of people living in an urban area.

RuralPercent = Percent of people living in an urban area.

Model Summary (LiveBirthPercent)

R	*R Square*	*Adjusted R Square*	*Std. Error of the Estimate*
.70	.49	.23	.71

ANOVA (Live Birth Percent)

	Sum of Squares	*df*	*Mean Square*	*F*	*Sig.*
Regression	7.74	8	.97	1.90	.131
Residual	8.15	16	.51		
Total	15.89	24			

Coefficients (LiveBirthPercent)

	Unstandardized Coefficients		*Standardized Coefficients*		
	B	*Std. Error*	*Beta*	*t*	*Sig.*
(Constant)	104.49	4.67	.00	22.36	.000
BedRate	-.01	.00	-.53	-2.56	.021
VaginalAvg	-.04	.02	-.46	-1.91	.074
Literacy	-.01	.06	-.05	-.14	.887
SecondaryM	-.03	.05	-.21	-.65	.525
Income	.00	.00	-.50	-1.82	.088
UrbanPercent	.02	.01	.29	1.24	.235
OBGYN	.02	.03	.11	.48	.636
PostOB	.00	.02	-.03	-.10	.919

FIGURE 11.14 Multiple Regression Analysis Table

OBGYN = Percent of births attended by an OBGYN.

PostOB = Percent of postnatal care attended by an OBGYN.

The table provides partial results of a multiple regression analysis with live births as the response variable.

1. The variable *RuralPercent* was not included in the regression model, along with the variable *CesareanDelivery*. Observe the other variables that were included in the model. Why might these two variables have been removed?
2. What is the multiple regression equation that predicts *LiveBirthPercent* from the other variables?
3. How much of the variation of *LiveBirthPercent* can be explained by the explanatory variables?
4. Some of the variables have a negative coefficient estimate. Interpret the meaning of these variables on the impact of *LiveBirthPercent*.
5. What is the *F*-statistic for the overall *F*-test? Provide the statistics with the distribution and degrees of freedom. Also, provide the null and alternative hypotheses for this test.
6. Summarize the results of the analyses that answer the research question. (Note: Assume a significance level of 0.1.)

Use these questions as a self-assessment checklist for this chapter:

1. Do you know the difference between correlation and causation?
2. Do you know how to perform simple linear regression?
3. Do you know how to perform multiple linear regression?
4. Do you know how to perform model diagnostics?
5. Do you know how to obtain the correlation coefficient and regression parameters using R?
6. Do you know how to obtain various values for model diagnostics using R?

References

Ai, T., Yang, Z., Hou, H., Zhan, C., Chen, C., Lv , W., Tao, Q., Sun, Z., & Xia, L. (2020). Correlation of chest CT and RT-PCR testing in coronavirus disease 2019 (COVID-19) in China: A report of 1014 cases. *Radiology*. Advance online publication. https://doi.org/10.1148/radiol.2020200642.

Li, Z., Huang., X., Zhang, J., Zeng, C., Olatosi, B., Li, X., Weissman, S., (2020). Human mobility, policy, and COVID-19: A preliminary study of South Carolina. http://shorturl.at/lACZ0

Liu, A., Wang, L., Li, H., Gong, J., & Liu, X., (2017). Correlation between posttraumatic growth and posttraumatic stress disorder symptoms based on Pearson correlation coefficient: A meta-analysis. *The Journal of Nervous and Mental Disease*, *205*(5), 380–389. https://doi.org/10.1097/NMD.0000000000000605

Miller et al. (2003). Quality of care in institutionalized deliveries: The paradox of the Dominican Republic. *International Journal of Gynecology & Obstetrics*, *82*(1), 89-103. doi:http://dx.doi.org/10.1016/S0020-7292(03)00148-6

Rotham, J., Jackson, M. C., Sellers, K F., Williams, T., Lele, S. R., & Waller, L. A. (2020). Correlation induced by missing spatial covariates: A connection between variance components models and kriging. *Journal of Mathematics and Statistical Science*, *5*, 333–344. http://www.ss-pub.org/wp-content/uploads/2019/12/JMSS19082101.pdf

Weichenthal, S., Van Ryswyk, K., Goldstein, A., Bagg, S., Shekkarizfard, M., & Hatzopoulou, M. (2016). A land use regression model for ambient ultrafine particles in Montreal, Canada: A comparison of linear regression and a machine learning approach. *Environmental Research*, *146*, 65–72. https://doi.org/10.1016/j.envres.2015.12.016

Figure Credits

Fig. 11.1: Copyright © Unsplash/Nori Webb.
Fig. 11.2: Copyright © Unsplash/Sydney Sims.
Fig. 11.3: Copyright © Unsplash/Aw Creative.
Fig. 11.6: Copyright © 2019 by Melpomeni Kalliri. Reprinted with permission.
Fig. 11.7: Copyright © Unsplash/Sergio Souza.
Fig. 11.8: Copyright © Unsplash/Jordan Opel.
Fig. 11.9: Copyright © Unsplash/Rajiv Perera.
Fig. 11.12: Copyright © Unsplash/Chantal.
Fig. 11.13: Copyright © Unsplash/Patricia Prudente.

CHAPTER 12

Nonparametric Statistics

CHAPTER OUTLINE

CHAPTER OBJECTIVES

After completing this chapter, you will be able to do the following:

1. Determine the difference between parametric and nonparametric statistics.
2. Know when to use nonparametric alternatives to parametric tests.
3. Test hypotheses using sign tests.
4. Test hypotheses using Wilcoxon tests.
5. Test hypotheses using Kruskal–Wallis tests.
6. Carry out various nonparametric tests in R and RStudio.

Loutraki is a seaside resort in Corinthia, Greece. Loutraki is also home of the Molecular Ecology Backshop. Scientists from this group collaborated with scientists worldwide to study the taxonomy of Aegean green lizards. Their research used nonparametric statistics to provide a clearer picture of the phylogenetic groupings of Aegean green lizards. In biology, phylogenetic classification attempts to arrange species into groups based on their evolutionary origins and relationships. This research lead to the identification of two new species of the Aegean green lizard in the group and region, hence, providing a better representation of the biodiversity that will benefit conservation management (Kornilios, et al., 2019). In this chapter you will learn about the field of nonparametric statistics including several nonparametric statistical methods. There are many nonparametric statistical methods. This chapter will focus on nonparametric hypothesis tests. The benefit of nonparametric methods is that these methodologies, including hypothesis tests, do not make distribution assumptions such as normality.

FIGURE 12.1 Loutraki, Corinthia, Greece

Chapter Vocabulary

- nonparametric tests are methodologies that do not require distributional assumptions to be satisfied.
- When a test or procedure carries with it a set of distributional assumptions, it is called a parametric test.

12.1 Sign Tests

Sign tests are a type of distribution-free or nonparametric test. The difference between a parametric test, such as a *t*-test, and a nonparametric test, such as the chi-square test, is that the power of a parametric test is typically greater than that of a nonparametric test. However, this is only when parametric assumptions are met. When parametric assumptions are not met, you should choose alternative statistical tests. This chapter discusses alternatives to parametric tests. They are called nonparametric tests. In the field of statistics, nonparametric tests are methodologies that do not require distributional assumptions to be satisfied.

12.1.1 Nonparametric Tests

Most statistical tests employed in this textbook thus far have had distributional assumptions, such as normality, to be satisfied in order to use the test. Otherwise, the results from the test may be invalid. When a test or procedure carries with it a set of distributional assumptions, it is called a parametric test.

Recall that, for example, in Chapter 8, when constructing a one-sample confidence interval for the population mean, if the sample size is small and the data are not normal, then neither a *t*-distribution nor a standard normal distribution would be appropriate for determining the critical value. When distributional assumptions are not met or are not close to being met, it is simply incorrect to use parametric tests.

For this reason, this chapter is as important as the 11 chapters that preceded it. Nonparametric Statistics is another course that is taken by students who major in statistics. In fact, some statistics professors specialize in the field of nonparametric statistics. We will cover a few nonparametric tests, starting with sign tests. We will give their parametric equivalents when appropriate.

12.1.2 One-Sample Sign Test

The one-sample sign test is a nonparametric test used to test the value of a population median. There are two cases for the sign test. The first is when the sample size is less than or equal to 25. The other is when the sample size is greater than 25. In a one-sample sign test, each data value is first assigned a plus or a minus sign. If the data value is above the hypothesized median, it is assigned a plus sign. If it is below the hypothesized median, it is assigned a minus sign. If it equals the median, it is assigned a 0.

The null and alternative hypotheses for the one-sample sign test are either

$$H_0 : \text{median} = k$$

$$H_a : \text{median} \neq k$$

or the null and alternative hypotheses are

$$H_0 : \text{median} = k$$

$$H_a : \text{median} > k.$$

The test statistic for a one-sample sign test depends on the case:

Case 1: The test statistic is the smaller of the number of plus or minus signs if the sample size $n \leq 25$.

Case 2: If the sample size $n > 25$, then the test statistic is

$$z = \frac{(x + 0.5n)}{\frac{\sqrt{n}}{2}},$$

where x is the smaller of either the number of plus signs or (n − the number of plus signs). The method for determining the critical value depends on the sample size. If $n \leq 25$, use the sign-test table in Appendix A (see Table 12: Critical Values for the Sign Test) or software to determine the critical value. Otherwise, use the normal distribution or software with $\mu = np$ and $\sigma = \sqrt{npq}$.

12.1.3 Paired-Sample Sign Test

The sign test is also used to test two medians or two means. The null hypothesis can be stated as one of three cases: "There is no difference between the population means," "There is no difference between the population medians," or "There is no difference between the populations." The alternative hypothesis may be indicated as a lower-tailed, upper-tailed, or two-tailed test, depending on the research question. The paired-sample sign test is used in before-and-after tests when parametric assumptions for a *t*-test are not satisfied. It is a nonparametric alternative to the *t*-test when testing the difference between two means in the case where the samples are small and dependent. The paired-sample sign test is used to test the difference between two population medians, given the samples are dependent. The only assumptions of the paired-sign test is that the samples are random, and the variables are dependent or paired. The paired-sample sign test can be left-, right-, or two-tailed.

The difference between each ordered pair is taken, and then the sign of each difference is noted as being a positive difference, a negative difference, or no difference. If there is no difference, then it is noted as a 0. If the difference of an ordered pair is 0, it is ignored. From here, it is very simple. If the number of plus signs from the number of positive difference is approximately equal to the number of minus signs from the number of negative differences, then the null hypothesis is not rejected. Otherwise, the null hypothesis is rejected.

The steps of conducting a paired-sample sign test are itemized here:

Step 1: State the null and alternative hypotheses.
Step 2: State the level of significance.

Step 3: Determine the test statistic as follows:

- **i.** Find the difference between each ordered pair.
- **ii.** Note whether each difference is positive or negative. If a difference is 0, then it is ignored.
- **iii.** Count the number of positive differences, and the number of negative differences.
- **iv.** The test statistic is the smaller of the number of positive or negative differences.

Step 4: Determine the critical value. If using the sign test table (Table 12 in Appendix A), locate the critical value in the body of the table. The first column of the table indicates the number of paired data values. The table's header contains two rows of numbers that indicate the levels of significance. The top row in the header contains the levels of significance for a one-tailed test. The second row of numbers in the header contains the levels of significance for a two-tailed test.

Step 5: Make a decision. If using the table, compare the critical value from the table to the test statistic. Reject the null hypothesis if the test statistic, the smaller number of positive or negative signs from the paired differences, is less than or equal to the critical value found in the table. If using software, make a decision using the p-value approach, and reject the null hypothesis if the p-value is less than or equal to the level of significance.

Step 6: Interpret the results in the context of the problem.

12.1.4 Exercises

Understanding Concepts

1. What is another name for a nonparametric test?

2. How does the power of a nonparametric test compare to that of a parametric test?

3. When should you use a nonparametric test?

4. What is the power of a hypothesis test?

5. Which nonparametric test is useful for testing before-and-after hypotheses?

True or false? In Exercises 6–8, determine whether the statement is true or false. If it is false, rewrite it as a true statement.

6. If the assumptions of a parametric test are not met or not close to being met, you should use a nonparametric test.

7. There are nonparametric alternatives to hypothesis tests, but not for other statistical procedures such as constructing confidence intervals.

8. There are statisticians who specialize in nonparametric statistical methodologies.

Skill Building

9. Provide a reason that may require the use of a nonparametric test for statistical analysis.

10. Which non-parametric test can replace a one-sample *t*-test?

11. What is the only assumption necessary for a one-sample sign test or a paired-sample sign test?

Use the following to answer questions 12–16:

FIGURE 12.2 U.S. Universities

The tuition prices, in U.S. dollars, at six different U.S. universities are displayed in the table below. Students are concerned that the median tuition price is over $25,000.

	University					
	A	B	C	D	E	F
Tuition	$50,000	$30,000	$22,580	$31,000	$25,000	$17,000

12. State the null and alternative hypotheses to be tested.

13. Perform the first step of the one-sample sign test, and the state the number of "+" and "–" for these data.

14. What is the value of the test statistic that is used to test the hypothesis in Exercise 12?

15. Provide the distribution and the appropriate parameters that are to be used to test the hypothesis.

16. State the p-value. Is it significant at a 0.05 significance level?

FIGURE 12.3 Empty Classrooms

Use the following to answer questions 17–20:

Are online classes more time consuming for professors to teach than classes taught in traditional face-to-face methods? The data below contains the amount of time, in hours, five different professors spent developing class material for one lecture of their face-to-face class and the same class taught online.

	Professor				
	A	B	C	D	E
Face-to-face	3	6	2	7	6
Online	5	8	5	2	6

17. What are the null and alternative hypotheses that are to be tested to determine if there are statistically significant differences between the two populations?

18. What sign test would you use to test your hypothesis in Exercise 17? Also, how many of each sign do you have to perform the test?

19. What is the test statistic and the distribution of the test statistic that is used to test the hypothesis stated in Exercise 17?

20. What is the p-value to test the hypothesis in Exercise 17? Are the results statistically significant at the 0.05 level?

Extending Concepts

21. Does every parametric statistical procedure have a nonparametric alternative? Explain your answer.

22. What are the mean and variance of the test statistic for a one-sample sign test when the sample size is greater than 25?

23. In the paired-sample sign test, is the assumption that the variables are dependent a reasonable assumption? Explain your answer.

24. When do we assign a score of 0 for a data point in a sign test?

25. In a paired-sample sign test, what does it mean that the two populations are dependent? Give an example.

12.2 Wilcoxon Tests

Note that sign tests do not consider how far a value is from the median. The only consideration is whether the value is above or below the median. Alternatively, Wilcoxon tests also take into consideration magnitude. They do this by using ranks.

These nonparametric tests were developed by American statistician and chemist, Frank Wilcoxon (1892–1965). Wilcoxon published many peer-reviewed research papers over the course of his career. He is best known for developing nonparametric alternatives to the parametric hypothesis tests for the population mean that were discussed in Chapter 9, the paired *t*-test and the unpaired t-test (Wilcoxon, 1945). These nonparametric alternatives are called the rank-sum test and the Wilcoxon signed-rank test, respectively.

12.2.1 Rank Tests

The rank of an observation plays a crucial role in nonparametric statics. The rank of the ith observation in a sample of observations is equal to the number of the observations that are less than or equal to the observation. In a rank test, computations are performed on the actual ranks of the observations.

This section discusses two Wilcoxon rank tests—the Wilcoxon signed-rank test and the Wilcoxon rank-sum test. The former is used for dependent data, and the later is used for independent data.

12.2.2 Wilcoxon Signed-Rank Test

The Wilcoxon signed rank test can also be used as a nonparametric alternative to the *t*-test for dependent samples. Because it is a nonparametric test, it does not require the population to have a normal distribution or any known distribution for that matter. The only assumptions are that the paired data have been obtained from a random sample and the population of differences have a distribution that is approximately symmetric.

The test statistic for the Wilcoxon signed-rank test depends on the case:

Case 1: If $n > 30$, the standard normal table can be used with

$$z = \frac{x - \dfrac{n(n-1)}{4}}{\sqrt{\dfrac{n(n+1)(2n+1)}{24}}},$$

where n is the number of ordered pairs whose difference is not 0, and x is the smaller of the number of positive and negative ranks.

Case 2: If $n \leq 30$, first rank the absolute value of the differences of each pair of data.

If the original differences were negative, assign a minus sign to the rank. If the original differences were positive, assign a plus sign to the rank. Next, sum the positive and negative ranks separately. Select the smaller of the number of positive and negative ranks. This sum of ranks is the test statistic.

Note that unlike parametric tests, the test statistic for some nonparametric tests may not be determined from an equation per say. As is the case with the Wilcoxon signed-rank test, the test statistic is the sum or ranks as described in Case 2 above.

The North Face and Environmental Sustainability

FIGURE 12.4 John A. Dobelman, PhD, Supporting Environmental Sustainability

In business, environmental sustainability involves making decisions and taking actions that are in the best interest of protecting the natural world. In particular, preserving the capability of the environment to support human life is emphasized. Some businesses, such as The North Face, have a sustainability statement posted on their website. Conscientious consumers like John A. Dobelman, PhD, take sustainability into consideration when making purchases such as the jacket he purchased from The North Face. Some investors value sustainability as well. Biktimirov and Afego (2022) studied whether investors value environmental sustainability by using data from the Financial Times Stock Exchange (FTSE) Environmental Opportunities 100 index. They compared the distributions of abnormal stock returns 30 days prior to qualification day for two types of firms in the repeated regular additions group. One type of firm had prior environmental conditions, while the other had no prior environmental conditions. *Environmental conditions* refer to several measures, such as recycling to combat waste, sourcing materials responsibly, reducing the environmental footprint, and packaging sustainably. The sample size for the abnormal stock returns 30 days prior to qualification day was n = 26, and the Wilcoxon sign-rank test statistic was determined to be 2.34. Is there a statistically significant difference between the population distributions of the firms that had prior environmental conditions and the firms that had no prior environmental conditions? The data are not normally distributed. Which statistical test is appropriate for use here and why?

Answer:

Because of the nonnormality of the data, we use the Wilcoxon sign-rank test. The test statistic is computed using Case 2 above because the sample size is less than 30. Using the Wilcoxon sign-rank table (Table 13) in the back of the book, the critical value for a two-tailed test is 7. The example states that the Wilcoxon sign-rank test statistic is 2.34. Since the critical value is less than 7, reject the null hypothesis at the 0.05 level of significance. Conclude that there is a statistically significant difference in the distribution of abnormal returns in the 30-day period prior to qualification day for firms in the repeated regular additions group who had prior environmental conditions to firms in the repeated regular additions group who had no prior environmental conditions.

12.2.3 Wilcoxon Rank-Sum Test

The Wilcoxon rank-sum test is a nonparametric test that uses ranks to determine if two independent samples were selected from populations that have the same distribution. In this test, the values of the data from both samples are combined and ranked. The null hypothesis is that there is no difference in the population distributions. The alternative hypothesis is that there is a difference in the population distributions.

There are two assumptions—that the samples are random and independent of each other. The size of each sample must be greater than or equal to 10. The critical value is found in the standard normal table. The test statistic is

$$z = \frac{x - \mu}{\sigma},$$

where

- $\mu = \dfrac{n_1(n_1 + n_2 + 1)}{12}$.
- $\sigma = \sqrt{\dfrac{n_1 n_2(n_1 + n_2 + 1)}{12}}$.
- x is the sum of the ranks for the smaller sample (the sample with n_1 values).
- n_1 is the number of data values in the smaller sample.
- n_2 is the number of data values in the larger sample.

12.2.4 Mann–Whitney U Test

The Mann-Whitney U test is sometimes called the Mann–Whitney–Wilcoxon test. It is a nonparametric alternative to the two-sample *t*-test. It is a hypothesis test used to compare the differences between two independent groups when the variables are either ordinal or continuous, but not normally distributed. By focusing on the median as a measure of location, the Mann–Whitney test determines whether there has been a shift in location. It expresses the null and alternative hypotheses in terms of the medians.

Example:

Splicing factor 1 (SF1) is a widely expressed alternative splicing factor that can process each piece of genetic information to generate different types of messenger RNAs (ribonucleic acid). RNA is a nucleic acid present in all living cells. Its main function is to act as a messenger carrying instructions for DNA to control the synthesis of proteins. Godavarthi et al. (2020) conducted a nonparametric statistical study of colon polyp development in mice with genotype $Apc^{min/+}$ and $Apc^{min/+};Sf1^{+/-}$ (Group 1 and Group 2, respectively) to determine whether the total number of polyps differed between the two groups. The data, which were obtained from lab results, represented the total number of polyp development in mice. Determine the test statistics for the Mann–Whitney U test on the mice polyp data. Refer to Godavarthi et al. (2020) for the data set.

Answer:

H_0: Median of Group 1 > Median of Group 2

H_a: Median of Group 1 < Median of Group 2

Test Statistic = W (smaller of W_1 and W_2)

Where

$W_1 = [n_1 n_2 + n_1(n_1 + 1)]* ½ - R_1$

$W_2 = [n_1 n_2 + n_2(n_2 + 1)]* ½ - R_2$

and R_1 is the sum of the ranks for Group 1, R_2 is the sum of the ranks for Group 2

Therefore, the test statistics is W = 23.5.

12.2.5 Exercises

Understanding Concepts

1. What is null hypothesis for the Wilcoxon rank-sum test?
2. What is the null hypothesis of the Wilcoxon signed-rank test?
3. What is another name for the Mann–Whitney U test?

True or false? In Exercises 4–6, determine whether the statement is true or false. If it is false, rewrite it as a true statement.

4. In a Wilcoxon signed-rank test that has more than 30 pairs of data, the test is still a nonparametric test even though the test statistic is normally distributed in this case.
5. The Wilcoxon rank-sum test assumes the samples are independent. However, the Wilcoxon signed-rank test assume the samples are dependent.
6. The Mann–Whitney U test is a nonparametric alternative to the two-sample *t*-test.

Skill Building

7. Explain how observations are ranked when using Wilcoxon nonparametric rank tests.

Use the following to answer questions 8–13:

Dr. Sellers, the head of the Mathematics department at a local university, is interested in how the students feel about a certain professor's performance throughout the semester. In order to figure this out, she asks students to evaluate the professor during the second week of class as well as during the final week of instruction. The responses from four students can be found in the table below.

SECOND WEEK OF CLASS	6	7	9	3
LAST WEEK OF CLASS	6	1	10	6

8. What would be the rank for the value of 9 and the value of 6 shown in the table?

9. Compute the absolute value of the differences of the student evaluations between the second week of class and the last week of class. Rank these differences from smallest to largest and indicate which ones were positive differences.

10. What is the value of the Wilcoxon signed-rank statistic?

11. If the Wilcoxon signed-rank test were to be used to analyze these data, what would be the null and alternative hypotheses being tested?

12. Based on Exercise 11, NOT 4, what is the mean and standard deviation of the sampling distribution for W+?

13. Compute the p-value to test your hypothesis in Exercise 11, NOT 4. Is it significant at the 0.05 level?

Use the following to answer questions 14–18:

Ethan, a first-year college student, is trying to decide on a major. Ethan has decided that he would like to choose a major that will maximize the number of job offers he receives upon graduation. He conducted a survey of students majoring in either physical sciences or natural sciences. The table below contains the number of job offers received from the surveyed students.

FIGURE 12.5 Physical or Natural Sciences?

PHYSICAL SCIENCES	10	3	1	3
NATURAL SCIENCES	12	3	8	2

14. Provide a table of the rank transformation of the data.

15. What is the value of the Wilcoxon rank-sum statistic?

16. What hypothesis is tested using the Wilcoxon rank-sum statistic? Are the assumptions met to perform the test? Explain.

17. What are the mean and standard deviation for the sampling distribution of the Wilcoxon rank-sum statistic, under the null hypothesis?

18. Calculate the p-value to test your hypothesis in Exercise 17, NOT 10. Are the results statistically significant at the 0.05 level?

Extending Concepts

19. In a Wilcoxon signed-rank test, the null hypothesis is rejected if the test statistic is less than or equal to the critical value found in the table. Explain the rationale for rejecting

the null hypothesis when such conditions are met, but not rejecting when the null hypothesis when the test statistic is greater than the critical value.

20. Compare and contrast the Wilcoxon signed-rank test and the Wilcoxon rank-sum test.

21. Compare and contrast the Wilcoxon signed-rank test, the Wilcoxon rank-sum test, and the Mann–Whitney–Wilcoxon test.

22. What test do we use to compare the medians of two populations?

23. Which test is more powerful: Wilcoxon signed-rank test or Wilcoxon rank-sum test? Explain your answer.

12.3 Kruskal–Wallis Test

When the assumptions of an analysis of variance (ANOVA) cannot be satisfied, a nonparametric alternative is the Kruskal–Wallis test. Like the ANOVA, it is used to compare three or more population means. The Kruskal–Wallis test must satisfy the following two assumptions: There are at least three random samples, and the size of each sample must be at least five.

The Kruskal–Wallis test was devised by William Henry Kruskal (1919–2005), an American statistician and mathematician, and by W. Allen Wallis (1912–1998), an American statistician and economist. The Kruskal–Wallis test was first published in the highly ranked, peer-reviewed *Journal of the American Statistical Association* (Kruskal & Wallis, 1952).

12.3.1 Kruskal–Wallis Formula

In the Kruskal–Wallis test, we consider all the data values as a group, and then we rank them from lowest to highest. For example, the smallest value in the entire data set receives the rank 1. Next, the ranked data are placed back in the group from which the sample originated, and the following are determined for each of the k samples

R_1 = sum of ranks of the data in sample 1

n_1 = size of sample 1

R_2 = sum of ranks of the data in sample 2

n_2 = size of sample 2, and so on ...

R_k = sum of ranks of the data in sample k

n_k = size of sample k

The Kruskal–Wallis test statistic is

$$H = \frac{12}{N(N+1)}\left(\frac{R_1^2}{n_1} + \frac{R_2^2}{n_2} + \ldots + \frac{R_k^2}{n_k}\right) - 3(N+1),$$

where

$$N = n_1 + n_2 + n_3 + \ldots + n_k.$$

The Kruskal–Wallis test is always a right-tailed test. The χ^2 distribution with df = k − 1, or software can be used to determine the critical value.

12.3.2 Kruskal–Wallis Procedure

The null hypothesis for the Kruskal–Wallis test is that there is no difference among the groups. The alternative hypothesis is that there is a difference. Whereas ANOVA compares the population means among the groups, Kruskal–Wallis is valid for count data such as the number of items in each group.

The steps of conducting a Kruskal–Wallis test are:

Step 1: State the null and alternative hypotheses.

Step 2: Determine the critical value using the χ^2 distribution with $df = k - 1$.

Step 3: Compute the test statistics.

- **a.** Arrange the data from lowest to highest and rank each value.
- **b.** Determine the sum of the ranks for each group.
- **c.** Determine the test statistic, *H*.

Step 4: Make a decision.

Step 5: Interpret the results in the context of the problem.

12.3.3 Exercises

Understanding Concepts

1. The Kruskal–Wallis test is a nonparametric alternative to which parametric test?

2. What are the assumptions of the Kruskal–Wallis test?

True or false? In Exercises 3–4, determine whether the statement is true or false. If it is false, rewrite it as a true statement.

3. The Kruskal–Wallis test may be a left-tailed, right-tailed, or two-tailed test.

4. The Kruskal–Wallis test statistic has a chi-square distribution.

Skill Building

5. What test can the Kruskal–Wallis test replace? When would the Kruskal–Wallis test be preferred over this test?

6. What are the assumptions for a Kruskal–Wallis test, and how do they differ from the assumptions of the test you mentioned in Exercise 5?

Use the following to answer questions 7–12:

FIGURE 12.6 Social Media Platforms Generation

Gooflixle, a media platform company, is trying to decide where to spend its research budget. To help with the decision, it decides to do a research study on the amount of time students spend watching media content, such as TV shows and movies, on different media platforms (i.e., TV, laptop, and phone). It is interested in knowing if there is a difference in the amount of time students spend watching media content on the three different platforms. The data file "media" contains information from three independent samples on the amount of time (in minutes) students spend watching media content on different media platforms.

QR Code Sidebar 12.1

https://DataAnalysisUsingR.com/datasets/media.dat

7. What are the null and alternative hypotheses for this problem?

8. Provide the ranks and the rank sums for each of the media platforms (i.e., TV, laptop, and phone).

9. Provide the Kruskal–Wallis statistic to test your hypotheses from Exercise 7.

10. What is the distribution of the test statistic that is used to test your hypotheses?

11. Compute the p-value, and state your results, assuming a significance level of 0.05.

12. Redo the analysis using a one-way ANOVA. Do your results differ? If so, how? Does the one-way ANOVA provide valid results? Explain.

Extending Concepts

13. Compare and contrast the Kruskal–Wallis test and ANOVA.

14. Explain why a Kruskal–Wallis test is always a right-tailed test.

15. Will the null hypothesis of a Kruskal–Wallis test be rejected if the test statistic is less than or greater than the critical value? Explain your answer.

16. Can we use Kruskal–Wallis test for normally distributed data?

17. A hospital develops three new vaccines. They administer each vaccine to five participants. After a week, doctors measure the amount of antibodies in participants' blood. Explain why ANOVA cannot be used for this study.

18. Can we use Kruskal–Wallis test for the example in exercise 17? What is the null hypothesis in this case?

12.4 R and RStudio

12.4.1 Programming Assignments

Exercise 12.1

Students use a 3D printer to print cubic plastic dies. They are pretty sure that the sizes of the cube are precisely the same down to 1/10 mm. In their 3D model they also design small semi-spherical carvings on each face that will eventually be filled with ink, so that to indicate the rank of each face. However, they are concerned that because there is more material removed from face ⚅ than from face ⚀, because there are simply more holes carved, the center of mass of the cube moves away from cube's center toward face ⚀ so that the die will be more likely to land on that face, creating an unfair die with more probability for the opposing face ⚅.

Students decide to do careful testing. In one experiment they release the die 235 times and observed the face ⚅ coming up 50 times. From this data they need to decide whether the die is fair or not. A nonparametric sign test, or binomial test, would use directly the binomial distribution and calculate the probability to obtain the observed number of outcome or worse, under the null hypothesis that the die is fair. This quantity is therefore the p-value that can be used to decide to reject, or fail to reject H_0 at the desired level of confidence. Here is the R code:

```
N = 235
k6 = 50
p = 1/6
```

```
p.val = sum(dbinom(k6:N, N, p))
reject.decision = (p.val < 0.05)
cat("should reject H0: ", reject.decision, "(p-value = ", p.val,")")

## should reject H0: TRUE (p-value = 0.03835268 )
```

This calculation is extremely difficult in general because it involves calculation of factorials of very large numbers, so care should be taken to ensure the accuracy of the results. See this, for example:

```
choose(N, 55)

## [1] 2.088671e+54
```

We show the code here just to illustrate the principle, because R has a function that does exactly this code. For example:

```
binom.test(k6, N, p, alternative = "greater")
```

How do the results compare? What else do you learn from R's `binom.test()`.

Under the same assumption, the face ⚀ should come up less times than expected. In their experiment they obtain ⚀ 32 times. Run the binomial test and decided whether or not the die is fair. Note that this time we are interested in events that have ⚀ less times than the observed one, so you need to use `alternative="less."`

Exercise 12.2

In the 3D printed die experiment, students fill the holes in the cube with ink, so they are not sure what effect that is going to have for face ⚅, so you need to run a two-sided test. Write the R code and compare it with results from function `binom.test`. Be careful how you deal with defining the left and right tails because the binomial distribution is not symmetrical.

Exercise 12.3

In the two-sample sign test we make the hypothesis that two samples X and Y are taken from the same population. Without assuming any special distribution or shape for the population, quite generally we have that $P(X < Y) = 1/2$. Therefore we can look at this experiment as if it a coin flip experiment (binomial with p = 0.5), so we count the number of head $(X > Y)$ and number of tails $(X > Y)$ and use the`binom.test()` to decide whether or not the "coin" is fair. We ignore cases where $X = Y$. Like before, we have the option to choose among three versions of the test: `two.sided`, `less`, or `greater`.

Suppose we are interested whether consumers prefer product B over product A. A sample of 10 consumers are asked to gives a mark from 1 to 9 for each product. Product A obtained the following grades A: 3,7,8,5,6,4,7,2,5,6, while product B got 3,7,8,5,6,4,7,2,5,6, where grades are given in the same order of consumers. With the following, make the null hypothesis that consumers have no preference for B over A, and the worst case scenario is that even more consumers prefer B over A, than the ones observed.

```
A = c(3,7,8,5,6,4,7,2,5,6)
B = c(5,8,7,9,8,5,7,9,8,9)
binom.test(sum(B>A), sum(B<A)+sum(B>A),0.5, alternative = "greater")
```

```
##
## Exact binomial test
##
## data: sum(B > A) and sum(B < A) + sum(B > A)
## number of successes = 8, number of trials = 9, p-value = 0.01953
## alternative hypothesis: true probability of success is greater
than 0.5
## 95 percent confidence interval:
## 0.5708645 1.0000000
## sample estimates:
## probability of success
##         0.8888889
```

What conclusion do you draw from this test? Can you use the function `dbinom()` to arrive at the same result?

Exercise 12.4

In a sense, the sign test does not have too much power because the magnitude information is lost and only the signs are taken into account. The Wilcoxon rank test fixes this deficiency and checks whether the differences between two matched populations have a symmetric distribution around zero depending on the position of specific score *W* with respect to precalculated critical values imposed by the required level of confidence. The distribution of *W* scores is universal and does not depend on any assumption regarding the distribution of the population under test. In R, this distribution is encoded as usual in function `*wilcox()` with `*=p, d, q, or r`.

Run a Wilcoxon rank-sum test on the data from Exercise 12.3 by using the test function `wilcox.test()`.

Note that results returned by this function refer to a "location shift," which means that we are looking for evidence that the medians of the two population differ.

Exercise 12.5

Two companies make the same product. We record samples of weights of the product and build a data frame with this code:

```
A <- c(117.1, 121.3, 127.8, 121.9, 117.4, 124.5, 119.5, 115.1)
B <- c(123.5, 125.3, 126.5, 127.9, 122.1, 125.6, 129.8, 117.2)
dat <- data.frame(weight = c(A,B), company = rep(c("A","B"), each=8))
```

This data comes from Hogg & Tanis, example 8.4-6. A quick inspection

```
boxplot(weight ~ company, data = dat)
```

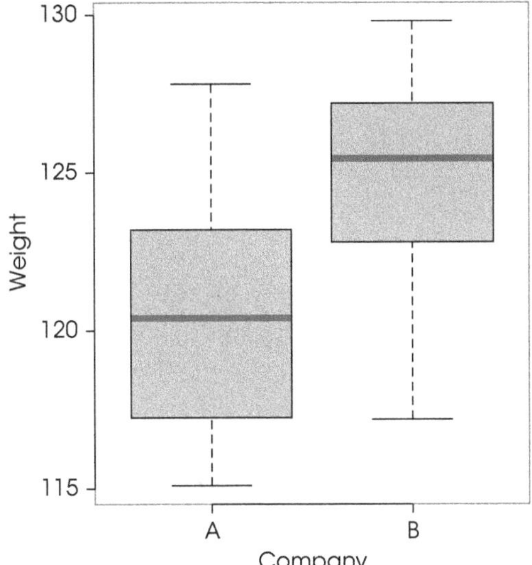

FIGURE 12.7 A Boxplot of Weight Data

shows that data have similar spread but may be skewed. For such a small sample it is hard to justify the normality of data.

Since the data is unpaired, we run a Wilcoxon rank-sum test under the H_0 hypothesis that there is no difference in the medians of the two populations.

```
wilcox.test(weight ~ company, data = dat)
```

```
##
## Wilcoxon rank sum test
##
## data: weight by company
## W = 13, p-value = 0.04988
## alternative hypothesis: true location shift is not equal to 0
```

The score returned is *W=13*. This is actually the number of times the weight of a B-product is less than one of an A-product. We can make all possible pair combinations for A- and B-products and count how many entries in the resulting 8x8 matrix are positive:

```
sum(outer(A, B,">"))
```

```
## [1] 13
```

We obtain the same result. Therefore the probability that $P(A > B) = 13/(8x8)$. With this score we can calculate the probability to get worse results by using the cumulative Wilcoxon distribution. If *W=13*, then we calculate $P(W <= 13)$:

```
pwilcox(q=13, m=8, n=8)*2

## [1] 0.04988345
```

This value corresponds to the p-value reported by the test.

Exercise 12.6

The anxiety score is measured for patients before and after a treatment and we need to evaluate the effect of the treatment. The before scores are: 1.83, 0.50, 1.62, 2.48, 1.68, 1.88, 1.55, 3.06, 1.30, while the after scores are: 0.878, 0.647, 0.598, 2.05, 1.06, 1.29, 1.06, 3.14, 1.29.

The samples here are paired so you need to run a Wilcoxon signed-rank test, which is selected with the option `paired = TRUE`. Also we believe that the scores improved so we need to use `alternative = "greater."`

What are the conclusions of the test?

Exercise 12.7

The built-in R data set named `airquality` recorded the daily air quality measurements in New York during the period May–September 1973. The variables are `Ozone, Solar.R, Wind, Temp, Month,` and `Day`.

The question we want to decide is if the ozone density has the same distribution every month. Therefore the null hypothesis is the ozone density sampled from the same monthly population.

We avoid assuming that data has normal distribution, so you need to apply a Kruskal–Wallis test with R function `kruskal.test()`.

At 0.05 significance level, what conclusion results from the test?

Exercise 12.8

Write a R function that reproduces the results of Exercise 12.7, without using the built-in function.

Apply the function to the built-in data set `PlantGrowth`. The function should also make a box plot automatically for the given data set. This data set has the growth information of a plant under three treatments. What is your interpretation?

Exercise 12.9

The `mtcars` data set that comes pre-installed in R has mileage information for several 1974 U.S. automobiles with automatic and manual transmission. Therefore we have two samples of mileage information. There is little evidence of normality for the *mpg* data, and the samples are independent, so you will use a Wilcoxon rank-sum test to verify that gas mileage data of manual and automatic transmissions have identical distribution.

Declare the hypotheses for this experiment. At 0.05 significance level, does the `wilcox.test()` give you evidence to reject the null hypothesis or not?

Exercise 12.10

The weight of 10 lab mice is measured to be in grams: 20.6, 22.2, 15.3, 20.9, 21.0, 18.9, 18.9, 18.9, 18.2. We are interested to know if the median weight of the mice population differs from 22 grams. Run a Wilcox one-sample test and decide. What if you want to know if the median weight of mice is less or greater than 22g ? How are the results different? Also, do a *t*-test on the sample and argue why the results are not very useful in this case.

12.4.2 Group Experiments

Research Journals

In this activity students are asked to find in the journal literature examples nonparametric tests, to make the point that the concepts learned in class are really used in the field by professional scientists. With the skill acquired in the class students are able to achieve the same results as obtained by the authors.

Students form groups of two to three people and discuss a search strategy for finding research papers published in scientific journal where statistical nonparametric tests are used to derive conclusions. The field of science is really not important, and students do not have to have to deep understanding of the details. Each group should identify five papers. Each paper should be summarized and analyzed as containing sufficient information reported, with summary data to permit recalculation. One best paper should then be selected to carry careful recalculation and confirm the author's conclusions.

Question 1:
How did you decide to search for relevant papers?

Question 2:
How many paper did contain enough summary information to be able to recalculate the results?

Question 3:
Explain and describe the data in the one paper you chose for detailed analysis.

Question 4:
Build a different graphical representation of the data that was not used in the paper.

Question 5:
In your opinion, comment about the quality of the data presented.

Question 6:
Is there another test or alternate procedure you can run to confirm the results?

Question 7:
Is there any evidence that authors tried to "tilt" the results toward their declared conclusions.

Question 8:
Did your calculation agree with the published result?

Question 9:
Do you agree with the conclusions of the paper? Are they complete or are some aspects not discussed. Speculate on the reasons.

Question 10:
What recommendation would you make to improve the published result?

12.4.3 Case Scenarios

CASE SCENARIO

Breast Cancer Awareness, Part I

FIGURE 12.8 International Women's Day

Breast cancer is the leading cause of cancer deaths among Latinas. Compared to non-Hispanic white women, Hispanic women are disproportionately diagnosed with breast cancer at later stages, have lower rates of screening mammography participation, and have delayed follow-up of abnormal screening results or self-discovered breast abnormalities (Miller, Hankey, & Thomas 2002).

Knowledge of breast cancer and breast cancer prevention was assessed before and after an educational intervention. The pre- and post-survey consisted of 13 true-or-false items addressing information gaps and misconceptions about breast cancer and breast cancer prevention, as identified in a focus group of eight women. Examples of items were: A strong blow to a breast can cause breast cancer over time; most of the lumps found in the breasts are cancerous; a mammography is a test that detects breast cancer in its earliest stage, before symptoms develop. The knowledge pre- and post-score was computed respectively by the number of items the participant answered correctly, with a possible range of scores on each test from 0–13. The data are in the file "Breast cancer." The variables in the data file include:

PreKnowledge = The score on the test before the educational intervention.

PostKnowledge = The score on the test after the educational intervention.

1. Perform a preliminary analysis of the data and report your findings.
2. What nonparametric test would you use for the analysis?
3. Explain why a matched pairs test or a two-sample *t*-test would not be appropriate for these data.
4. State the null and alternative hypotheses for your test in question 2.
5. Perform the analysis, and write a short summary of your results. Assume a significance level of 0.05.

QR Code Sidebar 12.2

https://DataAnalysisUsingR.com/datasets/breast_cancer.dat

CASE SCENARIO

Breast Cancer Awareness, Part II

The previous case scenario explored how educational intervention impacted breast cancer knowledge. The researchers for this study were also interested in how the method of education intervention impacted the change in survey score (*PreKnowledge – PostKnowledge*).

Participants in the study were randomly assigned to one of the three groups prior to the beginning of the educational intervention, determining the type of intervention strategy each participant would receive. The first group received two personalized, culturally and linguistically tailored automated voice educational messages per week for one month (i.e., 12 messages in total). The second group received two personalized, culturally and linguistically tailored automated text messages per week for a month (i.e., 12 messages in total). The series of text messages contained the same information as the voice messages. The mail group (control group) received the same information via a letter. In this three-arm study, the main study objective was to compare automated cell phone voice messages versus automated text messages versus a mail group (control group) to determine which strategy was more likely to enhance the women's knowledge of breast cancer and breast cancer prevention. The data are in the file "Breast cancer" with the *Group* variable identifying which group the participants were assigned: 1 = *voice*, 2 = *text*, 3 = *mail*.

1. For this case scenario, you will use a Kruskal–Wallis test to determine whether there is a difference in knowledge scores for the three groups. First, compute the difference of the scores (*PreKnowledge – PostKnowledge*). This new variable will serve as the response variable.
2. Perform a preliminary analysis of the data. Have the assumptions for the Kruskal–Wallis test been met?
3. State the null and alternative hypotheses being tested.
4. Perform the Kruskal–Wallis test. Write a short summary of your results.
5. Explain why a one-way ANOVA may not be appropriate for these data.
6. Would your results in question 4 change if you had used a one-way ANOVA instead? Explain.

Use these questions as a self-assessment checklist for this chapter:

1. Do you know the difference between parametric and nonparametric statistics?
2. Do you know the nonparametric equivalents of various parametric tests presented in this textbook?
3. Do you know how to perform sign tests?
4. Do you know how to perform Wilcoxon tests?
5. Do you know how to perform the Kurskal–Wallis test?
6. Do you know how to perform the aforementioned tests with R?

References

Biktimirov, E. N., & Afego, P. N. (2022). Do investors value environmental sustainability? Evidence from the FTSE Environmental Opportunities 100 index. *Finance Research Letters, 44*, 1–9.

Godavarthi, J. D., Polk, S., Nunez, L., Shivachar, A., Glenn Griesinger, N. L., & Matin, A. (2020). Deficiency of splicing factor 1 (SF1) reduces intestinal polyp incidence in Apc$^{Min/+}$ mice. *Biology, 9*(1), 1–13.

Kornilios, P., Thanou, E., Lymberakis, P., Ilgaz, C., Kumlutaş, Y, & Leaché, A. (2019). A phylogenomic resolution for the taxonomy of Aegean green lizards. *Zoologica Scripta, 49*, 14–27.

Kruskal, W. H., & Wallis, W. A. (1952). Use of ranks in one-criterion variance analysis. *Journal of the American Statistical Association, 47*(260), 583–621.

Miller, B. A., Hankey, B. F., & Thomas, T. L. (2002). Impact of sociodemographic factors, hormone receptor status, and tumor grade on ethnic differences in tumor stage and size for breast cancer in US women. *American Journal of Epidemiology, 155*, 534.

Wilcoxon, F. (1945). Individual comparisons by ranking methods. *Biometrics Bulletin, 1*, 80–83.

Figure Credits

Fig. 12.1: Copyright © 2019 by Melpomeni Kalliri. Reprinted with permission.
Fig. 12.2: Copyright © Unsplash/Elisabeth Lindsay.
Fig. 12.3: Copyright © Unsplash/Nathan Dumlao.
Fig. 12.5: Copyright © Unsplash/Riccardo Chiarini.
Fig. 12.6: Copyright © Unsplash/Jakob Owens.
Fig. 12.8: Copyright © Unsplash/Peter Boccia.

Appendix A Tables

Table 1 Factorials

n	n!	n	n!
1	1	16	20922789888000
2	2	17	355687428096000
3	6	18	6402373705728000
4	24	19	121645100408832000
5	120	20	2432902008176640000
6	720	21	51090942171709440000
7	5040	22	1124000727777607680000
8	40320	23	25852016738884976640000
9	362880	24	620448401733239439360000
10	3628800	25	15511210043330985984000000
11	39916800	26	403291461126605635584000000
12	479001600	27	10888869450418352160768000000
13	6227020800	28	304888344611713860501504000000
14	87178291200	29	8841761993739701954543616000000
15	1307674368000	30	265252859812191058636308480000000

Table 2A The Binomial Distribution *dbinom(k,n,p)*

p	0.05	0.1	0.2	0.3	0.4	0.5	0.6	0.7	0.8	0.9	0.95
k	n = 2										
0	0.902	0.810	0.640	0.490	0.360	0.250	0.160	0.090	0.040	0.010	0.003
1	0.095	0.180	0.320	0.420	0.480	0.500	0.480	0.420	0.320	0.180	0.095
2	0.003	0.010	0.040	0.090	0.160	0.250	0.360	0.490	0.640	0.810	0.902
k	n = 3										
0	0.857	0.729	0.512	0.343	0.216	0.125	0.064	0.027	0.008	0.001	0.000
1	0.135	0.243	0.384	0.441	0.432	0.375	0.288	0.189	0.096	0.027	0.007
2	0.007	0.027	0.096	0.189	0.288	0.375	0.432	0.441	0.384	0.243	0.135
3	0.000	0.001	0.008	0.027	0.064	0.125	0.216	0.343	0.512	0.729	0.857
k	n = 4										
0	0.815	0.656	0.410	0.240	0.130	0.062	0.026	0.008	0.002	0.000	0.000
1	0.171	0.292	0.410	0.412	0.346	0.250	0.154	0.076	0.026	0.004	0.000
2	0.014	0.049	0.154	0.265	0.346	0.375	0.346	0.265	0.154	0.049	0.014
3	0.000	0.004	0.026	0.076	0.154	0.250	0.346	0.412	0.410	0.292	0.171
4	0.000	0.000	0.002	0.008	0.026	0.062	0.130	0.240	0.410	0.656	0.815
k	n = 5										
0	0.774	0.590	0.328	0.168	0.078	0.031	0.010	0.002	0.000	0.000	0.000
1	0.204	0.328	0.410	0.360	0.259	0.156	0.077	0.028	0.006	0.000	0.000
2	0.021	0.073	0.205	0.309	0.346	0.312	0.230	0.132	0.051	0.008	0.001
3	0.001	0.008	0.051	0.132	0.230	0.312	0.346	0.309	0.205	0.073	0.021
4	0.000	0.000	0.006	0.028	0.077	0.156	0.259	0.360	0.410	0.328	0.204
5	0.000	0.000	0.000	0.002	0.010	0.031	0.078	0.168	0.328	0.590	0.774
k	n = 6										
0	0.735	0.531	0.262	0.118	0.047	0.016	0.004	0.001	0.000	0.000	0.000
1	0.232	0.354	0.393	0.303	0.187	0.094	0.037	0.010	0.002	0.000	0.000
2	0.031	0.098	0.246	0.324	0.311	0.234	0.138	0.060	0.015	0.001	0.000
3	0.002	0.015	0.082	0.185	0.276	0.312	0.276	0.185	0.082	0.015	0.002
4	0.000	0.001	0.015	0.060	0.138	0.234	0.311	0.324	0.246	0.098	0.031
5	0.000	0.000	0.002	0.010	0.037	0.094	0.187	0.303	0.393	0.354	0.232
6	0.000	0.000	0.000	0.001	0.004	0.016	0.047	0.118	0.262	0.531	0.735
k	n = 7										
0	0.698	0.478	0.210	0.082	0.028	0.008	0.002	0.000	0.000	0.000	0.000
1	0.257	0.372	0.367	0.247	0.131	0.055	0.017	0.004	0.000	0.000	0.000
2	0.041	0.124	0.275	0.318	0.261	0.164	0.077	0.025	0.004	0.000	0.000
3	0.004	0.023	0.115	0.227	0.290	0.273	0.194	0.097	0.029	0.003	0.000
4	0.000	0.003	0.029	0.097	0.194	0.273	0.290	0.227	0.115	0.023	0.004
5	0.000	0.000	0.004	0.025	0.077	0.164	0.261	0.318	0.275	0.124	0.041
6	0.000	0.000	0.000	0.004	0.017	0.055	0.131	0.247	0.367	0.372	0.257
7	0.000	0.000	0.000	0.000	0.002	0.008	0.028	0.082	0.210	0.478	0.698
k	n = 8										
0	0.663	0.430	0.168	0.058	0.017	0.004	0.001	0.000	0.000	0.000	0.000
1	0.279	0.383	0.336	0.198	0.090	0.031	0.008	0.001	0.000	0.000	0.000
2	0.051	0.149	0.294	0.296	0.209	0.109	0.041	0.010	0.001	0.000	0.000
3	0.005	0.033	0.147	0.254	0.279	0.219	0.124	0.047	0.009	0.000	0.000
4	0.000	0.005	0.046	0.136	0.232	0.273	0.232	0.136	0.046	0.005	0.000
5	0.000	0.000	0.009	0.047	0.124	0.219	0.279	0.254	0.147	0.033	0.005
6	0.000	0.000	0.001	0.010	0.041	0.109	0.209	0.296	0.294	0.149	0.051
7	0.000	0.000	0.000	0.001	0.008	0.031	0.090	0.198	0.336	0.383	0.279
8	0.000	0.000	0.000	0.000	0.001	0.004	0.017	0.058	0.168	0.430	0.663

Table 2B	The Binomial Distribution *dbinom(k,n,p)*										
p	**0.05**	**0.1**	**0.2**	**0.3**	**0.4**	**0.5**	**0.6**	**0.7**	**0.8**	**0.9**	**0.95**
k	n = 9										
0	0.630	0.387	0.134	0.040	0.010	0.002	0.000	0.000	0.000	0.000	0.000
1	0.299	0.387	0.302	0.156	0.060	0.018	0.004	0.000	0.000	0.000	0.000
2	0.063	0.172	0.302	0.267	0.161	0.070	0.021	0.004	0.000	0.000	0.000
3	0.008	0.045	0.176	0.267	0.251	0.164	0.074	0.021	0.003	0.000	0.000
4	0.001	0.007	0.066	0.172	0.251	0.246	0.167	0.074	0.017	0.001	0.000
5	0.000	0.001	0.017	0.074	0.167	0.246	0.251	0.172	0.066	0.007	0.001
6	0.000	0.000	0.003	0.021	0.074	0.164	0.251	0.267	0.176	0.045	0.008
7	0.000	0.000	0.000	0.004	0.021	0.070	0.161	0.267	0.302	0.172	0.063
8	0.000	0.000	0.000	0.000	0.004	0.018	0.060	0.156	0.302	0.387	0.299
9	0.000	0.000	0.000	0.000	0.000	0.002	0.010	0.040	0.134	0.387	0.630
k	n = 10										
0	0.599	0.349	0.107	0.028	0.006	0.001	0.000	0.000	0.000	0.000	0.000
1	0.315	0.387	0.268	0.121	0.040	0.010	0.002	0.000	0.000	0.000	0.000
2	0.075	0.194	0.302	0.233	0.121	0.044	0.011	0.001	0.000	0.000	0.000
3	0.010	0.057	0.201	0.267	0.215	0.117	0.042	0.009	0.001	0.000	0.000
4	0.001	0.011	0.088	0.200	0.251	0.205	0.111	0.037	0.006	0.000	0.000
5	0.000	0.001	0.026	0.103	0.201	0.246	0.201	0.103	0.026	0.001	0.000
6	0.000	0.000	0.006	0.037	0.111	0.205	0.251	0.200	0.088	0.011	0.001
7	0.000	0.000	0.001	0.009	0.042	0.117	0.215	0.267	0.201	0.057	0.010
8	0.000	0.000	0.000	0.001	0.011	0.044	0.121	0.233	0.302	0.194	0.075
9	0.000	0.000	0.000	0.000	0.002	0.010	0.040	0.121	0.268	0.387	0.315
10	0.000	0.000	0.000	0.000	0.000	0.001	0.006	0.028	0.107	0.349	0.599
k	n = 11										
0	0.569	0.314	0.086	0.020	0.004	0.000	0.000	0.000	0.000	0.000	0.000
1	0.329	0.384	0.236	0.093	0.027	0.005	0.001	0.000	0.000	0.000	0.000
2	0.087	0.213	0.295	0.200	0.089	0.027	0.005	0.001	0.000	0.000	0.000
3	0.014	0.071	0.221	0.257	0.177	0.081	0.023	0.004	0.000	0.000	0.000
4	0.001	0.016	0.111	0.220	0.236	0.161	0.070	0.017	0.002	0.000	0.000
5	0.000	0.002	0.039	0.132	0.221	0.226	0.147	0.057	0.010	0.000	0.000
6	0.000	0.000	0.010	0.057	0.147	0.226	0.221	0.132	0.039	0.002	0.000
7	0.000	0.000	0.002	0.017	0.070	0.161	0.236	0.220	0.111	0.016	0.001
8	0.000	0.000	0.000	0.004	0.023	0.081	0.177	0.257	0.221	0.071	0.014
9	0.000	0.000	0.000	0.001	0.005	0.027	0.089	0.200	0.295	0.213	0.087
10	0.000	0.000	0.000	0.000	0.001	0.005	0.027	0.093	0.236	0.384	0.329
11	0.000	0.000	0.000	0.000	0.000	0.000	0.004	0.020	0.086	0.314	0.569
k	n = 12										
0	0.540	0.282	0.069	0.014	0.002	0.000	0.000	0.000	0.000	0.000	0.000
1	0.341	0.377	0.206	0.071	0.017	0.003	0.000	0.000	0.000	0.000	0.000
2	0.099	0.230	0.283	0.168	0.064	0.016	0.002	0.000	0.000	0.000	0.000
3	0.017	0.085	0.236	0.240	0.142	0.054	0.012	0.001	0.000	0.000	0.000
4	0.002	0.021	0.133	0.231	0.213	0.121	0.042	0.008	0.001	0.000	0.000
5	0.000	0.004	0.053	0.158	0.227	0.193	0.101	0.029	0.003	0.000	0.000
6	0.000	0.000	0.016	0.079	0.177	0.226	0.177	0.079	0.016	0.000	0.000
7	0.000	0.000	0.003	0.029	0.101	0.193	0.227	0.158	0.053	0.004	0.000
8	0.000	0.000	0.001	0.008	0.042	0.121	0.213	0.231	0.133	0.021	0.002
9	0.000	0.000	0.000	0.001	0.012	0.054	0.142	0.240	0.236	0.085	0.017
10	0.000	0.000	0.000	0.000	0.002	0.016	0.064	0.168	0.283	0.230	0.099
11	0.000	0.000	0.000	0.000	0.000	0.003	0.017	0.071	0.206	0.377	0.341
12	0.000	0.000	0.000	0.000	0.000	0.000	0.002	0.014	0.069	0.282	0.540

Table 3 The Negative Binomial Distribution *dnbinom(k,r,p)*

p	0.05	0.1	0.2	0.3	0.4	0.5	0.6	0.7	0.8	0.9	0.95
k r= 1											
0	0.050	0.100	0.200	0.300	0.400	0.500	0.600	0.700	0.800	0.900	0.950
1	0.047	0.090	0.160	0.210	0.240	0.250	0.240	0.210	0.160	0.090	0.048
2	0.045	0.081	0.128	0.147	0.144	0.125	0.096	0.063	0.032	0.009	0.002
3	0.043	0.073	0.102	0.103	0.086	0.063	0.038	0.019	0.006	0.001	0.000
4	0.041	0.066	0.082	0.072	0.052	0.031	0.015	0.006	0.001	0.000	0.000
5	0.039	0.059	0.066	0.050	0.031	0.016	0.006	0.002	0.000	0.000	0.000
6	0.037	0.053	0.052	0.035	0.019	0.008	0.002	0.001	0.000	0.000	0.000
k r= 2											
0	0.003	0.010	0.040	0.090	0.160	0.250	0.360	0.490	0.640	0.810	0.902
1	0.005	0.018	0.064	0.126	0.192	0.250	0.288	0.294	0.256	0.162	0.090
2	0.007	0.024	0.077	0.132	0.173	0.188	0.173	0.132	0.077	0.024	0.007
3	0.009	0.029	0.082	0.123	0.138	0.125	0.092	0.053	0.020	0.003	0.000
4	0.010	0.033	0.082	0.108	0.104	0.078	0.046	0.020	0.005	0.000	0.000
5	0.012	0.035	0.079	0.091	0.075	0.047	0.022	0.007	0.001	0.000	0.000
6	0.013	0.037	0.073	0.074	0.052	0.027	0.010	0.003	0.000	0.000	0.000
k r= 3											
0	0.000	0.001	0.008	0.027	0.064	0.125	0.216	0.343	0.512	0.729	0.857
1	0.000	0.003	0.019	0.057	0.115	0.188	0.259	0.309	0.307	0.219	0.129
2	0.001	0.005	0.031	0.079	0.138	0.187	0.207	0.185	0.123	0.044	0.013
3	0.001	0.007	0.041	0.093	0.138	0.156	0.138	0.093	0.041	0.007	0.001
4	0.002	0.010	0.049	0.097	0.124	0.117	0.083	0.042	0.012	0.001	0.000
5	0.002	0.012	0.055	0.095	0.105	0.082	0.046	0.018	0.003	0.000	0.000
6	0.003	0.015	0.059	0.089	0.084	0.055	0.025	0.007	0.001	0.000	0.000
k r= 4											
0	0.000	0.000	0.002	0.008	0.026	0.062	0.130	0.240	0.410	0.656	0.815
1	0.000	0.000	0.005	0.023	0.061	0.125	0.207	0.288	0.328	0.262	0.163
2	0.000	0.001	0.010	0.040	0.092	0.156	0.207	0.216	0.164	0.066	0.020
3	0.000	0.001	0.016	0.056	0.111	0.156	0.166	0.130	0.066	0.013	0.002
4	0.000	0.002	0.023	0.068	0.116	0.137	0.116	0.068	0.023	0.002	0.000
5	0.000	0.003	0.029	0.076	0.111	0.109	0.074	0.033	0.007	0.000	0.000
6	0.000	0.004	0.035	0.080	0.100	0.082	0.045	0.015	0.002	0.000	0.000
k r= 5											
0	0.000	0.000	0.000	0.002	0.010	0.031	0.078	0.168	0.328	0.590	0.774
1	0.000	0.000	0.001	0.009	0.031	0.078	0.156	0.252	0.328	0.295	0.193
2	0.000	0.000	0.003	0.018	0.055	0.117	0.187	0.227	0.197	0.089	0.029
3	0.000	0.000	0.006	0.029	0.077	0.137	0.174	0.159	0.092	0.021	0.003
4	0.000	0.000	0.009	0.041	0.093	0.137	0.139	0.095	0.037	0.004	0.000
5	0.000	0.001	0.013	0.051	0.100	0.123	0.100	0.051	0.013	0.001	0.000
6	0.000	0.001	0.018	0.060	0.100	0.103	0.067	0.026	0.004	0.000	0.000
k r= 6											
0	0.000	0.000	0.000	0.001	0.004	0.016	0.047	0.118	0.262	0.531	0.735
1	0.000	0.000	0.000	0.003	0.015	0.047	0.112	0.212	0.315	0.319	0.221
2	0.000	0.000	0.001	0.008	0.031	0.082	0.157	0.222	0.220	0.112	0.039
3	0.000	0.000	0.002	0.014	0.050	0.109	0.167	0.178	0.117	0.030	0.005
4	0.000	0.000	0.003	0.022	0.067	0.123	0.150	0.120	0.053	0.007	0.001
5	0.000	0.000	0.005	0.031	0.080	0.123	0.120	0.072	0.021	0.001	0.000
6	0.000	0.000	0.008	0.040	0.088	0.113	0.088	0.040	0.008	0.000	0.000

Table 4A The Poisson Distribution *dpois(x, lambda)*

x	λ									
	0.1	**0.2**	**0.3**	**0.4**	**0.5**	**0.6**	**0.7**	**0.8**	**0.9**	**1**
0	0.9048	0.8187	0.7408	0.6703	0.6065	0.5488	0.4966	0.4493	0.4066	0.3679
1	0.0905	0.1637	0.2222	0.2681	0.3033	0.3293	0.3476	0.3595	0.3659	0.3679
2	0.0045	0.0164	0.0333	0.0536	0.0758	0.0988	0.1217	0.1438	0.1647	0.1839
3	0.0002	0.0011	0.0033	0.0072	0.0126	0.0198	0.0284	0.0383	0.0494	0.0613
4	0.0000	0.0001	0.0003	0.0007	0.0016	0.0030	0.0050	0.0077	0.0111	0.0153
5	0.0000	0.0000	0.0000	0.0001	0.0002	0.0004	0.0007	0.0012	0.0020	0.0031
6	0.0000	0.0000	0.0000	0.0000	0.0000	0.0000	0.0001	0.0002	0.0003	0.0005
7	0.0000	0.0000	0.0000	0.0000	0.0000	0.0000	0.0000	0.0000	0.0000	0.0001
	λ									
	1.1	**1.2**	**1.3**	**1.4**	**1.5**	**1.6**	**1.7**	**1.8**	**1.9**	**2**
0	0.3329	0.3012	0.2725	0.2466	0.2231	0.2019	0.1827	0.1653	0.1496	0.1353
1	0.3662	0.3614	0.3543	0.3452	0.3347	0.3230	0.3106	0.2975	0.2842	0.2707
2	0.2014	0.2169	0.2303	0.2417	0.2510	0.2584	0.2640	0.2678	0.2700	0.2707
3	0.0738	0.0867	0.0998	0.1128	0.1255	0.1378	0.1496	0.1607	0.1710	0.1804
4	0.0203	0.0260	0.0324	0.0395	0.0471	0.0551	0.0636	0.0723	0.0812	0.0902
5	0.0045	0.0062	0.0084	0.0111	0.0141	0.0176	0.0216	0.0260	0.0309	0.0361
6	0.0008	0.0012	0.0018	0.0026	0.0035	0.0047	0.0061	0.0078	0.0098	0.0120
7	0.0001	0.0002	0.0003	0.0005	0.0008	0.0011	0.0015	0.0020	0.0027	0.0034
8	0.0000	0.0000	0.0001	0.0001	0.0001	0.0002	0.0003	0.0005	0.0006	0.0009
9	0.0000	0.0000	0.0000	0.0000	0.0000	0.0000	0.0001	0.0001	0.0001	0.0002
	λ									
	2.1	**2.2**	**2.3**	**2.4**	**2.5**	**2.6**	**2.7**	**2.8**	**2.9**	**3**
0	0.1225	0.1108	0.1003	0.0907	0.0821	0.0743	0.0672	0.0608	0.0550	0.0498
1	0.2572	0.2438	0.2306	0.2177	0.2052	0.1931	0.1815	0.1703	0.1596	0.1494
2	0.2700	0.2681	0.2652	0.2613	0.2565	0.2510	0.2450	0.2384	0.2314	0.2240
3	0.1890	0.1966	0.2033	0.2090	0.2138	0.2176	0.2205	0.2225	0.2237	0.2240
4	0.0992	0.1082	0.1169	0.1254	0.1336	0.1414	0.1488	0.1557	0.1622	0.1680
5	0.0417	0.0476	0.0538	0.0602	0.0668	0.0735	0.0804	0.0872	0.0940	0.1008
6	0.0146	0.0174	0.0206	0.0241	0.0278	0.0319	0.0362	0.0407	0.0455	0.0504
7	0.0044	0.0055	0.0068	0.0083	0.0099	0.0118	0.0139	0.0163	0.0188	0.0216
8	0.0011	0.0015	0.0019	0.0025	0.0031	0.0038	0.0047	0.0057	0.0068	0.0081
9	0.0003	0.0004	0.0005	0.0007	0.0009	0.0011	0.0014	0.0018	0.0022	0.0027
10	0.0001	0.0001	0.0001	0.0002	0.0002	0.0003	0.0004	0.0005	0.0006	0.0008
11	0.0000	0.0000	0.0000	0.0000	0.0000	0.0001	0.0001	0.0001	0.0002	0.0002
12	0.0000	0.0000	0.0000	0.0000	0.0000	0.0000	0.0000	0.0000	0.0000	0.0001

Table 4B The Poisson Distribution *dpois(x, lambda)*

x	λ									
	3.1	**3.2**	**3.3**	**3.4**	**3.5**	**3.6**	**3.7**	**3.8**	**3.9**	**4**
0	0.0450	0.0408	0.0369	0.0334	0.0302	0.0273	0.0247	0.0224	0.0202	0.0183
1	0.1397	0.1304	0.1217	0.1135	0.1057	0.0984	0.0915	0.0850	0.0789	0.0733
2	0.2165	0.2087	0.2008	0.1929	0.1850	0.1771	0.1692	0.1615	0.1539	0.1465
3	0.2237	0.2226	0.2209	0.2186	0.2158	0.2125	0.2087	0.2046	0.2001	0.1954
4	0.1733	0.1781	0.1823	0.1858	0.1888	0.1912	0.1931	0.1944	0.1951	0.1954
5	0.1075	0.1140	0.1203	0.1264	0.1322	0.1377	0.1429	0.1477	0.1522	0.1563
6	0.0555	0.0608	0.0662	0.0716	0.0771	0.0826	0.0881	0.0936	0.0989	0.1042
7	0.0246	0.0278	0.0312	0.0348	0.0385	0.0425	0.0466	0.0508	0.0551	0.0595
8	0.0095	0.0111	0.0129	0.0148	0.0169	0.0191	0.0215	0.0241	0.0269	0.0298
9	0.0033	0.0040	0.0047	0.0056	0.0066	0.0076	0.0089	0.0102	0.0116	0.0132
10	0.0010	0.0013	0.0016	0.0019	0.0023	0.0028	0.0033	0.0039	0.0045	0.0053
11	0.0003	0.0004	0.0005	0.0006	0.0007	0.0009	0.0011	0.0013	0.0016	0.0019
12	0.0001	0.0001	0.0001	0.0002	0.0002	0.0003	0.0003	0.0004	0.0005	0.0006
13	0.0000	0.0000	0.0000	0.0000	0.0001	0.0001	0.0001	0.0001	0.0002	0.0002
14	0.0000	0.0000	0.0000	0.0000	0.0000	0.0000	0.0000	0.0000	0.0000	0.0001
	λ									
	4.1	**4.2**	**4.3**	**4.4**	**4.5**	**4.6**	**4.7**	**4.8**	**4.9**	**5**
0	0.0166	0.0150	0.0136	0.0123	0.0111	0.0101	0.0091	0.0082	0.0074	0.0067
1	0.0679	0.0630	0.0583	0.0540	0.0500	0.0462	0.0427	0.0395	0.0365	0.0337
2	0.1393	0.1323	0.1254	0.1188	0.1125	0.1063	0.1005	0.0948	0.0894	0.0842
3	0.1904	0.1852	0.1798	0.1743	0.1687	0.1631	0.1574	0.1517	0.1460	0.1404
4	0.1951	0.1944	0.1933	0.1917	0.1898	0.1875	0.1849	0.1820	0.1789	0.1755
5	0.1600	0.1633	0.1662	0.1687	0.1708	0.1725	0.1738	0.1747	0.1753	0.1755
6	0.1093	0.1143	0.1191	0.1237	0.1281	0.1323	0.1362	0.1398	0.1432	0.1462
7	0.0640	0.0686	0.0732	0.0778	0.0824	0.0869	0.0914	0.0959	0.1002	0.1044
8	0.0328	0.0360	0.0393	0.0428	0.0463	0.0500	0.0537	0.0575	0.0614	0.0653
9	0.0150	0.0168	0.0188	0.0209	0.0232	0.0255	0.0281	0.0307	0.0334	0.0363
10	0.0061	0.0071	0.0081	0.0092	0.0104	0.0118	0.0132	0.0147	0.0164	0.0181
11	0.0023	0.0027	0.0032	0.0037	0.0043	0.0049	0.0056	0.0064	0.0073	0.0082
12	0.0008	0.0009	0.0011	0.0013	0.0016	0.0019	0.0022	0.0026	0.0030	0.0034
13	0.0002	0.0003	0.0004	0.0005	0.0006	0.0007	0.0008	0.0009	0.0011	0.0013
14	0.0001	0.0001	0.0001	0.0001	0.0002	0.0002	0.0003	0.0003	0.0004	0.0005
15	0.0000	0.0000	0.0000	0.0000	0.0001	0.0001	0.0001	0.0001	0.0001	0.0002
	λ									
	5.1	**5.2**	**5.3**	**5.4**	**5.5**	**5.6**	**5.7**	**5.8**	**5.9**	**6**
0	0.0061	0.0055	0.0050	0.0045	0.0041	0.0037	0.0033	0.0030	0.0027	0.0025
1	0.0311	0.0287	0.0265	0.0244	0.0225	0.0207	0.0191	0.0176	0.0162	0.0149
2	0.0793	0.0746	0.0701	0.0659	0.0618	0.0580	0.0544	0.0509	0.0477	0.0446
3	0.1348	0.1293	0.1239	0.1185	0.1133	0.1082	0.1033	0.0985	0.0938	0.0892
4	0.1719	0.1681	0.1641	0.1600	0.1558	0.1515	0.1472	0.1428	0.1383	0.1339
5	0.1753	0.1748	0.1740	0.1728	0.1714	0.1697	0.1678	0.1656	0.1632	0.1606
6	0.1490	0.1515	0.1537	0.1555	0.1571	0.1584	0.1594	0.1601	0.1605	0.1606
7	0.1086	0.1125	0.1163	0.1200	0.1234	0.1267	0.1298	0.1326	0.1353	0.1377
8	0.0692	0.0731	0.0771	0.0810	0.0849	0.0887	0.0925	0.0962	0.0998	0.1033
9	0.0392	0.0423	0.0454	0.0486	0.0519	0.0552	0.0586	0.0620	0.0654	0.0688
10	0.0200	0.0220	0.0241	0.0262	0.0285	0.0309	0.0334	0.0359	0.0386	0.0413
11	0.0093	0.0104	0.0116	0.0129	0.0143	0.0157	0.0173	0.0190	0.0207	0.0225
12	0.0039	0.0045	0.0051	0.0058	0.0065	0.0073	0.0082	0.0092	0.0102	0.0113
13	0.0015	0.0018	0.0021	0.0024	0.0028	0.0032	0.0036	0.0041	0.0046	0.0052
14	0.0006	0.0007	0.0008	0.0009	0.0011	0.0013	0.0015	0.0017	0.0019	0.0022
15	0.0002	0.0002	0.0003	0.0003	0.0004	0.0005	0.0006	0.0007	0.0008	0.0009
16	0.0001	0.0001	0.0001	0.0001	0.0001	0.0002	0.0002	0.0002	0.0003	0.0003

Table 5 Uniform Random Numbers *runif()*

0.26045	0.45255	0.08243	0.11702	0.77174	0.59544	0.00434	0.32668	0.21756	0.32884	0.95214	0.74265
0.32421	0.80570	0.89146	0.71256	0.99249	0.10285	0.79897	0.96661	0.37763	0.14452	0.18652	0.36675
0.72592	0.12659	0.53533	0.60053	0.26672	0.87521	0.02552	0.25434	0.12797	0.24618	0.65108	0.64513
0.71840	0.08513	0.23371	0.02415	0.43554	0.05493	0.88436	0.41926	0.65170	0.79179	0.59458	0.04382
0.53730	0.26542	0.56482	0.72914	0.43531	0.78484	0.30489	0.03490	0.87762	0.89947	0.10485	0.36763
0.53009	0.81887	0.40481	0.86507	0.47260	0.94143	0.10507	0.42944	0.84748	0.15869	0.22194	0.90786
0.13244	0.18098	0.91291	0.60472	0.33724	0.31437	0.38023	0.03852	0.09715	0.50061	0.17050	0.82029
0.75747	0.67811	0.49845	0.88445	0.38439	0.22307	0.62127	0.13408	0.15820	0.37085	0.57577	0.01993
0.74058	0.41499	0.89102	0.73489	0.37543	0.65296	0.76141	0.07636	0.12641	0.18704	0.03580	0.53164
0.37995	0.00084	0.76149	0.82307	0.41687	0.99487	0.65669	0.08654	0.73599	0.18841	0.37058	0.08042
0.68364	0.99516	0.62631	0.56188	0.69964	0.12542	0.59097	0.27089	0.92112	0.24140	0.89183	0.61436
0.79564	0.70279	0.71969	0.68245	0.70334	0.21555	0.33227	0.93017	0.66524	0.56216	0.27590	0.08240
0.09321	0.08613	0.52274	0.84394	0.58626	0.27791	0.87987	0.70912	0.93716	0.22967	0.30107	0.98514
0.88879	0.03996	0.07819	0.93514	0.30262	0.04448	0.44624	0.51893	0.01440	0.50706	0.57082	0.27091
0.89181	0.77628	0.88659	0.05844	0.20766	0.02693	0.24419	0.76749	0.99971	0.97993	0.84579	0.44386
0.35929	0.32231	0.63343	0.79622	0.97920	0.25704	0.02932	0.74395	0.09865	0.61020	0.06410	0.50310
0.50129	0.78609	0.31604	0.61329	0.35325	0.18382	0.03873	0.55580	0.09346	0.27389	0.16918	0.21134
0.36496	0.46037	0.30461	0.81452	0.53345	0.19104	0.86362	0.55637	0.09098	0.72606	0.95548	0.49740
0.98389	0.31701	0.32705	0.44758	0.63069	0.26742	0.46233	0.55544	0.17752	0.26402	0.17765	0.86384
0.61070	0.35065	0.67802	0.40588	0.14595	0.47502	0.95638	0.82110	0.92669	0.63935	0.06547	0.80803
0.09130	0.08863	0.29354	0.78679	0.57487	0.69037	0.59067	0.59630	0.94073	0.04777	0.46844	0.73461
0.36299	0.09387	0.19838	0.71771	0.45717	0.81545	0.03106	0.06779	0.54076	0.28766	0.33251	0.58446
0.19061	0.98582	0.37645	0.57549	0.92324	0.34528	0.25491	0.28024	0.82136	0.57264	0.38061	0.39045
0.55205	0.11415	0.71101	0.96230	0.61362	0.41804	0.13503	0.05054	0.33201	0.59870	0.46453	0.49440
0.88609	0.21311	0.47853	0.65404	0.42697	0.79679	0.89558	0.23173	0.83146	0.68273	0.67547	0.63697
0.84976	0.83497	0.39602	0.03092	0.30428	0.43751	0.41733	0.19779	0.71576	0.00977	0.55365	0.91174
0.69274	0.73962	0.06509	0.85213	0.95080	0.95649	0.29667	0.25019	0.20914	0.95624	0.10788	0.78189
0.17920	0.41607	0.52394	0.64460	0.90272	0.35259	0.86859	0.72531	0.18865	0.07641	0.92086	0.56384
0.79470	0.78273	0.79459	0.79159	0.46205	0.06821	0.26707	0.39472	0.76326	0.89925	0.78382	0.41056
0.85515	0.09759	0.23818	0.73604	0.53715	0.32567	0.91836	0.25756	0.23133	0.22724	0.88368	0.76172
0.02211	0.64273	0.62611	0.11866	0.85040	0.80515	0.26370	0.36005	0.10805	0.29207	0.07195	0.56385
0.07526	0.63875	0.62860	0.32895	0.71142	0.37213	0.54913	0.70052	0.38738	0.91253	0.98763	0.76070
0.56253	0.06819	0.53463	0.65495	0.32509	0.31364	0.82816	0.24706	0.83613	0.69571	0.27185	0.28150
0.05976	0.99120	0.79449	0.02408	0.06431	0.44003	0.68529	0.04345	0.29677	0.73441	0.86819	0.06398
0.31433	0.67372	0.47582	0.36025	0.43992	0.24349	0.38936	0.70662	0.59317	0.98039	0.35107	0.71279
0.05496	0.10931	0.37364	0.46287	0.71819	0.65004	0.02665	0.99846	0.44542	0.13603	0.09263	0.79295
0.31558	0.89560	0.65687	0.02941	0.64811	0.86453	0.36923	0.06865	0.20339	0.67074	0.26818	0.10026
0.89550	0.02150	0.54029	0.02745	0.38691	0.23837	0.93694	0.55979	0.47136	0.47120	0.76193	0.73475
0.31373	0.50761	0.06291	0.60640	0.10860	0.13291	0.20233	0.23532	0.54307	0.53908	0.54415	0.44746
0.37234	0.10612	0.30849	0.51793	0.69791	0.70961	0.04664	0.49120	0.75060	0.25763	0.79115	0.18276
0.49401	0.23880	0.77832	0.10183	0.47407	0.58064	0.77764	0.90514	0.81599	0.58603	0.16238	0.41738
0.24428	0.34958	0.69620	0.94477	0.04459	0.00309	0.47021	0.07034	0.53072	0.62322	0.07487	0.25765
0.80867	0.36851	0.16183	0.82675	0.45737	0.69821	0.15163	0.41232	0.10247	0.67875	0.02741	0.67550
0.72365	0.94833	0.45768	0.24785	0.36755	0.34085	0.90246	0.48430	0.14734	0.08267	0.73418	0.51305
0.68798	0.29518	0.24831	0.44418	0.23717	0.45857	0.20131	0.72744	0.58808	0.91476	0.75339	0.58143
0.72962	0.60418	0.16412	0.08700	0.56799	0.54024	0.01336	0.39290	0.33159	0.36715	0.18243	0.59687
0.39265	0.76290	0.39065	0.62015	0.23773	0.99269	0.92462	0.36855	0.49693	0.77447	0.75981	0.25707
0.77820	0.75591	0.42069	0.62261	0.67050	0.95338	0.78539	0.60962	0.16904	0.01911	0.06098	0.18148
0.92235	0.60504	0.26900	0.75977	0.17585	0.17589	0.37827	0.73405	0.37064	0.19840	0.22707	0.53079
0.56531	0.56800	0.67042	0.58552	0.10493	0.55123	0.53317	0.22061	0.28386	0.31886	0.37999	0.22154

Table 6 Normal Random Numbers *rnorm()*

1.41454	−0.01730	−2.36819	0.29493	0.50965	1.21490	0.07785	0.43732	1.09229	−1.10448	0.06672
−0.40859	0.45341	1.99087	−0.86667	−0.34753	0.81674	0.35439	−0.00307	−0.87258	1.06371	−0.77224
−0.84417	0.88097	−1.89494	0.51587	−0.35833	0.14322	0.89374	0.26242	−0.57621	0.54472	0.11631
−1.03085	0.28022	1.63994	0.31428	0.62237	−1.45487	−1.58922	−0.70650	−0.05959	0.16965	−1.22107
−0.29284	0.18224	0.34862	−0.33570	−1.59689	0.09538	1.08324	−1.50433	0.26166	0.19888	−0.13817
1.94815	1.25012	0.75006	0.13336	−3.01359	−0.08416	2.11394	0.49415	−1.00732	1.20540	0.35026
−0.28790	−0.73669	0.72904	0.43187	0.57001	−0.47086	−0.08548	0.37685	−0.05280	0.44200	0.48824
−0.20150	0.00414	0.61642	−0.59934	0.37483	−0.76223	0.96221	−0.85891	0.98695	−0.88989	1.40683
−0.46417	1.20743	0.27583	0.70954	0.19756	0.08720	1.39201	−0.68634	0.97974	0.13303	0.67667
0.88816	0.23222	−0.18307	−0.07550	−0.70191	−0.26851	−0.70018	0.46943	−2.29884	1.43193	−1.32409
2.10451	3.71241	−0.50259	0.48774	−0.52434	−1.60039	−1.08079	0.20215	0.20004	0.55507	0.21762
−0.33571	1.02325	0.00107	0.37945	0.08294	0.32854	−0.32797	0.15696	2.02390	−0.06944	−0.14846
−1.08655	1.59761	−1.46166	1.38814	0.88852	0.41167	0.64047	1.00082	0.16690	1.09976	−0.01619
−2.00716	1.19278	0.43605	1.26196	0.13018	0.31070	1.16807	0.04993	−1.14361	−0.15681	0.08715
2.19862	−0.29717	0.44549	−0.36705	−0.20489	0.01734	−0.17208	0.01978	−1.23604	1.50503	0.59908
−0.33989	−0.26465	2.83284	0.96599	1.42372	1.17499	1.94346	0.38380	0.77902	−0.03025	−0.38539
−0.71090	−0.25878	0.26900	−0.78089	−0.08410	0.30440	−0.27115	−0.35542	0.12565	−0.18920	−1.34452
0.70919	0.59750	−0.04583	−0.88405	1.60868	3.05433	0.70368	−1.29100	1.58245	0.11642	0.12345
−1.21620	−0.39730	0.38453	1.09984	−0.64246	−1.35791	0.34796	0.29378	−0.81288	−0.25805	1.19220
0.36807	0.18125	0.39018	−1.00071	0.19866	−1.40515	−0.24124	0.39821	1.18375	0.37369	−1.12025
−0.97891	−0.58646	0.33777	−0.82992	−0.13636	1.08891	−0.54916	0.27755	−0.47570	0.90053	0.41431
1.64239	1.54327	0.23385	0.61676	0.31595	1.21807	1.35788	−1.59685	0.43317	−0.73337	−0.35326
2.92797	0.88831	1.66457	0.63851	0.65766	−0.06684	−0.86212	−1.22031	1.29682	−0.66578	0.36904
1.32442	−0.80479	−0.78584	0.70325	0.67111	−0.24525	1.35534	0.48745	−0.96159	−0.75927	−1.19718
−0.35875	0.46107	0.58515	−0.07217	1.13902	−0.19510	−0.46537	−1.56974	0.41041	0.05467	−1.74370
−0.32602	−0.94723	−0.49068	−0.21759	0.63419	−0.89146	−0.78703	0.06821	0.75525	−1.01236	0.83680
0.07516	0.67230	−0.12423	−2.30127	2.12689	−0.09974	1.32146	0.88403	0.62865	0.24707	1.03212
1.86809	0.05537	−1.43947	0.85125	−0.15708	−1.26449	0.27738	1.94810	0.54179	1.05659	−0.95903
−0.22643	−1.35469	0.50925	−0.67050	−0.60714	−0.43223	−0.45260	1.34881	−0.19288	1.05904	−0.09501
1.70906	1.31515	−2.18747	1.08610	−1.06902	0.27804	−0.29293	−0.17445	−0.53751	−1.79979	−0.41721
−0.83390	0.46731	−0.56274	−2.20880	−0.27900	0.82870	1.07405	−0.97264	−1.02573	−0.29890	−0.48554
−0.51258	0.80417	−0.06920	0.40064	0.18906	0.33154	−0.58905	−1.46178	0.40877	1.63213	0.70093
−0.63941	0.39501	1.00943	−0.87322	−0.46130	−0.10074	0.05105	−1.39067	0.31018	−1.50217	0.50525
1.36665	1.74711	0.08899	−0.55434	1.30707	−0.26805	0.49918	0.29566	0.59670	0.23504	−0.24372
−1.40481	0.66860	−0.34508	−0.70946	−1.90081	−0.05226	−0.41017	0.27629	0.81197	0.28091	0.43705
0.89751	−0.82849	−1.10322	−0.70205	2.31094	0.31775	−1.10196	−0.01512	−0.96577	−1.23711	1.15663
−0.10625	0.87426	−0.36524	−0.28340	1.50529	1.18436	−2.96204	0.48695	1.53433	0.61426	3.49481
1.93813	−0.67592	1.07759	−0.17343	−0.34475	−0.06209	0.42699	−0.89233	0.78170	−0.66984	−0.27896
−0.90268	−1.34644	0.29699	−0.90468	0.34819	−0.25832	−0.47819	0.86988	0.41686	−0.80345	−0.19809
1.66307	0.53654	0.99816	−1.11934	−0.29584	−2.23558	−1.31746	0.52602	−0.90182	0.57381	1.83910
−0.50779	−0.83039	0.56605	−0.71431	1.63516	0.50691	−0.13062	−0.20598	0.67242	0.43727	−1.06699
−0.95078	0.76159	0.58282	−0.09880	−1.19036	1.14878	−0.13988	1.64719	0.78968	−0.78546	0.14191
0.61489	1.14312	0.91741	0.54070	0.62595	−0.51385	−0.12093	0.89387	0.50550	−2.56324	−1.33797
0.89686	0.89269	−1.24247	−0.75980	−1.48276	−1.29377	2.06290	1.69582	−1.30505	0.14456	−0.41667
0.03243	0.81627	−0.23586	1.43030	0.75656	0.44905	−0.77305	−1.61727	−0.44636	−0.14987	−0.28204
0.92752	−1.55510	−0.42709	0.19483	0.13888	−0.62455	−0.42029	−1.51817	−0.16898	0.87832	0.59636
1.67997	−0.07600	−0.58079	0.29822	−0.44670	−0.44328	0.48903	−2.34268	−0.16576	−0.16816	0.56294
0.21364	1.76015	−0.67186	−0.22039	−1.09916	0.43115	0.52821	−0.41856	−1.21243	0.21279	0.56905
−0.32614	1.25131	0.43976	−0.29192	−1.00316	0.60873	0.00913	−1.75542	−1.20400	0.73305	0.22079
0.85401	−0.69327	−0.55011	0.51770	1.05760	−1.35158	0.63512	0.16262	−1.57508	−0.28042	2.82785

Table 7A	Cumulative Standard Normal Distribution *pnorm()*									
z	0.00	0.01	0.02	0.03	0.04	0.05	0.06	0.07	0.08	0.09
−3.4	0.0003	0.0003	0.0003	0.0003	0.0003	0.0003	0.0003	0.0003	0.0003	0.0002
−3.3	0.0005	0.0005	0.0005	0.0004	0.0004	0.0004	0.0004	0.0004	0.0004	0.0003
−3.2	0.0007	0.0007	0.0006	0.0006	0.0006	0.0006	0.0006	0.0005	0.0005	0.0005
−3.1	0.0010	0.0009	0.0009	0.0009	0.0008	0.0008	0.0008	0.0008	0.0007	0.0007
−3.0	0.0013	0.0013	0.0013	0.0012	0.0012	0.0011	0.0011	0.0011	0.0010	0.0010
−2.9	0.0019	0.0018	0.0018	0.0017	0.0016	0.0016	0.0015	0.0015	0.0014	0.0014
−2.8	0.0026	0.0025	0.0024	0.0023	0.0023	0.0022	0.0021	0.0021	0.0020	0.0019
−2.7	0.0035	0.0034	0.0033	0.0032	0.0031	0.0030	0.0029	0.0028	0.0027	0.0026
−2.6	0.0047	0.0045	0.0044	0.0043	0.0041	0.0040	0.0039	0.0038	0.0037	0.0036
−2.5	0.0062	0.0060	0.0059	0.0057	0.0055	0.0054	0.0052	0.0051	0.0049	0.0048
−2.4	0.0082	0.0080	0.0078	0.0075	0.0073	0.0071	0.0069	0.0068	0.0066	0.0064
−2.3	0.0107	0.0104	0.0102	0.0099	0.0096	0.0094	0.0091	0.0089	0.0087	0.0084
−2.2	0.0139	0.0136	0.0132	0.0129	0.0125	0.0122	0.0119	0.0116	0.0113	0.0110
−2.1	0.0179	0.0174	0.0170	0.0166	0.0162	0.0158	0.0154	0.0150	0.0146	0.0143
−2.0	0.0228	0.0222	0.0217	0.0212	0.0207	0.0202	0.0197	0.0192	0.0188	0.0183
−1.9	0.0287	0.0281	0.0274	0.0268	0.0262	0.0256	0.0250	0.0244	0.0239	0.0233
−1.8	0.0359	0.0351	0.0344	0.0336	0.0329	0.0322	0.0314	0.0307	0.0301	0.0294
−1.7	0.0446	0.0436	0.0427	0.0418	0.0409	0.0401	0.0392	0.0384	0.0375	0.0367
−1.6	0.0548	0.0537	0.0526	0.0516	0.0505	0.0495	0.0485	0.0475	0.0465	0.0455
−1.5	0.0668	0.0655	0.0643	0.0630	0.0618	0.0606	0.0594	0.0582	0.0571	0.0559
−1.4	0.0808	0.0793	0.0778	0.0764	0.0749	0.0735	0.0721	0.0708	0.0694	0.0681
−1.3	0.0968	0.0951	0.0934	0.0918	0.0901	0.0885	0.0869	0.0853	0.0838	0.0823
−1.2	0.1151	0.1131	0.1112	0.1093	0.1075	0.1056	0.1038	0.1020	0.1003	0.0985
−1.1	0.1357	0.1335	0.1314	0.1292	0.1271	0.1251	0.1230	0.1210	0.1190	0.1170
−1.0	0.1587	0.1562	0.1539	0.1515	0.1492	0.1469	0.1446	0.1423	0.1401	0.1379
−0.9	0.1841	0.1814	0.1788	0.1762	0.1736	0.1711	0.1685	0.1660	0.1635	0.1611
−0.8	0.2119	0.2090	0.2061	0.2033	0.2005	0.1977	0.1949	0.1922	0.1894	0.1867
−0.7	0.2420	0.2389	0.2358	0.2327	0.2296	0.2266	0.2236	0.2206	0.2177	0.2148
−0.6	0.2743	0.2709	0.2676	0.2643	0.2611	0.2578	0.2546	0.2514	0.2483	0.2451
−0.5	0.3085	0.3050	0.3015	0.2981	0.2946	0.2912	0.2877	0.2843	0.2810	0.2776
−0.4	0.3446	0.3409	0.3372	0.3336	0.3300	0.3264	0.3228	0.3192	0.3156	0.3121
−0.3	0.3821	0.3783	0.3745	0.3707	0.3669	0.3632	0.3594	0.3557	0.3520	0.3483
−0.2	0.4207	0.4168	0.4129	0.4090	0.4052	0.4013	0.3974	0.3936	0.3897	0.3859
−0.1	0.4602	0.4562	0.4522	0.4483	0.4443	0.4404	0.4364	0.4325	0.4286	0.4247
−0.0	0.5000	0.4960	0.4920	0.4880	0.4840	0.4801	0.4761	0.4721	0.4681	0.4641

Table 7B Cumulative Standard Normal Distribution *pnorm()*

z	0.00	0.01	0.02	0.03	0.04	0.05	0.06	0.07	0.08	0.09
0.0	0.5000	0.5040	0.5080	0.5120	0.5160	0.5199	0.5239	0.5279	0.5319	0.5359
0.1	0.5398	0.5438	0.5478	0.5517	0.5557	0.5596	0.5636	0.5675	0.5714	0.5753
0.2	0.5793	0.5832	0.5871	0.5910	0.5948	0.5987	0.6026	0.6064	0.6103	0.6141
0.3	0.6179	0.6217	0.6255	0.6293	0.6331	0.6368	0.6406	0.6443	0.6480	0.6517
0.4	0.6554	0.6591	0.6628	0.6664	0.6700	0.6736	0.6772	0.6808	0.6844	0.6879
0.5	0.6915	0.6950	0.6985	0.7019	0.7054	0.7088	0.7123	0.7157	0.7190	0.7224
0.6	0.7257	0.7291	0.7324	0.7357	0.7389	0.7422	0.7454	0.7486	0.7517	0.7549
0.7	0.7580	0.7611	0.7642	0.7673	0.7704	0.7734	0.7764	0.7794	0.7823	0.7852
0.8	0.7881	0.7910	0.7939	0.7967	0.7995	0.8023	0.8051	0.8078	0.8106	0.8133
0.9	0.8159	0.8186	0.8212	0.8238	0.8264	0.8289	0.8315	0.8340	0.8365	0.8389
1.0	0.8413	0.8438	0.8461	0.8485	0.8508	0.8531	0.8554	0.8577	0.8599	0.8621
1.1	0.8643	0.8665	0.8686	0.8708	0.8729	0.8749	0.8770	0.8790	0.8810	0.8830
1.2	0.8849	0.8869	0.8888	0.8907	0.8925	0.8944	0.8962	0.8980	0.8997	0.9015
1.3	0.9032	0.9049	0.9066	0.9082	0.9099	0.9115	0.9131	0.9147	0.9162	0.9177
1.4	0.9192	0.9207	0.9222	0.9236	0.9251	0.9265	0.9279	0.9292	0.9306	0.9319
1.5	0.9332	0.9345	0.9357	0.9370	0.9382	0.9394	0.9406	0.9418	0.9429	0.9441
1.6	0.9452	0.9463	0.9474	0.9484	0.9495	0.9505	0.9515	0.9525	0.9535	0.9545
1.7	0.9554	0.9564	0.9573	0.9582	0.9591	0.9599	0.9608	0.9616	0.9625	0.9633
1.8	0.9641	0.9649	0.9656	0.9664	0.9671	0.9678	0.9686	0.9693	0.9699	0.9706
1.9	0.9713	0.9719	0.9726	0.9732	0.9738	0.9744	0.9750	0.9756	0.9761	0.9767
2.0	0.9772	0.9778	0.9783	0.9788	0.9793	0.9798	0.9803	0.9808	0.9812	0.9817
2.1	0.9821	0.9826	0.9830	0.9834	0.9838	0.9842	0.9846	0.9850	0.9854	0.9857
2.2	0.9861	0.9864	0.9868	0.9871	0.9875	0.9878	0.9881	0.9884	0.9887	0.9890
2.3	0.9893	0.9896	0.9898	0.9901	0.9904	0.9906	0.9909	0.9911	0.9913	0.9916
2.4	0.9918	0.9920	0.9922	0.9925	0.9927	0.9929	0.9931	0.9932	0.9934	0.9936
2.5	0.9938	0.9940	0.9941	0.9943	0.9945	0.9946	0.9948	0.9949	0.9951	0.9952
2.6	0.9953	0.9955	0.9956	0.9957	0.9959	0.9960	0.9961	0.9962	0.9963	0.9964
2.7	0.9965	0.9966	0.9967	0.9968	0.9969	0.9970	0.9971	0.9972	0.9973	0.9974
2.8	0.9974	0.9975	0.9976	0.9977	0.9977	0.9978	0.9979	0.9979	0.9980	0.9981
2.9	0.9981	0.9982	0.9982	0.9983	0.9984	0.9984	0.9985	0.9985	0.9986	0.9986
3.0	0.9987	0.9987	0.9987	0.9988	0.9988	0.9989	0.9989	0.9989	0.9990	0.9990
3.1	0.9990	0.9991	0.9991	0.9991	0.9992	0.9992	0.9992	0.9992	0.9993	0.9993
3.2	0.9993	0.9993	0.9994	0.9994	0.9994	0.9994	0.9994	0.9995	0.9995	0.9995
3.3	0.9995	0.9995	0.9995	0.9996	0.9996	0.9996	0.9996	0.9996	0.9996	0.9997
3.4	0.9997	0.9997	0.9997	0.9997	0.9997	0.9997	0.9997	0.9997	0.9997	0.9998

Table 8	The *t*-Distribution *qt((1+c)/2, df)*				
C. I.	**0.8**	**0.85**	**0.9**	**0.95**	**0.98**
one–tailed α	**0.1**	**0.075**	**0.05**	**0.025**	**0.01**
two–tailed α	**0.2**	**0.15**	**0.1**	**0.05**	**0.02**
df					
1	3.0777	4.1653	6.3138	12.706	31.821
2	1.8856	2.2819	2.9200	4.3027	6.9646
3	1.6377	1.9243	2.3534	3.1824	4.5407
4	1.5332	1.7782	2.1318	2.7764	3.7469
5	1.4759	1.6994	2.0150	2.5706	3.3649
6	1.4398	1.6502	1.9432	2.4469	3.1427
7	1.4149	1.6166	1.8946	2.3646	2.9980
8	1.3968	1.5922	1.8595	2.3060	2.8965
9	1.3830	1.5737	1.8331	2.2622	2.8214
10	1.3722	1.5592	1.8125	2.2281	2.7638
11	1.3634	1.5476	1.7959	2.2010	2.7181
12	1.3562	1.5380	1.7823	2.1788	2.6810
13	1.3502	1.5299	1.7709	2.1604	2.6503
14	1.3450	1.5231	1.7613	2.1448	2.6245
15	1.3406	1.5172	1.7531	2.1314	2.6025
16	1.3368	1.5121	1.7459	2.1199	2.5835
17	1.3334	1.5077	1.7396	2.1098	2.5669
18	1.3304	1.5037	1.7341	2.1009	2.5524
19	1.3277	1.5002	1.7291	2.0930	2.5395
20	1.3253	1.4970	1.7247	2.0860	2.5280
21	1.3232	1.4942	1.7207	2.0796	2.5176
22	1.3212	1.4916	1.7171	2.0739	2.5083
23	1.3195	1.4893	1.7139	2.0687	2.4999
24	1.3178	1.4871	1.7109	2.0639	2.4922
25	1.3163	1.4852	1.7081	2.0595	2.4851
26	1.3150	1.4834	1.7056	2.0555	2.4786
27	1.3137	1.4817	1.7033	2.0518	2.4727
28	1.3125	1.4801	1.7011	2.0484	2.4671
29	1.3114	1.4787	1.6991	2.0452	2.4620
30	1.3104	1.4774	1.6973	2.0423	2.4573
35	1.3062	1.4718	1.6896	2.0301	2.4377
40	1.3031	1.4677	1.6839	2.0211	2.4233
45	1.3006	1.4645	1.6794	2.0141	2.4121
50	1.2987	1.4620	1.6759	2.0086	2.4033
55	1.2971	1.4599	1.6730	2.0040	2.3961
60	1.2958	1.4582	1.6706	2.0003	2.3901
65	1.2947	1.4567	1.6686	1.9971	2.3851
70	1.2938	1.4555	1.6669	1.9944	2.3808
75	1.2929	1.4544	1.6654	1.9921	2.3771
80	1.2922	1.4535	1.6641	1.9901	2.3739
90	1.2910	1.4519	1.6620	1.9867	2.3685
100	1.2901	1.4507	1.6602	1.9840	2.3642
500	1.2832	1.4417	1.6479	1.9647	2.3338
1000	1.2824	1.4406	1.6464	1.9623	2.3301
∞	1.2816	1.4395	1.6449	1.9600	2.3264

Table 9 The Chi–Square Distribution *qchisq(alpha, df)*

	α									
df	**0.005**	**0.01**	**0.025**	**0.05**	**0.1**	**0.9**	**0.95**	**0.975**	**0.99**	**0.995**
1	0.0000	0.0001	0.0009	0.0039	0.0157	2.7055	3.8415	5.0239	6.6349	7.8794
2	0.0100	0.0201	0.0506	0.1025	0.2107	4.6052	5.9915	7.3778	9.2103	10.597
3	0.0717	0.1148	0.2158	0.3518	0.5843	6.2514	7.8147	9.3484	11.345	12.838
4	0.2069	0.2971	0.4844	0.7107	1.0636	7.7794	9.4877	11.143	13.277	14.860
5	0.4117	0.5543	0.8312	1.1455	1.6103	9.2364	11.070	12.833	15.086	16.750
6	0.6757	0.8720	1.2373	1.6354	2.2041	10.645	12.592	14.449	16.812	18.548
7	0.9892	1.2390	1.6899	2.1673	2.8331	12.017	14.067	16.013	18.475	20.278
8	1.3444	1.6465	2.1797	2.7326	3.4895	13.362	15.507	17.535	20.090	21.955
9	1.7349	2.0879	2.7004	3.3251	4.1682	14.684	16.919	19.023	21.666	23.589
10	2.1559	2.5582	3.2470	3.9403	4.8652	15.987	18.307	20.483	23.209	25.188
11	2.6032	3.0535	3.8157	4.5748	5.5778	17.275	19.675	21.920	24.725	26.757
12	3.0738	3.5706	4.4038	5.2260	6.3038	18.549	21.026	23.337	26.217	28.300
13	3.5650	4.1069	5.0088	5.8919	7.0415	19.812	22.362	24.736	27.688	29.819
14	4.0747	4.6604	5.6287	6.5706	7.7895	21.064	23.685	26.119	29.141	31.319
15	4.6009	5.2293	6.2621	7.2609	8.5468	22.307	24.996	27.488	30.578	32.801
16	5.1422	5.8122	6.9077	7.9616	9.3122	23.542	26.296	28.845	32.000	34.267
17	5.6972	6.4078	7.5642	8.6718	10.085	24.769	27.587	30.191	33.409	35.718
18	6.2648	7.0149	8.2307	9.3905	10.865	25.989	28.869	31.526	34.805	37.156
19	6.8440	7.6327	8.9065	10.117	11.651	27.204	30.144	32.852	36.191	38.582
20	7.4338	8.2604	9.5908	10.851	12.443	28.412	31.410	34.170	37.566	39.997
21	8.0337	8.8972	10.283	11.591	13.240	29.615	32.671	35.479	38.932	41.401
22	8.6427	9.5425	10.982	12.338	14.041	30.813	33.924	36.781	40.289	42.796
23	9.2604	10.196	11.689	13.091	14.848	32.007	35.172	38.076	41.638	44.181
24	9.8862	10.856	12.401	13.848	15.659	33.196	36.415	39.364	42.980	45.559
25	10.520	11.524	13.120	14.611	16.473	34.382	37.652	40.646	44.314	46.928
26	11.160	12.198	13.844	15.379	17.292	35.563	38.885	41.923	45.642	48.290
27	11.808	12.879	14.573	16.151	18.114	36.741	40.113	43.195	46.963	49.645
28	12.461	13.565	15.308	16.928	18.939	37.916	41.337	44.461	48.278	50.993
29	13.121	14.256	16.047	17.708	19.768	39.087	42.557	45.722	49.588	52.336
30	13.787	14.953	16.791	18.493	20.599	40.256	43.773	46.979	50.892	53.672
40	20.707	22.164	24.433	26.509	29.051	51.805	55.758	59.342	63.691	66.766
50	27.991	29.707	32.357	34.764	37.689	63.167	67.505	71.420	76.154	79.490
60	35.534	37.485	40.482	43.188	46.459	74.397	79.082	83.298	88.379	91.952
70	43.275	45.442	48.758	51.739	55.329	85.527	90.531	95.023	100.43	104.21
80	51.172	53.540	57.153	60.391	64.278	96.578	101.88	106.63	112.33	116.32
90	59.196	61.754	65.647	69.126	73.291	107.57	113.15	118.14	124.12	128.30
100	67.328	70.065	74.222	77.929	82.358	118.50	124.34	129.56	135.81	140.17

Table 10A The *F*-Distribution *qf(1–alpha, df1, df2)* for α = 0.005

df1 \ df2	1	2	3	4	5	6	7	8	9	10	11
1	16211	198.5	55.55	31.33	22.78	18.63	16.23	14.68	13.61	12.82	12.22
2	19999	199.0	49.79	26.28	18.31	14.54	12.40	11.04	10.10	9.427	8.912
3	21615	199.2	47.46	24.25	16.53	12.91	10.88	9.596	8.717	8.081	7.600
4	22500	199.2	46.19	23.15	15.55	12.02	10.05	8.805	7.956	7.343	6.881
5	23056	199.3	45.39	22.45	14.94	11.46	9.522	8.302	7.471	6.872	6.422
6	23437	199.3	44.83	21.97	14.51	11.07	9.155	7.952	7.134	6.545	6.102
7	23715	199.4	44.43	21.62	14.20	10.78	8.885	7.694	6.885	6.302	5.865
8	23925	199.4	44.12	21.35	13.96	10.56	8.678	7.496	6.693	6.116	5.682
9	24091	199.4	43.88	21.13	13.77	10.39	8.514	7.339	6.541	5.968	5.537
10	24224	199.4	43.68	20.96	13.61	10.25	8.380	7.211	6.417	5.847	5.418
11	24334	199.4	43.52	20.82	13.49	10.13	8.270	7.104	6.314	5.746	5.320
12	24426	199.4	43.38	20.70	13.38	10.03	8.176	7.015	6.227	5.661	5.236
13	24505	199.4	43.27	20.60	13.29	9.950	8.097	6.938	6.153	5.589	5.165
14	24572	199.4	43.17	20.51	13.21	9.877	8.028	6.872	6.089	5.526	5.103
15	24630	199.4	43.08	20.43	13.14	9.814	7.968	6.814	6.032	5.471	5.049
20	24836	199.4	42.77	20.16	12.90	9.589	7.754	6.608	5.832	5.274	4.855
30	25044	199.5	42.46	19.89	12.65	9.358	7.534	6.396	5.625	5.071	4.654
40	25148	199.5	42.30	19.75	12.53	9.241	7.422	6.288	5.519	4.966	4.551
50	25211	199.5	42.21	19.66	12.45	9.170	7.354	6.222	5.454	4.902	4.488
60	25253	199.5	42.14	19.61	12.40	9.122	7.309	6.177	5.410	4.859	4.445
120	25359	199.5	41.98	19.46	12.27	9.001	7.193	6.065	5.300	4.750	4.337
∞	25464	199.5	41.82	19.32	12.14	8.879	7.076	5.951	5.188	4.639	4.226

df1 \ df2	12	13	14	15	20	30	40	50	60	120	∞
1	11.75	11.37	11.06	10.79	9.944	9.180	8.828	8.626	8.495	8.179	7.879
2	8.510	8.186	7.922	7.701	6.986	6.355	6.066	5.902	5.795	5.539	5.298
3	7.226	6.926	6.680	6.476	5.818	5.239	4.976	4.826	4.729	4.497	4.279
4	6.521	6.233	5.998	5.803	5.174	4.623	4.374	4.232	4.140	3.921	3.715
5	6.071	5.791	5.562	5.372	4.762	4.228	3.986	3.849	3.760	3.548	3.350
6	5.757	5.482	5.257	5.071	4.472	3.949	3.713	3.579	3.492	3.285	3.091
7	5.525	5.253	5.031	4.847	4.257	3.742	3.509	3.376	3.291	3.087	2.897
8	5.345	5.076	4.857	4.674	4.090	3.580	3.350	3.219	3.134	2.933	2.744
9	5.202	4.935	4.717	4.536	3.956	3.450	3.222	3.092	3.008	2.808	2.621
10	5.085	4.820	4.603	4.424	3.847	3.344	3.117	2.988	2.904	2.705	2.519
11	4.988	4.724	4.508	4.329	3.756	3.255	3.028	2.900	2.817	2.618	2.432
12	4.906	4.643	4.428	4.250	3.678	3.179	2.953	2.825	2.742	2.544	2.358
13	4.836	4.573	4.359	4.181	3.611	3.113	2.888	2.760	2.677	2.479	2.294
14	4.775	4.513	4.299	4.122	3.553	3.056	2.831	2.703	2.620	2.423	2.237
15	4.721	4.460	4.247	4.070	3.502	3.006	2.781	2.653	2.570	2.373	2.187
20	4.530	4.270	4.059	3.883	3.318	2.823	2.598	2.470	2.387	2.188	2.000
30	4.331	4.073	3.862	3.687	3.123	2.628	2.401	2.272	2.187	1.984	1.789
40	4.228	3.970	3.760	3.585	3.022	2.524	2.296	2.164	2.079	1.871	1.669
50	4.165	3.908	3.698	3.523	2.959	2.459	2.230	2.097	2.010	1.798	1.590
60	4.123	3.866	3.655	3.480	2.916	2.415	2.184	2.050	1.962	1.747	1.533
120	4.015	3.758	3.547	3.372	2.806	2.300	2.064	1.925	1.834	1.606	1.364
∞	3.904	3.647	3.436	3.260	2.690	2.176	1.932	1.786	1.689	1.431	1.000

Table 10B The *F*-Distribution *qf(1–alpha, df1, df2)* for $\alpha = 0.01$

df1	df2										
	1	2	3	4	5	6	7	8	9	10	11
1	4052	98.50	34.11	21.19	16.25	13.74	12.24	11.25	10.56	10.04	9.646
2	4999	99.00	30.81	18.00	13.27	10.92	9.547	8.649	8.022	7.559	7.206
3	5403	99.17	29.45	16.69	12.06	9.780	8.451	7.591	6.992	6.552	6.217
4	5625	99.25	28.71	15.97	11.39	9.148	7.847	7.006	6.422	5.994	5.668
5	5764	99.30	28.23	15.52	10.96	8.746	7.460	6.632	6.057	5.636	5.316
6	5859	99.33	27.91	15.20	10.67	8.466	7.191	6.371	5.802	5.386	5.069
7	5928	99.36	27.67	14.97	10.45	8.260	6.993	6.178	5.613	5.200	4.886
8	5981	99.37	27.48	14.79	10.28	8.102	6.840	6.029	5.467	5.057	4.744
9	6022	99.39	27.34	14.65	10.15	7.976	6.719	5.911	5.351	4.942	4.632
10	6056	99.40	27.22	14.54	10.05	7.874	6.620	5.814	5.257	4.849	4.539
11	6083	99.41	27.13	14.45	9.963	7.790	6.538	5.734	5.178	4.772	4.462
12	6106	99.42	27.05	14.37	9.888	7.718	6.469	5.667	5.111	4.706	4.397
13	6126	99.42	26.98	14.30	9.825	7.657	6.410	5.609	5.055	4.650	4.342
14	6143	99.43	26.92	14.24	9.770	7.605	6.359	5.559	5.005	4.601	4.293
15	6157	99.43	26.87	14.19	9.722	7.559	6.314	5.515	4.962	4.558	4.251
20	6209	99.45	26.69	14.02	9.553	7.396	6.155	5.359	4.808	4.405	4.099
30	6261	99.47	26.50	13.83	9.379	7.229	5.992	5.198	4.649	4.247	3.941
40	6287	99.47	26.41	13.74	9.291	7.143	5.908	5.116	4.567	4.165	3.860
50	6303	99.48	26.35	13.69	9.238	7.091	5.858	5.065	4.517	4.115	3.810
60	6313	99.48	26.31	13.65	9.202	7.057	5.824	5.032	4.483	4.082	3.776
120	6339	99.49	26.22	13.55	9.112	6.969	5.737	4.946	4.398	3.996	3.690
∞	6366	99.50	26.12	13.46	9.020	6.880	5.650	4.859	4.311	3.909	3.602

df1	12	13	14	15	20	30	40	50	60	120	∞
1	9.330	9.074	8.862	8.683	8.096	7.562	7.314	7.171	7.077	6.851	6.635
2	6.927	6.701	6.515	6.359	5.849	5.390	5.179	5.057	4.977	4.787	4.605
3	5.953	5.739	5.564	5.417	4.938	4.510	4.313	4.199	4.126	3.949	3.782
4	5.412	5.205	5.035	4.893	4.431	4.018	3.828	3.720	3.649	3.480	3.319
5	5.064	4.862	4.695	4.556	4.103	3.699	3.514	3.408	3.339	3.174	3.017
6	4.821	4.620	4.456	4.318	3.871	3.473	3.291	3.186	3.119	2.956	2.802
7	4.640	4.441	4.278	4.142	3.699	3.304	3.124	3.020	2.953	2.792	2.639
8	4.499	4.302	4.140	4.004	3.564	3.173	2.993	2.890	2.823	2.663	2.511
9	4.388	4.191	4.030	3.895	3.457	3.067	2.888	2.785	2.718	2.559	2.407
10	4.296	4.100	3.939	3.805	3.368	2.979	2.801	2.698	2.632	2.472	2.321
11	4.220	4.025	3.864	3.730	3.294	2.906	2.727	2.625	2.559	2.399	2.248
12	4.155	3.960	3.800	3.666	3.231	2.843	2.665	2.562	2.496	2.336	2.185
13	4.100	3.905	3.745	3.612	3.177	2.789	2.611	2.508	2.442	2.282	2.130
14	4.052	3.857	3.698	3.564	3.130	2.742	2.563	2.461	2.394	2.234	2.082
15	4.010	3.815	3.656	3.522	3.088	2.700	2.522	2.419	2.352	2.192	2.039
20	3.858	3.665	3.505	3.372	2.938	2.549	2.369	2.265	2.198	2.035	1.878
30	3.701	3.507	3.348	3.214	2.778	2.386	2.203	2.098	2.028	1.860	1.696
40	3.619	3.425	3.266	3.132	2.695	2.299	2.114	2.007	1.936	1.763	1.592
50	3.569	3.375	3.215	3.081	2.643	2.245	2.058	1.949	1.877	1.700	1.523
60	3.535	3.341	3.181	3.047	2.608	2.208	2.019	1.909	1.836	1.656	1.473
120	3.449	3.255	3.094	2.959	2.517	2.111	1.917	1.803	1.726	1.533	1.325
∞	3.361	3.165	3.004	2.868	2.421	2.006	1.805	1.683	1.601	1.381	1.000

Table 10C The *F*-Distribution *qf(1−alpha, df1, df2)* for α = 0.05

df1	df2 1	2	3	4	5	6	7	8	9	10	11
1	161.4	18.51	10.12	7.709	6.608	5.987	5.591	5.318	5.117	4.965	4.844
2	199.5	19.00	9.552	6.944	5.786	5.143	4.737	4.459	4.256	4.103	3.982
3	215.7	19.16	9.277	6.591	5.409	4.757	4.347	4.066	3.863	3.708	3.587
4	224.6	19.25	9.117	6.388	5.192	4.534	4.120	3.838	3.633	3.478	3.357
5	230.2	19.30	9.013	6.256	5.050	4.387	3.972	3.687	3.482	3.326	3.204
6	234.0	19.33	8.941	6.163	4.950	4.284	3.866	3.581	3.374	3.217	3.095
7	236.8	19.35	8.887	6.094	4.876	4.207	3.787	3.500	3.293	3.135	3.012
8	238.9	19.37	8.845	6.041	4.818	4.147	3.726	3.438	3.230	3.072	2.948
9	240.5	19.38	8.812	5.999	4.772	4.099	3.677	3.388	3.179	3.020	2.896
10	241.9	19.40	8.786	5.964	4.735	4.060	3.637	3.347	3.137	2.978	2.854
11	243.0	19.40	8.763	5.936	4.704	4.027	3.603	3.313	3.102	2.943	2.818
12	243.9	19.41	8.745	5.912	4.678	4.000	3.575	3.284	3.073	2.913	2.788
13	244.7	19.42	8.729	5.891	4.655	3.976	3.550	3.259	3.048	2.887	2.761
14	245.4	19.42	8.715	5.873	4.636	3.956	3.529	3.237	3.025	2.865	2.739
15	245.9	19.43	8.703	5.858	4.619	3.938	3.511	3.218	3.006	2.845	2.719
20	248.0	19.45	8.660	5.803	4.558	3.874	3.445	3.150	2.936	2.774	2.646
30	250.1	19.46	8.617	5.746	4.496	3.808	3.376	3.079	2.864	2.700	2.570
40	251.1	19.47	8.594	5.717	4.464	3.774	3.340	3.043	2.826	2.661	2.531
50	251.8	19.48	8.581	5.699	4.444	3.754	3.319	3.020	2.803	2.637	2.507
60	252.2	19.48	8.572	5.688	4.431	3.740	3.304	3.005	2.787	2.621	2.490
120	253.3	19.49	8.549	5.658	4.398	3.705	3.267	2.967	2.748	2.580	2.448
∞	254.3	19.50	8.526	5.628	4.365	3.669	3.230	2.928	2.707	2.538	2.404

df1	df2 12	13	14	15	20	30	40	50	60	120	∞
1	4.747	4.667	4.600	4.543	4.351	4.171	4.085	4.034	4.001	3.920	3.841
2	3.885	3.806	3.739	3.682	3.493	3.316	3.232	3.183	3.150	3.072	2.996
3	3.490	3.411	3.344	3.287	3.098	2.922	2.839	2.790	2.758	2.680	2.605
4	3.259	3.179	3.112	3.056	2.866	2.690	2.606	2.557	2.525	2.447	2.372
5	3.106	3.025	2.958	2.901	2.711	2.534	2.449	2.400	2.368	2.290	2.214
6	2.996	2.915	2.848	2.790	2.599	2.421	2.336	2.286	2.254	2.175	2.099
7	2.913	2.832	2.764	2.707	2.514	2.334	2.249	2.199	2.167	2.087	2.010
8	2.849	2.767	2.699	2.641	2.447	2.266	2.180	2.130	2.097	2.016	1.938
9	2.796	2.714	2.646	2.588	2.393	2.211	2.124	2.073	2.040	1.959	1.880
10	2.753	2.671	2.602	2.544	2.348	2.165	2.077	2.026	1.993	1.910	1.831
11	2.717	2.635	2.565	2.507	2.310	2.126	2.038	1.986	1.952	1.869	1.789
12	2.687	2.604	2.534	2.475	2.278	2.092	2.003	1.952	1.917	1.834	1.752
13	2.660	2.577	2.507	2.448	2.250	2.063	1.974	1.921	1.887	1.803	1.720
14	2.637	2.554	2.484	2.424	2.225	2.037	1.948	1.895	1.860	1.775	1.692
15	2.617	2.533	2.463	2.403	2.203	2.015	1.924	1.871	1.836	1.750	1.666
20	2.544	2.459	2.388	2.328	2.124	1.932	1.839	1.784	1.748	1.659	1.571
30	2.466	2.380	2.308	2.247	2.039	1.841	1.744	1.687	1.649	1.554	1.459
40	2.426	2.339	2.266	2.204	1.994	1.792	1.693	1.634	1.594	1.495	1.394
50	2.401	2.314	2.241	2.178	1.966	1.761	1.660	1.599	1.559	1.457	1.350
60	2.384	2.297	2.223	2.160	1.946	1.740	1.637	1.576	1.534	1.429	1.318
120	2.341	2.252	2.178	2.114	1.896	1.683	1.577	1.511	1.467	1.352	1.221
∞	2.296	2.206	2.131	2.066	1.843	1.622	1.509	1.438	1.389	1.254	1.000

Table 10D The *F*-Distribution *qf(1−alpha, df1, df2)* for $\alpha = 0.1$

df1	df2										
	1	2	3	4	5	6	7	8	9	10	11
1	39.86	8.526	5.538	4.545	4.060	3.776	3.589	3.458	3.360	3.285	3.225
2	49.50	9.000	5.462	4.325	3.780	3.463	3.257	3.113	3.006	2.924	2.860
3	53.59	9.162	5.391	4.191	3.619	3.289	3.074	2.924	2.813	2.728	2.660
4	55.83	9.243	5.343	4.107	3.520	3.181	2.961	2.806	2.693	2.605	2.536
5	57.24	9.293	5.309	4.051	3.453	3.108	2.883	2.726	2.611	2.522	2.451
6	58.20	9.326	5.285	4.010	3.405	3.055	2.827	2.668	2.551	2.461	2.389
7	58.91	9.349	5.266	3.979	3.368	3.014	2.785	2.624	2.505	2.414	2.342
8	59.44	9.367	5.252	3.955	3.339	2.983	2.752	2.589	2.469	2.377	2.304
9	59.86	9.381	5.240	3.936	3.316	2.958	2.725	2.561	2.440	2.347	2.274
10	60.19	9.392	5.230	3.920	3.297	2.937	2.703	2.538	2.416	2.323	2.248
11	60.47	9.401	5.222	3.907	3.282	2.920	2.684	2.519	2.396	2.302	2.227
12	60.71	9.408	5.216	3.896	3.268	2.905	2.668	2.502	2.379	2.284	2.209
13	60.90	9.415	5.210	3.886	3.257	2.892	2.654	2.488	2.364	2.269	2.193
14	61.07	9.420	5.205	3.878	3.247	2.881	2.643	2.475	2.351	2.255	2.179
15	61.22	9.425	5.200	3.870	3.238	2.871	2.632	2.464	2.340	2.244	2.167
20	61.74	9.441	5.184	3.844	3.207	2.836	2.595	2.425	2.298	2.201	2.123
30	62.26	9.458	5.168	3.817	3.174	2.800	2.555	2.383	2.255	2.155	2.076
40	62.53	9.466	5.160	3.804	3.157	2.781	2.535	2.361	2.232	2.132	2.052
50	62.69	9.471	5.155	3.795	3.147	2.770	2.523	2.348	2.218	2.117	2.036
60	62.79	9.475	5.151	3.790	3.140	2.762	2.514	2.339	2.208	2.107	2.026
120	63.06	9.483	5.143	3.775	3.123	2.742	2.493	2.316	2.184	2.082	2.000
∞	63.33	9.491	5.134	3.761	3.105	2.722	2.471	2.293	2.159	2.055	1.972

df1	12	13	14	15	20	30	40	50	60	120	∞
1	3.177	3.136	3.102	3.073	2.975	2.881	2.835	2.809	2.791	2.748	2.706
2	2.807	2.763	2.726	2.695	2.589	2.489	2.440	2.412	2.393	2.347	2.303
3	2.606	2.560	2.522	2.490	2.380	2.276	2.226	2.197	2.177	2.130	2.084
4	2.480	2.434	2.395	2.361	2.249	2.142	2.091	2.061	2.041	1.992	1.945
5	2.394	2.347	2.307	2.273	2.158	2.049	1.997	1.966	1.946	1.896	1.847
6	2.331	2.283	2.243	2.208	2.091	1.980	1.927	1.895	1.875	1.824	1.774
7	2.283	2.234	2.193	2.158	2.040	1.927	1.873	1.840	1.819	1.767	1.717
8	2.245	2.195	2.154	2.119	1.999	1.884	1.829	1.796	1.775	1.722	1.670
9	2.214	2.164	2.122	2.086	1.965	1.849	1.793	1.760	1.738	1.684	1.632
10	2.188	2.138	2.095	2.059	1.937	1.819	1.763	1.729	1.707	1.652	1.599
11	2.166	2.116	2.073	2.037	1.913	1.794	1.737	1.703	1.680	1.625	1.570
12	2.147	2.097	2.054	2.017	1.892	1.773	1.715	1.680	1.657	1.601	1.546
13	2.131	2.080	2.037	2.000	1.875	1.754	1.695	1.660	1.637	1.580	1.524
14	2.117	2.066	2.022	1.985	1.859	1.737	1.678	1.643	1.619	1.562	1.505
15	2.105	2.053	2.010	1.972	1.845	1.722	1.662	1.627	1.603	1.545	1.487
20	2.060	2.007	1.962	1.924	1.794	1.667	1.605	1.568	1.543	1.482	1.421
30	2.011	1.958	1.912	1.873	1.738	1.606	1.541	1.502	1.476	1.409	1.342
40	1.986	1.931	1.885	1.845	1.708	1.573	1.506	1.465	1.437	1.368	1.295
50	1.970	1.915	1.869	1.828	1.690	1.552	1.483	1.441	1.413	1.340	1.263
60	1.960	1.904	1.857	1.817	1.677	1.538	1.467	1.424	1.395	1.320	1.240
120	1.932	1.876	1.828	1.787	1.643	1.499	1.425	1.379	1.348	1.265	1.169
∞	1.904	1.846	1.797	1.755	1.607	1.456	1.377	1.327	1.291	1.193	1.000

Table 11 Critical Values for Pearson Correlation Coefficient

Reject $H_0 : \rho = 0$ if the absolute value of r is greater than the value given in the table. The values are for a two–tailed test; df = $n - 2$.

	α				α		
df	**0.1**	**0.05**	**0.01**	**df**	**0.1**	**0.05**	**0.01**
1	0.9877	0.9969	0.9999	20	0.3598	0.4227	0.5368
2	0.9000	0.9500	0.9900	21	0.3515	0.4132	0.5256
3	0.8054	0.8783	0.9587	22	0.3438	0.4044	0.5151
4	0.7293	0.8114	0.9172	23	0.3365	0.3961	0.5052
5	0.6694	0.7545	0.8745	24	0.3297	0.3882	0.4958
6	0.6215	0.7067	0.8343	25	0.3233	0.3809	0.4869
7	0.5822	0.6664	0.7977	26	0.3172	0.3739	0.4785
8	0.5494	0.6319	0.7646	27	0.3115	0.3673	0.4705
9	0.5214	0.6021	0.7348	28	0.3061	0.3610	0.4629
10	0.4973	0.5760	0.7079	29	0.3009	0.3550	0.4556
11	0.4762	0.5529	0.6835	30	0.2960	0.3494	0.4487
12	0.4575	0.5324	0.6614	35	0.2746	0.3246	0.4182
13	0.4409	0.5140	0.6411	40	0.2573	0.3044	0.3932
14	0.4259	0.4973	0.6226	45	0.2429	0.2876	0.3721
15	0.4124	0.4821	0.6055	50	0.2306	0.2732	0.3542
16	0.4000	0.4683	0.5897	60	0.2108	0.2500	0.3248
17	0.3887	0.4555	0.5751	70	0.1954	0.2319	0.3017
18	0.3783	0.4438	0.5614	80	0.1829	0.2172	0.2830
19	0.3687	0.4329	0.5487	90	0.1726	0.2050	0.2673
20	0.3598	0.4227	0.5368	100	0.1638	0.1946	0.2540

Table 12 Critical Values for the Sign Test

Reject the null hypothesis if the smaller number of positive or negative signs is less than or equal to the value in the table

	one–tailed α				
	0.005	**0.01**	**0.025**	**0.05**	**0.10**
	two–tailed α				
n	**0.01**	**0.02**	**0.05**	**0.10**	**0.20**
8	0	0	0	1	1
9	0	0	1	1	2
10	0	0	1	1	2
11	0	1	1	2	2
12	1	1	2	2	3
13	1	1	2	3	3
14	1	2	2	3	4
15	2	2	3	3	4
16	2	2	3	4	4
17	2	3	4	4	5
18	3	3	4	5	5
19	3	4	4	5	6
20	3	4	5	5	6
21	4	4	5	6	7
22	4	5	5	6	7
23	4	5	6	7	7
24	5	5	6	7	8
25	5	6	7	7	8
26	6	6	7	8	9
27	6	7	7	8	9
28	6	7	8	9	10
29	7	7	8	9	10
30	7	8	9	10	10

Table 13 Critical Values for the Wilcoxon Signed-Rank Test

	one–tailed α						
	0.0005	0.0025	0.005	0.0125	0.025	0.05	0.10
	two–tailed α						
n	0.001	0.005	0.01	0.025	0.05	0.10	0.20
5	--	--	--	--	--	0	2
6	--	--	--	--	0	2	3
7	--	--	--	0	2	3	5
8	--	--	0	2	3	5	8
9	--	0	1	3	5	8	10
10	--	1	3	5	8	10	14
11	0	3	5	8	10	13	17
12	1	5	7	10	13	17	21
13	2	7	9	13	17	21	26
14	4	9	12	17	21	25	31
15	6	12	15	20	25	30	36
16	8	15	19	25	29	35	42
17	11	19	23	29	34	41	48
18	14	23	27	34	40	47	55
19	18	27	32	39	46	53	62
20	21	32	37	45	52	60	69
21	25	37	42	51	58	67	77
22	30	42	48	57	65	75	86
23	35	48	54	64	73	83	94
24	40	54	61	72	81	91	104
25	45	60	68	79	89	100	113
26	51	67	75	87	98	110	124
27	57	74	83	96	107	119	134
28	64	82	91	105	116	130	145
29	71	90	100	114	126	140	157
30	78	98	109	124	137	151	169

Table 14 Critical Values for Spearman's Rank Correlation Coefficient

	two–tailed α				
n	**0.20**	**0.10**	**0.05**	**0.02**	**0.01**
5	0.700	0.800	0.900	0.900	1.000
6	0.714	0.829	0.943	1.000	1.000
7	0.607	0.750	0.821	0.893	0.929
8	0.548	0.667	0.762	0.833	0.881
9	0.500	0.617	0.700	0.783	0.833
10	0.467	0.576	0.648	0.733	0.782
11	0.436	0.536	0.618	0.700	0.755
12	0.413	0.507	0.587	0.668	0.720
13	0.390	0.484	0.560	0.643	0.692
14	0.371	0.464	0.538	0.622	0.670
15	0.357	0.446	0.521	0.600	0.645
16	0.344	0.432	0.503	0.579	0.626
17	0.331	0.417	0.485	0.561	0.610
18	0.321	0.404	0.472	0.546	0.593
19	0.311	0.391	0.458	0.532	0.578
20	0.302	0.380	0.447	0.518	0.564
21	0.293	0.371	0.434	0.505	0.550
22	0.286	0.362	0.425	0.494	0.539
23	0.279	0.353	0.415	0.483	0.528
24	0.272	0.345	0.406	0.473	0.516
25	0.266	0.338	0.398	0.464	0.506
26	0.261	0.331	0.389	0.454	0.497
27	0.256	0.324	0.382	0.446	0.487
28	0.251	0.318	0.375	0.438	0.479
29	0.246	0.312	0.368	0.431	0.471
30	0.241	0.307	0.362	0.423	0.464

Appendix B Index of Terminology

Chapter 1 Terms

Chapter 2 Terms

Chapter 3 Terms

mean, population, 45
mean, sample, 45
mean, weighted mean, 45
variance, population, 45
variance, sample, 45
standard deviation, 46, 67, 68, 69, 73
coefficient of variation, 46
z-score, 69, 79
Chebyshev's theorem, 68, 69
median, 66
quartile, 70
fractile, 70
interquartile range, 67
mode, 66
outlier, 67
range, 67
fractiles, 70
steam-and-leaf plot
box plot, 72, 73, 74, 79, 80
box-and-whisker plot, 72
ogive, 64
histogram, 62, 64, 77, 78, 82
Pareto plot, 64
pie chart, 62, 63, 76
dot plot, 80

Chapter 4 Terms

probability, 85
outcome, 85
sample space, 85
event, 85
probability, theoretical, 85
probability, empirical, 85
probability, subjective, 85
probability, conditional, 96–102
law of large numbers, 85
contingency table, 85
tree diagram, 85
event, compound, 85
event, mutually exclusive, 85
Venn diagram, 85
event, independent, 85
event, mutually independent, 85
rule, multiplication, 85
rule, addition, 92–96
events, dependent, 85
events, conditional
permutation, 85
combination, 85
factorial, 85
counting principle, 90

Chapter 5 Terms

random variable, 121
support, 121
random variable, discrete, 121
random variable, continuous, 121
countable set, 121
random variable, 121
distribution, 121
probability distribution, discrete, 121
expected value, 121
mean, 121
variance, 123
standard deviation, 123
probability distribution, geometric, 140
probability distribution, Poisson, 135
probability distribution, uniform continuous, 141
birthday paradox, 142–145

Chapter 6 Terms

probability distribution, binomial, 149
Bernoulli trial, 149
binomial experiment, 149
mean, binomial, 149
standard deviation, binomial, 149
standard deviation, binomial, 149
variance, binomial, 149

Chapter 7 Terms

probability distribution, normal, 175
probability density function, 175
probability distribution, standard normal, 175
probability distribution transformation, 175
standard error of the mean, 175

Chapter 8 Terms

Chapter 9 Terms

Chapter 10 Terms

Chapter 11 Terms

Chapter 12 Terms

Appendix C
Index of Applications

Chapter 1. Introduction to Statistics

Chapter 2. Introduction to R

Chapter 3. Descriptive Statistics

Chapter 4. Probability

Games
Section 4.5.3 Game Night, 116

Chapter 5. Probability Distributions

Games
Section 5.1.1 Coin Tossing, 122

Business
Section 5.1.1 Commercial Finance and Banking, 122
Section 5.4.1 Merchandise Warranty, 134
Section 5.5.3 American Football Franchise, 145

Sciences—Climate
Section 5.1.2 Weather, 123

Health Care
Section 5.1.2 Sunscreen, 123

Government
Section 5.2.2 U.S. Internal Revenue Service, 126
Section 5.3.1 Tax Returns, 129

Sciences—Geography
Section 5.4.2 Rural America, 136

Sports
Section 5.5.3 Kansas City, 145

Chapter 6. Binomial Probability Distributions

Engineering
Section 6.1.1 Injection Molding, 150

Health Care
Section 6.1.2 COVID-19 and Infants, 151
Section 6.4.2 Blood Type, 169
Section 6.4.3 COVID-19 and World Health Organization, 171
Section 6.4.3 Surgical Site Infections, 172

Sciences—Linguistics
Section 6.2.1 Folk Heritage and Storytelling, 155
Section 6.2.2 Gullah Language, 157
Section 6.3.1 Gullah Social Sciences Research, 162

Chapter 7. Normal Probability Distributions

Engineering
Section 7.1.1 Ceramic Engineer, 177
Section 7.3.1 Tensile Strength, 188

Health Care
Section 7.3.2 Physical Fitness, 190
Section 7.5.3 Genetic Counseling, 206

Sciences—Climate
Section 7.4.3 Indian Meteorological Studies, 195

Sports
Section 7.5.2 Basketball Player's Weights, 203
Section 7.5.3 Bowling Night, 205

Chapter 8. Confidence Intervals

Engineering
Section 8.1.2 Tensile Strength, 213
Section 8.2.2 Concrete Strength, 219

Sciences—Linguistics
Section 8.4.1 Gullah Language, 228
Section 8.4.2 Web of Science Database and Social Sciences, 229

Section 8.4.3 Social Science Linguistics Publications, 231

Government

Section 8.5.2 Place of Birth, 239

Section 8.5.3 Campus Crime, 241

Education

Section 8.5.3 Statistical Software, 242

Chapter 9. Hypothesis Testing

Engineering

Section 9.1.1 Tensile Strength, 251

Section 9.1.1 Engineering Invention, 250

Business

Section 9.2.1 Salary Equity, 256

Section 9.4.2 New York Stock Exchange, 273

Health Care

Section 9.2.2 Weight Loss, 258

Section 9.2.3 Body Mass Index (BMI), 260

Government

Section 9.3.2 U. S. Congress, 265

Education

Section 9.4.3 Traditional and Online Learning, 275

Chapter 10. Chi-Square Tests and *F*-Distribution

Business

Section 10.1.1 U.S. Small Business Association, 279

Section 10.1.1 Small Business Challenges, 279, 281–282

Section 10.4.2 M&M Candies, 310

Section 10.4.3 Pizza Crust, 312

Health Care

Section 10.1.2 Alcoholism, 284

Section 10.1.3 Pediatric Optometry, 289

Section 10.2.2 Cholesterol Level, 291–292

Government

Section 10.3.1 Consumer Protection Organization , 295–296

Sciences—Agriculture

Section 10.4.3 Tomato Plant Yield, 314

Sciences—Environmental

Section 10.4.3 Total Dissolved Solids, 313

Chapter 11. Correlation

Health Care

Section 11.1.2 Post-Traumatic Stress Disorder, 320

Section 11.5.2 Body Measurements, 346

Section 11.5.3 Maternal Mortality Ratio, 348

Education

Section 11.1.3 Childhood Vocabulary, 321

Sciences—Environmental

Section 11.2.3 Ambient Ultrafine Particles, 327

Section 11.3.3 Consumption Expenditure, 332

Section 11.5.3 Crustacean Ecological Study, 347

Chapter 12. Nonparametric Statistics

Sciences—Biology

Section 12.2.4 Splicing Factor 1, 359

Environment

Section 12.2.1 Environmental Sustainability, 358

Education

Section 12.4.2 Undergraduate Research, 371

Health Care

Section 12.4.3 Breast Cancer Awareness and Ethnic Background, 372

Section 12.4.3 Breast Cancer Education, 373

Appendix D Glossary of Symbols

Chapter 1. Introduction to Statistics

N/A

Chapter 2. Introduction to R

N/A

Chapter 3. Descriptive Statistics

μ	population mean $\Sigma x/N$ for a population of size N
Σ	summation of values in a list
$\overline{x}$	sample mean $\Sigma x/n$ for a sample of size n from a bigger population
σ^2	population variance $\Sigma(x-\mu)^2/N$ for a population of size N
σ	population standard deviation $\sqrt{\Sigma(x-\mu)^2 / N}$
s^2	sample variance $\Sigma(x- \ )^2/(n-1)$ for a sample of size n
s	sample standard deviation $\sqrt{\Sigma(x-\overline{x})^2 / (n-1)}$
CV	coefficient of variation (σ/μ)*100% or $(s/\overline{x})$*100%
z	z-score $(x-\mu)/\sigma$ for a value x from a bell-shaped distribution
Q_1	first quartile; 25% of values in a set are smaller than this
Q_2	second quartile, or median; 50% of values in a set are smaller than this
Q_3	third quartile; 75% of values in a set are smaller than this
IQR	interquartile range Q_3-Q_1

Chapter 4. Probability

P(E)	probability of an event, or outcome, E from a sample space
$\emptyset$	empty set; events or outcomes that never happen; $P(\emptyset) = 0$
$A \cup B$	union of two events that realizes when Event A **or** Event B are observed
$A \cap B$	intersection of two events that realizes when Event A **and** Event B are observed
B|A	conditional event; Event B realized when Event A occurs
$n!$	factorial of number $n = n(n-1)(n-2) \ldots (2)(1)$, by definition $0! = 1$ is the number of permutations of n objects
${}_nP_r$	the number of ways r objects, in a given order, can be arranged in a group of n object $= n!/(n-r)!$
${}_nC_r$	the number of many ways r objects can be selected from a group of n objects, regardless of their order; also known as the combination of r chosen from n: $n!/r!/(n-r)!$
$\binom{n}{r}$	the same as ${}_nC_r$

Chapter 5. Probability Distributions

$E[X]$, μ	expected value, or mean, of random variable $X = \Sigma xP(x)$
$Var[X]$, σ^2	variance of random variable $X = E[X^2] - (E[X])^2 = E[X^2] - \mu^2$

Chapter 6. Binomial Probability Distributions

N/A

Chapter 7. Normal Probability Distributions

N/A

Chapter 8. Confidence Intervals

c level of confidence; the percentage of all possible samples that can be expected to be included in the true population parameter.

z_c critical values for the *z*-score that separate statistics that are probable from those that are improbable at the chosen level of confidence

E margin of error; defines the interval of the random variable corresponding to the critical value, such that the confidence interval is $(\overline{x} - E, \overline{x} + E)$

df degrees of freedom; the number of free choices left after the sample statistics have been calculated

t_c critical value for *t*-distribution corresponding to the chosen level of confidence, *c*

χ^2 the square of the Greek letter chi.

χ_L^2, χ_R^2 left-tail and right-tail critical values in χ^2 distribution corresponding to a given level of confidence

$\hat{p}$ sample proportion, and an estimate of the population proportion

Chapter 9. Hypothesis Testing

H_0 null hypothesis; the status quo.

H_a alternative hypothesis; the research hypothesis

α level of significance; the maximum allowable probability for making a Type I error in hypothesis testing

β the probability of a Type II error

$1 - \beta$ power of a statistical test

p-value probability value of obtaining a sample statistic with a value as extreme or more extreme that the one determined from sample data; H_0 is rejected if *p*-value is smaller than or equal to α

d the difference between two paired (dependent) samples

$\overline{d}$ the mean difference between dependent samples

Chapter 10. Chi-Square Tests and *F*-Distribution

E_i expected frequency in a multinomial experiment

O_i observed frequency in a multinomial experiment

F *F*-test statistic that can be used to compare the variance for two populations

$\overline{\overline{x}}$ the grand mean over all samples $\Sigma S_k / \Sigma n_k$ in an ANOVA test for *K* samples, where each sample has size is n_k, the sum of values $S_k = \Sigma x$ and sum of squares $SS_k = \Sigma x^2$

N total number of values in all samples $\Sigma nk = n_1 + n_2 + ... n_K$

SS_B sum of squared deviations between mean of each sample and the grand mean, weighted by the sample size = $\Sigma n_k (S_k/n_k - \overline{\overline{x}})^2$

SS_W sum of squared deviations within each sample from sample mean = $\Sigma S_k^2 (n_k-1) = \Sigma(SS_k - S_k/n_k)^2$

MS_B variance between samples SS_B/df_N where $df_N = K - 1$

MS_W variance within samples SS_W/df_D where $df_D = N - K$

SStot total sum of squares of deviations from the grand mean = $\Sigma[x-(\Sigma x)/N]^2 = \Sigma SS_k - (\Sigma S_k)^2/N$

Chapter 11. Correlation

r correlation coefficient between two samples

d_i residuals between observed values, y_i, and values predicted by the model, $\hat{y}(x_i)$, of the dependent variable for a given value of the independent variable, x_i

r^2 coefficient of variation; the ratio of the explained variation to the total variation

$cov(X,Y)$ covariance of two random variables X and Y = $E[(X-E[X])(Y-E[Y])]$

r coefficient of determination = $cov(X,Y)/[var(X)var(Y)]^{1/2}$

Chapter 12. Nonparametric Statistics

N/A

Appendix E
Most Common R Commands

Getting Help and Packages

`help(topic)` documentation on topic

`?topic` documentation of topic; special characters need quotes; for example, `?'&&'`

`help.search("topic")` search the help system; same as `??topic`

`apropos("topic")` the names of all objects in the search list matching "topic"

`summary(x)` give a summary about object *x*

`str(x)` display the internal structure of an object

`ls()` list all objects in the search path

`dir()` show files in the current directory

`q(), quit(), ctrl-D` (ctrl-Z on Windows) quit R session

`install.packages("pkgs",lib)` download and install packaged from CRAN repositories

`library(pkg)` load and activate a package

`detach("package:pkg")` deactivate a library

Operators

`<-` Left assignment

`->` Right assignment

`=` Left assignment

`-` Subtract or negative sign

`+` Add

`~` Tilde used to formulate models

`:` Sequence of consecutive numbers,

For example: `a = 1:5` is the same with `a=c(1,2,3,4,5)`

`::` Refers to a function in a package

`*` Multiplication

`/` Division

`^` Power

`**` Power

`%%` Reminder of a division

`%/%` Integer divide

`%*%` Matrix product

`%o%` Outer products of vectors

`%in%` Matching operator

`!x` negation, *NOT x*

`x & y` elementwise logical *AND*

`x && y` vector logical *AND*

`x | y` elementwise logical *OR*

`x || y` vector logical *AND*

`==` test for equality

`<=` test for less than or equal

`>=` test for greater than or equal

Flow Control

`if(cond) {expr}` conditional execution of expression

`for(var in seq){expr}` repeated execution of expression for each value in list seq

`while(cond){expr}` execute expression in a loop as long as condition is verified

`repeat{expr}` execute expression in infinite loop

`break` stop a loop

`next` advance to the next iteration within a loop

Data Structures

`c(item1,item2,....)` combine arguments to form a vector of values with the same type

`seq(from, to)` generate a sequence; optional argument `by=` to specify increment

`rep(x, times)` create a vector with 'x' replicated a number of times. Optional argument `each=`

`x[n]` value at index *n* in vector *x*; the first value is `x[1]`

`x[-n]` drop the element at index *n*

`x[2:n]` get a slice of vector *x*

`x["name"]` get the element labeled by `name`

`x[x>3]` get all elements obeying a condition

`data.frame(...)` combines vectors of the same size into a data frame

`list(...)` create a list of the named or unnamed arguments with the same or different types; `list(a=c(1,2),b="hi", c=3)`

`attributes(x)` labels for various values in *x*

`x[[n]]` return a single element from list *x*

`x$name` select a column or element in list

`array(x, dim)` array with data *x* in a shape specified by argument dim; `dim=c(3,3)` creates a 3x3 matrix

`matrix(x, nrow, ncol)` create a `nrow x col` matrix from a vector *x*

`gl(n,k,length=n*k,labels=1:n)` generate levels (factors) by specifying the pattern of their levels, where *k* is the number of levels and *n* the number of replications

`as.array(x), as.character(x), as.numeric(x)` a set of functions to convert between types

`is.array(x), is.character(x), is.numeric(x)` a set of functions to test data types

`head(x)` return the first part of an object

`tail(x)` return the last part of an object

`summary(x)` give a summary of an object

`length(x)` the number of elements in *x*

`dim(x)` retrieve the dimensions of *x*

Data Manipulation

`max(x)` return the greatest element of *x*

`which.max(x)` return the position of the greatest element of *x*

`min(x)` return the smallest element of *x*

`which.min(x)` return the position of the smallest element of *x*

`rev(x)` reverse the order of elements in *x*

`sort(x)` sort *x* in increasing order

`cut(x,breaks)` divide *x* into intervals; breaks is the number of cut intervals

`match(x,y)` return a vector of the same length as *x*; each elements of *x* replaced by the index of matching element in `y` and `NA` otherwise

`which(x==a)` return a vector of indices of *x* that have elements equal to *a*

`na.omit(x)` eliminate NA records from *x*

`complete.cases(x)` return rows with no NA

`unique(x)` a vector with no duplicates

`table(x)` a list with the number of different values (factors) in *x*

`tabulate(x)` count the number of times each integer appears in *x*

`factor(x)` encode a vector as a list of factors

`split(x,f)` divide the vector *x* into groups

`subset(x)` a selection of *x* based on some criteria

`sample(x, size)` random sample of elements of *x*

`sweep(x,margin,stats)` transform an array by sweeping out summary statistics column- and row-wise

`xtabs(a,b,data=x)` a contingency table from cross-classifying factors

`replace(x, list, values)` replace elements of *x* corresponding to indexes in list

`merge(a,b)` conjoin two data frames by common column or row names

`stack(x,..)` concatenate vectors

`rbind(x,..)` combine matrices or data frames

`reshape(x)` reshape an array or data frame

Functions

`function(arguments) {..}` define a function

`apply(x,index, fun)` apply function `fun` to all elements *x*

`lapply(x, fun)` apply function to list elements

`sapply(x, fun)` friendly interface to `lapply`

`aggregate(x, by, fun)` apply function to groups of elements of *x*

`ave(data, by, fun=mean)` get the mean or other operation of subsets of *x*

`missing(a)` test inside a function if *a* was given as argument

`require(lib)` load a package within a function

`return(value)` return the result from a function

`invisible(value)` return but do not print

Math

`sin, cos, tan, asin, acos, atan, exp` trigonometric, inverse trigonometric, and exponential functions

`atan2(y,x)` the second form of tangent that takes into account the quadrant of (x,y) point

`log(x), log10(x), log(x, base)` natural logarithm; logarithm in base 10 and arbitrary base

`min(x), max(x)` extremum values in a list

`range(x)` both min and max of a list

`sum(x)` sum of elements in a list

`diff(x)` lagged and iterated differences

`scale(x)` center and normalize a vector

`pmin(x,y,...), pmax(x,y,...)` find min and max of a set of vectors

`union(x,y), intersect(x,y), setdiff(x,y)` set operations on vectors

`abs(x), Mod(x)` absolute value

`Re(z), Im(z), Arg(z), Conj(z)` complex numbers function; a complex number example: `z = 3+2i`

`convolve(x,y)` convolve vectors *x* and *y*

`fft(x)` fast Fourier transform of vector *x*

`filter(x,f)` apply linear filter f on vector *x*

`solve(a,b)` solve a linear set of equations

`rowsum(x), colsum(x)` column and row sum of matrices

`t(x)` transpose of matrix *x*

`diag(x)` diagonal vector of matrix *x*

Descriptive Statistics

`mean(x)` arithmetic mean of values in *x*

`median(x)` median value of a vector

`quantile(x, probs)` sample quantile corresponding to given probabilities

`weighted.mean(x,w)` mean of *x* weighted by *w*

`summary(x)` report several measured for *x*

`sd(x)` standard deviation for values in *x*

`density(x)` computes kernel density estimates

`var(x), cov(x,y), cor(x,y)` variance of *x* and covariance (or correlation) of *x* and *y* `tabulate(x)` count occurrences and bin values

Distributions

There are about 20 by default in R and many more in packages. There are four functions for each distribution that handle different aspects, depending on the first letter: `d` probability density, `p` cumulative distribution, `q` the inverse of cumulative distribution (or quantile function), and `r` random number generator. The most popular ones are:

`dnorm(x, mean, sd)` normal distribution with mean and standard deviation specified

`dunif(x, min, max)` uniform distribution between min and max

`dbinom(x, size, prob)` binomial distribution of given size and probability

`dgeom(x, prob)` geometric distribution with given probability

`dpois(x, lambda)` Poisson probability with parameter lambda

`dexp(x, rate)` exponential distribution with given rate

`dchisq(x,df)` chi-square distribution with *df* degrees of freedom

`dt(x,df)` Student *t*-distribution with *df* degrees of freedom

`df(x,df1,df2)` *F*-distribution with *df1* and *df2* degrees of freedom

Statistical Tests

`cor.test(a,b)` test for association between paired samples

`prop.test(x)` test the null hypothesis that the proportions in some groups are the same

`binom.test(x)` test the hypothesis about the probability of success in a Bernoulli experiment

`chisq.test(x)` chi-square contingency table test and goodness-of-fit tests

`ks.test(x,y)` one- or two-sample Kolmogorov–Smirnov test

`wilcox.test(x)` Wilcoxon signed rank test

`var.test(x,y)` check if two samples have same variance

Models

Formulas used for fitting have the form:

`resp ~ termA + termB`

Other operators are: `:`,`*`,`^`,`%in%`

`lm(formula, data)` fit data with a linear model

`aov(formula, data)` analysis of variance model

`glm(formula, data)` generalized linear model

`nls(formula, data)` nonlinear least square model

`anova(fit, data)` analysis of variance table

`summary(fit)` summary of fit model

`predict(fit)` use the model to predict values

Strings

`paste(vectors, sep, collapse)` concatenate vectors after converting to characters

`substr(x,start,stop)` extract or replace parts of a string

`strsplit(x)` split a string into substrings

`grep(pattern,x)`, `regexpr(pattern, text)` search for patterns in a string, eventually replace

Base Graphics and Plots

`plot(x,y,main="Title", col="-color", xlab="x-axis-label", ylab`

="y-axis-label") draw points at coordinates given by vectors x and y and annotate the plot

`hist(x)` draw a histogram for values in x

`barplot(x)` barplot for values in x

`boxplot(x)` box-and-whiskers plot

`symbols(x,y)` place symbols at coordinates x, y

`lines(x,y)` add lines to the current graphics

`text(x,y,labels)` place string labels at x, y

`par(...)` set or query graphical parameters

`pdf(file), postscript(file), png(file)` produce graphics to a file

Input and Output

`read.csv(file), read.table(file)` read a data frame from comma separated file or URL

`write.table(x, file)` write a table to a file

`data()` load a specified build-in data set or list available data set

`edit(x)` invoke an editor to edit object x

[illegible] draw points at coordinates given by vectors x and y and annotate the plot [illegible]

[illegible]

Input and Output

[illegible]

CPSIA information can be obtained
at www.ICGtesting.com
Printed in the USA
LVHW060108051022
729968LV00001B/6